I Guess I Just Wasn't Thinking

Part Three:
The CIA Secret Airline
and Eureka! She Exists!

W.K. "Jake" Wehrell

*This series is dedicated to my four savvy kids,
who in spite of my flagrant and prolonged absence,
have grown up to be loving and capable parents,
unremittingly supportive of each other, and exceptionally
successful professionals. I would have to say,
all credit to their great mom.*

Published by
AfterWit Books
afterwitbooks@gmail.com

This is a conceivable work of non-fiction. Names, characters, places, and incidents are the product of the author's imagination or his recollections. Any resemblance to actual persons, living or dead, events, or locales is possible.

ISBN: 978-0-9987632-4-8 (print)
ISBN: 978-0-9987632-5-5 (e-book)
Library of Congress Control Number: 2017936006

TABLE OF CONTENTS

Continued on next page

TABLE OF CONTENTS *Continued*

ABOUT THE SERIES

I GUESS I JUST WASN'T THINKING is a four-part, first-person memoir that rides the rails of high adventure. You will be at Roger Yahnke's side in five continents while he struggles to overcome (or even survive) a diverse assortment of challenges; in the jungle and in the desert; in the cockpit and in the bedroom. Between aviation exploits occur repeated daring but questionable escapades on terra firma. Above all it is a compelling tale of one man's battle with a very personal shortcoming; an honest and revealing account of his uniquely driven life. His head-shaking array of adult activities include a proud beginning as a Marine Corps carrier-based pilot, being hired by the CIA, flying covert missions for foreign governments, and other less provident activities; some of which result in him appearing in TV documentaries, having his photo in weekly news magazines, and residences worldwide; including everything from a bougainvillea-draped cottage on the French Riviera to a bamboo cage in Laos.

All this transpires in the midst of frequent (and always fruitless) feminine involvements. Every contemplated activity—besides its actual merit, is heavily weighted as to its likelihood of being graced by a certain female partner. This motivation evokes a plight of skewed perceptions, flawed decisions and overly zealous undertakings. Although it well could— the import of the Series is not so much in the action, intriguing venues or colorful characters, as in the frank and intimate narrative of Roger's condition; its all-embracing mastery of him and the crushing embarrassment when seeing the perplexed disillusionment of yet another unsatisfied female partner. Roger is consumed by the search for that one woman with the right chemistry to unlock his manhood. To the dismissal of all else he remains hopelessly fettered to the quest to find her. Wives and girlfriends who have blamed themselves for a failed union may be comforted by this surprising explanation for their husband's or boyfriend's apparent womanizing.

V

A SHORT REVIEW OF PARTS ONE AND TWO

Part One: Instead of Skipping Stones is an unlikely prelude to his future duplicitous global adventures; a warmly entertaining collection of innocent and endearing admissions; a fresh and confidentially narrated pre-teen to adult memoir. As the reader you will be caught up in a succession of delicate, weighty, and progressively more thought-provoking scenarios, unable to resist the bonding, as it is obvious Roger trusts you, is willing to confide in you and share with you his innermost hopes and fears. The end of each chapter will find you with a knowing smile or tear in your eye; wincing at Roger's adolescent doubts, conclusions, and best guess responses; up to and including his almost happenstance choice of a life's work. But stick with this harmless narrative; it's going somewhere! Part One is a necessary step: Roger's only chance to win your approval and maybe even a bit of affection, before a devastating impasse besets him and his actions appear non-defensible. Only in the last chapters will you get a hint of the dilemma awaiting him; one that would provoke and mitigate the possible consequences of his future all too-risky undertakings!

Part Two: The French Riviera, Leo, June, and Big Trouble is set some years later and finds a young Captain Yahnke cruising the Mediterranean aboard a US super carrier. You will be with him—teeth clenched and hands clamping the armrests, during harrowing airborne operations and icy night landings. And equally as important, accompany him on his desperate search for that one woman (who he hopes could well be one of those foreign-speaking, exciting European women). You'll be with him as he traipses the Continent, cavorts with rogues and royalty and blunders into barely credible scenarios, about which much doubt should ensue. You'll spend the night with Roger in an Istanbul jail cell with a famous German actor and a storied Middle East princess, and travel with him and his new friend Leo when they journey to Bulgaria to meet with the KGB. The cover photo is the English dancer June, who you will meet and forever admire. You may wince and condemn him, or find yourself unable not to be on his side—earnestly pulling for him in each new inscrutable endeavor. The question is, the cruise over and returning to the states, how will he ever be able to face his family again, look his wife in the eyes and pick up where he left off?

Chapter One
IT'S OVER!

The USA, My First Day Back

April 18th, 1965: made it across and finally to this dreaded day. 100 miles out of Norfolk we launched, and I needed the catapult shot to jar me back to the reality that awaited me. I was leaving the USS *Forrestal*—my habitat for the last ten months, below and behind me—a hopefully not-too-long-lasting, haunting memory. Almost a year of shameful experimentation was over; a terrifying refit was imminent. I was on the final leg to what was—and still is, my home (and my family)! An hour and twenty later our flight was overhead Beaufort Marine Corps Air Station. We all landed smoothly, but just for show—with too little interval. This allowed us to be close enough together to taxi to the ramp in a tight twelve-plane formation. When the last plane was chocked the Skipper gave the radio command to simultaneously shut down the engines and let all the canopies swing open in unison. Out of the cockpit and down the ladder. After almost a year, USA concrete under my feet (but nothing USA in my head).

The panorama of chairs and bodies were as mirages; no more real than the nostalgic kaleidoscope of images behind my eyes. No idea what was in store for me, but I was back. Everything that had dominated my being for the last ten months was over. And I feared—as the imposter I was, it would only be a matter of hours (or minutes) before I was exposed. But I kept moving towards the waiting families—staying abreast my joyfully innocent squadron mates, stabbing one leg out in front of the other. I was afraid to imagine the expression on my face—or lack thereof, which had to be broadcasting my guilt. Blurred figures were passing me in all directions, or I was passing them. In spite of my fright, churning stomach, and worst fears, I continued towards Sara and the kids; hopped over a half row of toppled chairs and bumped into Major Burnham (who was there 'glad-handing' everyone he could get to). Past him—no time for that now. It's not whether this is going to happen. It's happening. It's just how long it will take and if I get through it. *Lord help me.*

Before I knew it Sara and I were in an embrace. It was a big hug and I felt I was being kissed. Some rushed bubbly greetings between us, a couple expected comments, and then an awkward silence. *Quick, reintroduce yourself to the kids.* Hugged them all. Scooped up the two little ones. With Stacy and Kevin in my arms I leaned over towards the other two, asking questions, answering questions—most with not very original answers. And then, the euphoria, what of it there was, quickly faded. Sara and I found ourselves making small talk—ordinary talk, about buying some trash bags when we passed the 7-11, and what I would want for supper. Not what one would have expected to hear on this occasion, but it was a dull comfort and so far I didn't think I'd been discovered. *Don't think about the adventures; particularly the Barcelona late nights.* I forced myself into the midst of the reunion and listened with my best show of enthusiasm. The kids began a chorus of commentaries on their present activities and best friends, while just under the 'listening' surface a riptide of contrasting emotions lurked. I was being handed Kevin again. Stacy was tugging at my wrist. Mark was talking a blue streak and shoving a piece of paper towards me. How could I feel so much confusion on the inside, and not have it glaringly apparent on the outside? A least twenty minutes now. I may have pulled it off so far.

Off the ramp and to the parking area. Bob and Don sauntered by. Our eyes met. *They knew.* For sure they knew. I was no more than a walking stick-figure, a scarecrow being pulled along—the returning hero being escorted home. I spied our Ford Esquire station wagon. It looked the same, like I just stepped out of it yesterday. Sara got in the driver's seat; never offered me the keys. Guess by now she's used to being the chauffer. And fine with me. Nausea was only inches away. I heard words coming from my mouth that I didn't realize I was forming. Was hoping this first afternoon would be the worst of it. Tried not to visualize Leo, or June, or Ardith, or Ingrid, or the airport in Sofia, or the Carlton hotel in Cannes; a year's worth of fruitless experimenting (infidelity). It was more than a series of failed attempts. I'd sold my soul. Now I was here face-to-face with reality and what I was sure was as good a wife as anyone ever had. The engine was missing each time Sara accelerated; knew one of the first things I would have to do was get it to a garage. At first the drive was quiet—for about five minutes. The silence was broken by Donna. "Daddy, Daddy, I'm getting perfect report cards."

"No she's not," added Mark non-committedly, only commenting as a disinterested bystander.

"I am too," she shouted, twisting around and glaring at Mark. He slunk back into his seat (apparently satisfied with a sole remark). I suspected he'd had experience contradicting Donna and chose to avoid further combat. Even at seven she was in the habit of prevailing. Stacy was crying in the back seat. I didn't see what started it. Kevin was in his car seat on the other side, making a horrible mess with some sort of chocolate snack. An animated conversation began between Donna and Mark, involving alternately harder pokes. Soon, between the four of them it was approaching bedlam. My heart was racing. Sara looked over at me with a sheepish smile. (I couldn't see the situation deserving of a smile.) She glanced at the kids, then back to me and just shrugged her shoulders.

I could feel a rushing in my ears. The noise in the car was mounting. Sara looked over and smiled again. There was a chorus of voices mounting from the rear seat. They all were shouting at the same time. Sara gave a rote command to quiet them, to which they paid absolutely no attention; words which I was sure even Sara did not think would have any effect. It was just a script—an expected drill. Like so many other things she did, I was beginning to remember these responses. As it continued, she exhaled and made some "waving off" motion with her hand. I could see she had immunized herself to this sort of thing. I felt a cramping between my shoulders and became aware I was rumpling Mark's drawing in my hand. I was afraid if the car stopped I might open the door and run. I hated myself. I had been in over my head before, but nothing like this. This could not be ended by jumping in a liberty boat and returning to the carrier, or pulling out of port. This was permanent. *This was my real life!*

Into the driveway and a chance to scan the property—examine the house, the carport, the bad lawn, the ripped screens, the stained brick front, the peeling white paint. It looked just like the house I left, but now not necessarily one I should be living in (a far cry from King Constantine's cliff-top cottage on the island of Rhodes). The house was more common-looking and less appealing than I remembered. Lots of work awaiting me here, but that's okay. Inside, after a tour of cracked tiles, chipped enamel, soap-ringed bath tubs, corroded faucets, torn shower curtains and loose corner moldings, I knew I had to do something quick, so retreated into our bedroom, busying myself unpacking and hanging things up. Sara made a light lunch while I played with the kids—could do that. And they were looking up at me so admiringly, my heart could not do other than be heavy with remorse. Sara hollered in with local and family news—the latest updates on our neighbors and relatives. That was okay, I could handle that; keep it coming. *Just don't ask about the cruise.*

About six, Sara cooked dinner—special dishes she said were my favorites. Which while this was typical of her thoughtfulness I couldn't remember they were my favorites (or that I even had any favorites). After the meal things felt somewhat normal as I willingly helped her with the dishes. Before putting the kids to bed, as a family we went through snapshots of the carrier, and I gave the best running commentary truth would allow. That accomplished, Sara and I watched a little TV, and then what I was dreading since my arrival: *bedtime*. As you might imagine, I knew I was almost certainly in for trouble. My recent trysts—however incomplete, would be sufficient to keep me from being the love-starved husband I should be. And the deserved weight of shame would no doubt play a role in me once again not being able to consummate the act. You can bet I was praying to the good Lord to make an exception and grant me what would be necessary—even if only for this one night.

Nothing was familiar and yet it was; in bed with a woman—that wasn't so long ago. But now it was complicated with so much more than before. Over there I had been flailing in the dark, truly experimenting—searching and hoping to find that one woman! Now I was actually where I should be and that could have made it right. But of course it didn't and it wasn't. I had a proper enough exposure to good role models (my own parents) to know my obligations; to feel a deep and deserved respect for this woman and realize the debt I owed her. No doubt about that. But once again, what I didn't feel or have—*was what the male partner needs*. I kept imagining being someplace else—anywhere else, where I wouldn't be faced with this encounter. Sara was unusually aggressive, moving her pelvis in hard thrusting sexual movements that while they would have helped any other man, succeeded only in derailing any progress I might have been making. Finally and mercifully I had a measure of what I would need and was afraid to wait for something better. A semblance of the act was accomplished. But I suspect—for her, as it had consistently been before I left (and similar to my repeated 'falling short' performances on the Continent), certainly nothing worth any woman waiting ten months for. Though I felt no better than when I climbed down from the cockpit, I was pretty sure I would eventually fall asleep.

The Old Grind, Almost

Back to work, but not to the old pre-cruise squadron. We were now undergoing a complete turnover of personnel. VMA 331 wasn't tactical anymore; just the remnants of a previously formidable fighting force. After a squadron completes its fleet tour, it's yanked back and dismantled. The cycle starts all over again. There would soon be an influx of new, 'green' pilots replacing us, ready to begin their Phase One training. We were just hanging around waiting to see which of us would be first to be plucked out—for new and non-tactical jobs; assignments such as Disbursing Officer or Base fire Marshall, or the like—which none of us wanted. After having reached the highest state of readiness, instead of taking advantage of it, we were going to be recycled into God knew what. Now, no longer with a tactical mission and the imminent breakup of the squadron, a cavalier attitude prevailed among the returning pilots. I soon came to the almost certain conclusion that no matter where I was assigned, I would not be able to endure this day to day ordinary existence on a permanent basis. And if I was going to do something about it, it would have to be soon.

My Nostalgia was Overwhelming

I was taunted by an assortment of images: cities, train stations, restaurants, cab rides, places and faces—most frequently June, whose every move—everything she ever said, was exactly what I would have anticipated and wanted (although tragically she did not 'turn the key' for me and I knew a permanent arrangement could eventually prove unsatisfactory to her, with heart-breaking sad results). These reminiscences were of such intensity that I often found myself unknowingly shaking my head or emitting a moan (which more than once provoked a quizzical look from Sara or whoever was next to me). I was in no frame of mind to look favorably on any new duty station; especially a non-glamorous commonplace assignment. Nothing could allay the undoubtedly foolish but persistent feeling I had—that I was being 'missed' on the Continent. As a result of my personal involvements in Europe, I believed I had made a difference in several other people's lives, and was thinking (ridiculously) that things were somehow 'on hold' over there until I could get back. *But how and where, and for who?!* What in the hell was I thinking? The discontent, often interrupted by my own reproaches had me stumbling robot-like through these first days, and deservedly so.

Things Around the House

In spite of this period being one of somber thoughts, desperate speculations, and painful deliberations, and in spite of the anguish and unsettled nature of my existence, I acted out the role of a respected head of household, taking care of necessary things—no matter how mundane. The end of the week I took the car to the local Ford dealer and got the engine problem fixed. I passed the evenings and weekends with a myriad of long-overdue repairs: replacing the linoleum in the kitchen, enameling the porch floor, changing all the bathroom faucets, and repairing just about every window and screen. And there was barely a blade of grass in the back yard—lots of work there. This activity at least kept my mind off other things. When I moved the refrigerator I couldn't believe what I found behind it: *the same utensils and cups we'd lost before I went on the cruise.*

Sara told me a raccoon had been getting into our garbage can almost every night; in the morning—egg shells, coffee grinds, and greasy napkins all over the yard. I told her I'd spend the night on the roof and catch it in the act. About three in the morning I heard some action below and saw a dark figure digging in the can. I leaped off the roof with a blood curdling scream, flailing the broom in his direction. I must have scared the wits out of him because I passed him going up as I was going down. And it wasn't a raccoon, it was a dog!

The dog began a race for his life, around the perimeter of our fenced-in yard, me after him—beating the ground with the broom just inches behind him. After two complete circles he suddenly skids to a stop, turns and leaps at my throat! I dodge him. He hits the ground behind me and escapes under the fence. I'm over the fence and hot on his tail, continuing to beat the ground behind him. He races through our front yard, across the street, and into the car port across the street. The unused carport was full of leaves. The dog slips and slides ten feet before thudding into the far wall. I likewise—in trying to stop, fall and slide, creating a second loud thump on the same far wall. We're both lying there in the leaves when the carport light comes on and the side door whips open. The dog's master steps out in wonderment at the sight of me laying there in the leaves, with his dog—

who turned out to be dead!

Memories Revived. Exactly What I Didn't Need

One night watching the Ed Sullivan show, he introduces a new sensation from England: *Cilla Black!* Out she walks on the stage right here in the USA. My heart almost stopped when she commenced to sing "You're My World" (June and my 'special' song from our times together in Spain). No sooner had this started than the phone starts ringing off the hook; one after the other of my cruise buddies telling me to quick turn on the TV. (Evidently the awareness of my activities during the cruise was more widespread than I thought.) Seeing and hearing Cilla Black again would make forgetting the memories of the cruise even more difficult. I could contemplate no other course of action than to somehow find a way to again bring about a similar domestic situation to the one that had existed during the cruise. This would grant me at least a chance to give those memories another life.

To do such, I could not exclude the necessity of resigning my Commission—*getting out of the service?!* However when you're a Regular Officer it's no easy thing, and with nine years' service it means sacrificing all your retirement benefits when you're halfway there. And the worst, your fellow Marines view you as a traitor. It conveys that you're dissatisfied with the Corps and your squadron mates. (Of course while they don't say it, they know *you're* the misfit, not the Corps.) And I *was* real proud being a Marine, but I was doomed to never find out if there was another life (woman) for me as long as I was in the Corps. On rare moments I allowed the word "divorce" to enter my mind (but not for long). The consequences would be devastating. I knew how it would disappoint my folks, who deservedly loved Sara. And owning up to a divorce in front of all our military friends would be something I couldn't face. What a conundrum (that of course I deserved). So what can I do? I was racked with such guilt each time I even contemplated broaching divorce to Sara, I never did. Most likely because I was a coward, or in my defense, because I just couldn't bear to hurt her. As far as the kids were concerned it was like I had never left. But to Sara I'm sure it must have been as if someone other than her husband had returned. Or perhaps she had always tolerated this selfishness on my part; this distancing of myself from her. Maybe I'd always been this way, in which case her excellence as a loving wife is even more laudable.

A Possible Plan

One day in the mailbox was a response to a query I had sent. The first line of the Washington return address read *Air America Inc*. (Remember? The CIA secret airline in S E Asia that I heard about while on the carrier.) I had already mentioned it to Sara—sort of readying her for that possibility, without actually going into the details of where I would live, and where she would live, or how it would affect us, other than that I could make a lot of money and assure her a better life and the kids a college education. I felt deceitful opening the letter in the house and sought refuge in the carport. There I nervously pulled out the single page. It said little else besides I could come for an interview, but it caused my heart to pound. Suddenly the idea of resigning of my Commission and a possibly innocent way to affect a physical separation from Sara might be possible. This could be the light at the end of the tunnel. A scary tunnel and a faint light; one I might never reach, or reach and sorely regret. But the hint of it was there.

It was just about the hardest thing I ever did. I can't imagine how I got the courage to approach Major Burnham and tell him I wanted out. But I did. The biggest hurt was I dared not voice the real reason behind my wanting to leave the Corps. My weakly voiced stumbling explanations did not justify my intended action. I felt terrible because I had inflicted a hurt upon the Major—professionally and personally. And there would be others—my squadron mates, who may have previously respected me (or at least tolerated my off-duty behavior) who would now think I didn't approve of their choice for a way of life. This really hurt, but somehow in spite of all and a total lack of surety I stuck to my guns. The paperwork was sent off. I'd persevered, but I wasn't at all confident in the wisdom of this decision. My legs went weak every time I thought about it. I prayed that my memories of Europe and June would not fade; now needing them close by to see me through this.

The following week I was able to get one of our aircraft and flew to Andrews Air Force Base outside Washington. I landed at 0930, changed clothes, got transportation, was off the shuttle bus at Independence Avenue at 10:50, and at 1725 K St N.W. at 1100 (the Air America stateside office). *Exactly when I had said I would be there.* I was ushered inside and waited nervously in a sterile-looking area that could have been the entrance to any bona fide business. There were no wall decorations that hinted at the pursuit of this organization. A gracious lady with a manila folder approached me, smiled, shook my hand, and escorted me into Red's office. I was favorably impressed by a down-to-earth sort of guy; about fifty, paunchy, with an experienced air, nice smile and thinning red hair.

"Red Dawsond here, glad to meet you." I was praying there would be no embarrassing or disqualifying questions. Sadly the salaries he outlined fell short of what I had heard, but I had pretty much committed to this fork in the road. He asked me if I had really considered the consequences of getting out of the Marine Corps after nine years. "You're halfway there you know." (Major Burnham would have approved of Red's counselling.) I told him my official separation should be in just a couple weeks. *I had no idea of the emptiness and loss that would accompany leaving the only employment I had ever known.* Had I known, I doubt I could have gone through with the resignation. I guess in my naiveté or reliance on providence, I was just assuming I'd be a Marine pilot one day, and a gainfully employed Air America pilot the next.

It Happened!

Just one week later, on a day filled with doubts and speculation regarding my present and future work possibilities, everything changed: a packet from Red arrived. It showed my hire date to be in one week—at 2400 hours on June 13th (making me wonder if it was a coincidence that my separation from the Corps was going to be on 2359 hours on the 12th)! Included were my itinerary, all my tickets, and a list of items to bring along (as well as those not to bring). I was excited. In my ignorance of the import of all this, I at least began to savor again the mystique of jumping off for 'parts unknown', as I had done so often in Europe

And when I shared all this with Sara? As usual she went along with everything. *If I thought it was for the best, she would conclude it was.* I didn't know if her passiveness was because of a great inner tranquility, or that she never understood the theme of my machinations, or that she doubted she could make a difference if she tried. *Sara! Speak out! Please make your thoughts known.* I don't know how she ever let me go through with it. Perhaps she was numbed from years of inattention and my lack of prioritizing what might be important in her life. Perhaps having never experienced a devoted husband she had accustomed herself to me—this kind of interface being the norm. Certainly her calmness in this instance wasn't due to my confidence or enthusiasm, since I wasn't expressing any.

Just under the surface I was experiencing grave doubt; in fact downright fear! The kids—what do they know? Like I said before, they know about when supper is on the stove, they know when they're on your lap. They know when their mom and dad are laughing, but they don't know about separations, either temporary physical ones, or later, legal ones. I'm sure I didn't know.

The night before my official separation, my carrier buddies threw a hell of a party for me. The punch was potent (a variety of fruit juices, ice cream, and rum), but tasted like fruit slushies. I drank way more than my share. I don't know how I was allowed to drive home (or made it)! This was before the war on DUI. No one even blinked at me staggering out the door. I remember patches of roadway, an occasional yellow line, tree limbs streaking by, going airborne after passing over humps in the road, before thankfully, in what seemed like three minutes—finding myself in our driveway. *God was I lucky.*

Can't Believe I was Able to See It Through

Sara had probably not yet accustomed herself to my return, and here I was bounding out of her life again. I told her that even though I was taking a job halfway around the world, in 90 days she could join me, and we'd have a great life abroad. I'm not sure she felt at ease with my explanation. (I know I didn't.) If the Air America thing had been any later arriving—even a week or two, I may not have been able to do it. I realized, but only as I was packing (too late) that I was becoming more comfortable here—settling into a family routine, the normality of it, the comfort of it. Not that the faces and places I had visited for ten months had faded. No, they were still right there.

Sara followed me around the house, while I gathered up articles of clothing, checked a list and assembled all the documentation I would need. I was whistling in the dark, alternately feeling moments of excitement and then waves of breath-taking apprehension. I was saying whatever I had to, to make this quick exodus go calmly. Sara's feelings I could see, were not so complex. She was worried. She was watching all this come together with absolutely no understanding of why, or what would evolve. As I reflect on my selfish departure, if she would have shed one tear I doubt I would have been able to carry it off. But she didn't. She just stood there, or sat there; the expression on her face saying, "I guess you know what you're doing. I hope you know what you're doing." *I didn't.* Good thing she didn't know I didn't.

The drive to the Charleston airport was quiet. I knew I should try to make it upbeat, and be talking about how they'd be living in a big house in Bangkok or Singapore. I knew that's where most the Vietnam pilots domiciled their wives and kids. I'd heard (and enthusiastically told Sara) about big homes, maids, cooks, and personal drivers, which would introduce her to a new and privileged lifestyle. And there was a modern International School which should provide a rewarding experience for the kids. I wasn't at all sure of anything. Maybe the realities of my motives were so well known to me, I couldn't make this hyping up of the situation credible to myself. Maybe I had at least some conscience. Somehow the goodbyes were accomplished. I made it inside the terminal, to the gate, to the aircraft, and collapsed onboard.

Chapter Two
SOUTHEAST ASIA!

Arriving in Taipei, Taiwan

The flights transited San Francisco and Hong Kong before arriving in Taipei—the S.E. Asia headquarters for Air America. It was (secretly) located there, inside the Civil Air Transport offices (CAT airlines—the face-saving flag carrier of Nationalist China). The airline was a commercial venture begun after WWII, initially run by retired Army Air Corps General Claire Chenault, who had gained respect and notoriety as the head of the storied "Flying Tigers," and who I was to hear time and time again was a true giant among men. He, Chiang Kai Shek (the military leader of the old Republic of China), and many other opponents of Chairman Mao fled to Taiwan (then Formosa) from mainland China in 1949. As you might imagine, often found among the CAT pilot group were aging members of the original "Flying Tigers. Unknown to me and most others, it had been covertly purchased for intelligence-gathering purposes by the CIA.

I was impressed. Upon landing at one in the morning a van was there to meet me and one other arriving new hire. It took us to our hotel and picked us up in the morning (a little earlier than I would have preferred). There, I and several other new hires learned we were to be instructed in Taiwanese aviation regulations and then take tests to qualify us to fly in their country. (Never mind we weren't ever going to be flying in Taiwan.) It was easy to see, based on the regulations and heartfelt sincerity of the instructors, Taiwan worried every day about an attack from the Army of The People's Republic of China, now ruling the mainland under Chairman Mao. The regulations stated huge fines, long sentences, and even the death penalty, for any aviator caught making radio transmissions to the mainland (just 110 miles away, across the Formosa Straits). None of us had too much trouble passing the tests, but were very much impressed by the earnest delivery by the Chinese instructors. Most of them had been pilots in the Republic of China Air Force in their loss to Mao's revolutionaries. We could see that they were still fighting that war, and to the man believed that they would one day return, face Mao's soldiers again, defeat them, and again retake control of the mainland.

Bangkok, Thailand

After finishing in Taipei we boarded a flight for Bangkok on CAT Airlines, aboard their top-of-the-line *Mandarin Jet*—the airline's only jet; a many-times-over refurbished, secondhand Convair 880. In no other airline did one airplane spend less time on the ground and more time in the air. You would have thought CAT had ten of them. It seemed to be in Bangkok, Hong Kong, and Tokyo the same night (and usually was). The aircraft was highly polished, trimmed with white and gold, and boasted a long dragon stretching the length of the fuselage. The interior was done up like the executive dining room in a Chinese restaurant. The stewardesses wore silk brocade, sheath dresses, with the high slit up the leg. There were hot towels, spring rolls, rice bowls, and chop sticks. It was my first experience to Oriental hospitality.

I was excited about what I would find in Bangkok. I'd heard a lot about it—*the massage capital of the world!* It was almost two in the morning when we taxied up to the arrival gates at Bangkok's Don Muang Airport. I couldn't believe how hot it was when I stepped out of the airplane. Middle of the night and the temperature and humidity were in the high nineties! I had my first exposure to the unmistakable fragrance of Bangkok—the fragrance of sweet flowers; almost too sweet. Once having smelled it (I think Frangipani) you would forever be able to identify arriving there even without opening your eyes. I was tired and I guess, irritable. I'd sweated through my clothes several times already. The airport was virtually deserted. Ours was the only aircraft on the ramp, and we were the only passengers in the terminal. It was 1965. The U.S. Military buildup in Vietnam was just getting rolling, so Bangkok had not yet become the wild "R&R" (Rest and Recuperation) spot it would shortly become. At the moment it was a ghost airport.

I wasn't the lone Air America employee. There were four other pilots including a short and boisterous guy named Harry Bonetta. He was about 35 and acting as if he was an old hand at all this—attempting to take over the whole show. He wasn't a 'new-hire' like we were. He was just returning from his first home leave. He wasn't based in Saigon. He was assigned to our overt air transport operation in Tachikawa, Japan. Had a hard time believing he was a pilot (maybe an engineer or navigator). I couldn't decide if Harry was real, a phony, or a real phony. "They owe us a van. They knew we were coming." Harry wasn't about to fork over money for a cab. Me, I would have spent it in a minute. I was tired. Who cares if they forgot to send a van, but Harry was not inviting anyone to intervene. I couldn't tell if the other guys were humoring him or counting on him. He had nice wavy black hair, which I later learned lifted off at night. In all fairness, five years later when I bumped into Harry, and saw how many friends he had, the guy must have had something going for him.

Harry's calls paid off. The van finally arrived (though I would have been asleep in my hotel by then if I would have taken a cab). It must've been about 10 miles to the city, on a wide, straight, new concrete road. There were canals on both sides and I could make out the shapes of huge water buffalos alongside them. As we approached the city limits, Bangkok's arrival on the world scene was evidenced by cranes and new construction in every direction. Brightly colored cabs with added chrome ornaments continued to shoot past us. Their license plates were encircled with flashing peanut lights and loud Thai music was blaring out their open windows. Once in the city I noticed an unusually large number of girls wandering the streets; shapely young girls, in high heels and too-short dresses.

The City

Downtown: The corner of Silom and Sukhumvit—the crossroads of Bangkok. Only two blocks up Silom, a right turn onto Pat Pong street, and there was the Air America office on the right. This storied street was in the process of gaining world acclaim as a hangout for mercenaries, journalists, and horny single guys—with its share of girly bars and upstairs massage parlors. While at this point it was on its way, Pat Pong still had respectability. Besides Air America it boasted the Japan Air Lines office and the Air France office. The bars still had some innocence; all being sport-drinking pubs with darts and shuffleboard, and lots of camaraderie. I was to soon discover that before CNN, it was the best place to get the latest Southeast Asian news and rumors. There was a bar for just about every foreign nationality represented in the city. We went by a bar for the Germans with a giant pewter stein mounted above the door; a bar for the Swedes with a brightly enameled Swedish flag carved out of teak hanging outside; an Australian bar with its 'yard of ale' over the door; and a bar called The Red Door which you can guess how it was distinguished. Bangkok was for just about everybody. And finally, there was Tigers—the bona-fide watering hole for all the Southeast Asia soldiers of fortune. (To this day you might find an old Air America pilot there.)

Around the far corner of Pat Pong, the van let us off at our hotel on Suriwongse Street. It was the Thai version of our Econo-Lodge. AAM had put us up there—at least for the first night. As tired as I was, any place would have been okay. I didn't even bother to shower. I was exhausted and fell into the rack. I was just drifting off when there was a loud knocking on the door:

"Who is it?"

"The Manager."

"Yes, what?"

"Do you have a girl in there?"

"No Goddamit, I don't have a girl in here!"

"Do you want one?"

Bangkok was for fun. Everyone knew it, and pitched in to do his or her part. The following morning I had to check-in at the AAM office with the other new pilots. We sat through a few more days of company indoctrination while we waited for our duty station assignments, and then the visas to go there. Except for the oppressive heat, it was beautifully clear. It was a bustling city, constantly on the move. Lots of traffic. When it wasn't racing at a frightening speed, it was at a dead stop. Usually it was curb-to-curb taxis (all Datsuns); their fares sweltering in the back seats on clear plastic seat covers. The smell of flowers and diesel fumes and feeling your shirt stuck to your back—that was Bangkok. In some tropical cities they've chosen to coexist with the heat, opting to just leave the doors and windows open. But not in Bangkok—every hotel, restaurant, bar, or shop you walked into, seemed to be kept near freezing! Hell with living with the heat. Lock it out. The motto of almost every establishment was "Step into our refrigerator and see your breath." Every building was trembling beneath a mega-ton air conditioner rumbling on its roof.

Bangkok was the 'safe haven' city where most the married Saigon pilots kept their families. Since in Saigon there was always the threat of Viet Cong terrorist action: a satchel charge here, a satchel charge there, sniper fire, or a car-bombing, keeping your family in Bangkok—only a short flight away and out of harm's way, was an accepted procedure. (And in fact that was my very intention.) Bangkok had good schools; an International school and an American School, all kinds of rental property to choose from, and lots of activities for the ladies. On the surface, keeping the wives and kids in Bangkok looked like the reasonable, practical thing to do. (No one interpreted this as a result of questionable marital preferences.) I spent as much time as I could cruising the areas where Americans chose to live (out Sukhumvit a few miles, near the American School). I tried to picture Sara and the kids in one locale or another. Knowing that a maid and cook were part of the deal, it was hard to believe she'd balk at this setup. And I was able to locate several large and modern houses in good areas, in walled compounds, with nice yards, that would do just fine. This should be easy. *Though now after many years, I can't believe I did and would, drag my family through so much—just to meet my ends.* I get a pain in my heart when I think of my behavior and selfishness.

On the outskirts of this new gleaming city, one could not help but be impressed by the obvious good health and fine figures of the indigenous residents, and their penchant for clean bodies. They must wash themselves more than any other ethnic group. Somewhere on every block was a neighborhood shower. Under it, men and women (but mostly well-physiqued men) wrapped below the waist in colorful plaid cotton sarongs, were energetically scrubbing themselves and dousing off. Those citizens living in lesser well-off areas could still be seen daily—using pails and pots to dump "clong" (canal) water over their heads. Washing appeared to be a national pastime, and the Thais have the most beautifully colored and textured skin. (Any guy who ever took a Thai girl to bed would forever rave about her silky skin.)

Here in Bangkok I was embarrassedly not just dwelling on my new employment and future responsibilities, but rather—once again was thinking of myself, and what possible liaisons I might stumble on here in the Far East. I couldn't avoid checking out the hotel lobbies and surveying American and European female tourists. Bangkok had a wide assortment of hotels: some were super modern, like the brand new Siam Intercontinental, and some for 'old money' like the famous Erawan Hotel—an all-wood classic like a New England old people's home. It was only two stories and sprawled over well-kept grounds. Lots of British and German tourists stayed there. I wasn't hitting any of the massage parlors and didn't plan to either. It wasn't my style. If at some time I was going to stumble into an association, I would prefer it to be with a proper Anglo-Saxon lady in a gray business suit, maybe with a briefcase (or if not one of that type, then some rebellious, stringy-haired flower child with no bra, on her way to Nepal).

Something of Which I'm Certainly Not Proud

One night before going back to the hotel, myself and another pilot decided to visit a neat little bar we'd recently found; a hole in the wall called Talk-of-the-Town. Being frequented by the Aussies (some real beer-drinking went on there). The draw was the piano player, who not only played like Billy Joel, but kept up a non-stop banter—insulting the patrons. Tonight, seated in a corner booth was a big, wide-mouthed, large-breasted, raven-haired woman, wearing a tight red knit dress and dark sun glasses. As such she was drawing a lot of attention (and reveling in it). She was with a short bald guy wearing a banker's suit—who didn't appear a likely companion. She was talking loud, gesturing wildly with big hands, and emitting sexy, throaty laughter. Not lady-like, but radiating a sexual boldness that demanded notice. You certainly couldn't use words like "cute" or "effeminate" to describe her. No, that she wasn't. She may have been an entertainer, perhaps a stripper. When Bob and I finished our first beer, he opted to call it an evening.

Her male companion—perhaps worried about having bitten off more than he could chew, had excused himself and left. I was sitting close enough to start a conversation and learned she was staying at the historic Erawan hotel, which surprised me, since it was the most discriminating hotel in town (and she was definitely not representative of their clientele). She asked if I'd like to hit her favorite place before calling it a night. With no overtures on my part, in lieu of the Bamboo Bar, she orders the driver take us to the Erawan. While I'm expecting her to jump out with some closing comment, she just up and tells me to give her thirty minutes and then come up to her room! *Whoaa, what am I doing—again? So soon!* While she was most definitely not a woman I would ever have pictured myself with, either once or on a continuing bases, *there was always that chance that her aggressive sexuality would jolt me into the expected male response* (which as you know after reading Part Two, I could not even claim to be an occasional occurrence)!

Here I Go Experimenting Again, So Soon!

I waited the thirty minutes (*Shades of Erica and the Carlton Hotel in Cannes*) and then walked, but with substantial second-thoughts—through the lobby and up to the second floor. There I tip-toed down the poorly lit, carpeted but musty, creaking old wooden-floored hallway. Being two in the morning this upper wing was deserted. There it was—room 217. I knocked softly (didn't want the adjacent room occupant accidently opening their door). She opened the door—naked, turned her back to me and led me into her room. It was completely dark. No overhead light, no lamp, not even a night-light in the bathroom. I could barely see anything. A harsh, bright street light was being kept out by the drawn window curtains. As I followed behind, I discerned a not too exciting silhouette. She didn't have a narrow waist, nor was it accented by a flare of the hips. She was straight from the armpits to the thighs. And she was not so tall. I was looking over her head, whereas in the club she was eye-to-eye with me. Must've had on four inch heels. As best I could see the huge head of hair wasn't as huge. It looked close-cropped (or maybe she'd taken a shower and it was combed back). A few minutes later while leaning on the back of the desk chair, I realized my hand was atop a wig. Here in her room, my date was not boasting any prominent female curves or the unsubdued sexuality she had flaunted in the club. Any amorous urges I was hoping to be in possession of had been eradicated.

Holy Shit!

Without a single embrace we were in the bed—or at least she was. I climbed in with a slight delay, feeling a pronounced impropriety (which was in addition to my great concern about my coming performance, or lack thereof). I was taken aback by her unusually urgent desire that I make love to her—immediately. She held on to me strongly—too strongly, almost with desperation, and implored me to enter her. It was way too much, way too soon. This great need on her part didn't make sense. I knew I was in the wrong place. I had no choice but to begin some foreplay, which she appeared to be enjoying beyond reality. Her skin was okay, but her stomach was wide and hard. I slid my hand down to her mound to excite her most sensitive spot; and it wasn't hard to find. It was high on top, like a big button. It was large—larger than my thumb. Something was not making sense! I reflected on everything up to this point, and it hit me like a ton of heart-stopping bricks. *I was in bed with a guy who had recently had a sex change operation!*

This explained the dark room, the short hair, the small nipples, the straight waist, the big hands, the husky voice. *Jesus Christ!* Needless to say this deduction ended any amorous feelings I might have been trying to generate. She (or he) was near to crying now; begging to be screwed. *By me? With what?* (After last year's experimentation, a hard-on with Miss America would not be a safe wager.) So what little chance there had been was for sure now gone. Even if I could have, I don't think I would have. Next thing I know, surprisingly not discouraged *she's talking about us getting married!?* She had friends in Argentina. They had a house for her. *We could go and live there for nothing.* "Please. It will be a paradise. I'll be so good for you."

While listening and waiting for an excuse to flee, she told me she was an entertainer and in two days was going to Hong Kong, *and did I have any contacts? Me?* Well as good fortune would have it, when I was in Taipei I had met Redd Foxx (of the long running TV sitcom "Sanford and Sons.") who had just had a gig in Hong Kong and was now performing at the Princess Hotel here in Bangkok. I called the hotel and to my amazement got Foxx between shows, and he remembered me! I told him I needed the name of an agent in Hong Kong. Without hesitation he gave me his agent's name and two clubs there. My date was impressed and almost trembling with gratitude. *At least I didn't turn out to be a complete bust;* she now had something to look forward to. There would be another city, another man, another chance for her. *I was out of there and on my way to a long, hot shower!*

Learning More About Vietnam

We got our station assignments—all of us were going to Saigon. Not well understood by me then, Vietnam used to be just one country (Indochina) and preferred as such by its citizens. After the defeat of the French at Dien Bien Phu in 1954, five nations (*none* of which was Vietnam), met in Geneva and declared that the country would be split in half at the east-west running Ben Hai river (more commonly referred to as the 17th parallel). This division was never accepted by either the residents of the new northern country or the new southern country. Or in other words one possible reason the war started, and why the war may have been unwinnable from the start! And evidently we don't learn well, because after WWII, the victors: the U.S. and Russia, cut Germany in half, right through the middle of Berlin; and then decided to do the same thing with

Korea; dividing it at the 38th parallel; the Russians taking the north half and we taking the south half (and we all know now how that is working out).

What? We Could Have Gone Somewhere Else?

Up to this time I was unaware there was another main base we could have been sent to: Vientiane, Laos. In Laos—although not making any headlines, a brutal country-wide covert CIA-administered military combat operation had been going on for at least five years. The Agency was in the process of arming and training just about every male member of the Laotian mountain tribes (the Hmong) to resist the continuing southerly incursions of the North Vietnamese Army into Laos. This military effort required many supply missions as well as the actual transport of the Hmong soldiers to and from the front lines. *All these airlift needs were taken care of by Air America personnel and aircraft based in the Laotian capital of Vientiane.* The old hands repeatedly told us that it was in Laos that the *real* war was going on, where the *real* (and dangerous) flying was being done, and where the *real* pilots were assigned. But for us—for now, we were going to Saigon. And now, with our visas in hand, we were all through in Bangkok and God willing—for better or worse, tomorrow our feet would be on the ground in Vietnam!

Chapter Three
OFF TO SAIGON CITY

A Pensive Flight There

Bangkok was sweltering. Just like yesterday and every other day, the temperature must have been 100 and the humidity the same. And inside this old French Caravelle it was worse. Thirty-six bodies in an aluminum oven, stuck to the seat, neck soaked. *Sure hope they get the air on quick.* Sitting alone I couldn't help but reflect on my week's shenanigans. Between the daytime class work and my sampling of Bangkok night life, I was feeling a little physically and mentally sapped. This hour and a half flight to Saigon would be a chance to rest and wonder; question for more than just a few minutes the decisions I'd made during the past year; where in the hell my life was going, and what this one was going to mean. On the same flight were the four guys I had gone through orientation with. One we had nick-named the "Baht-Kid" after his wild spending of the Thai currency in the Bangkok massage parlors. As we descended into Vietnamese airspace I sensed some of our bravado fading. The jokes were more forced as it began to sink in that we really had no idea what to expect. Soon we weren't speaking at all. A week ago the headlines in the Bangkok English-language newspaper announced that the Viet Cong had blown up the old US Embassy, and yesterday it said they had hit the famous *My Canh* floating restaurant—killing nine US personnel. *This could well turn out to be more than we bargained for.*

Arriving at Tan Son Nhut Airport

Gray skies and rain showers filled all quadrants as we commenced our descent into Tan Son Nhut airport. Approaching pattern altitude and anxious to get some idea of the terrain and structures of my new country of residence, I swiveled left and right, peering out alternate sides of the aircraft as it banked from side to side. Dissatisfied with the results I resigned myself to whatever success I might have looking out my own window (which was unfortunately half blocked by the seat in front of me). Patching together the glimpses I was able to get between the low clouds still beneath us I was observing a sea of rusted corrugated metal roofs; in fact every building I could see—regardless of its size, had this type roof. Although not as much greenery as I would have expected, there were a few palmed trees in and around the shacks. The majority of these structures, which may have been homes or small commercial establishments, were tilting or shored-up—appearing as nothing more than battered and oft repaired sheds or shacks; lots of fields with trash; lots of narrow red dirt roads—all cored with ruts and cluttered with puddles. Not that many cars, but a million scooters and bicycles. Tiny figures clothed in black were scurrying in all directions. Smoke was drifting up from the center of every small cluster of individuals. Turning on downwind leg I noticed at least one gathering on every street we flew over, which I would later learn was the neighborhood 'soup and noodle' stand. Our real point of interest— downtown Saigon City was about three or four miles from the airport, so unfortunately due to our low pattern altitude and banking of the aircraft, we were unable to get even a momentary sneak preview.

On the ramp—stopped; engines having spun down, for the moment everything was silent. A few nervous glances were exchanged as we got to our feet. We emerged from the aircraft into a pelting rain and had to use caution as we descended the soaked and slick aluminum stairway. Safely on the tarmac we made a quick dash to the terminal. Inside we became part of a similarly concerned group of travelers attempting to bear up while being herded one way then another; directed first into a queue on the left and then a moment later being yanked out of it and sent to the queue on the right. Very-much-in-charge officials (all thin as a rail and with gaunt faces) scanned the incoming passengers suspiciously— seemingly just waiting for someone to question their authority. The process of immigration and customs was being accomplished using decades-old French Colonial procedures. From behind high warped wood counters and chipped Formica tables, immigration officials were carrying out their duties with as much decorum as they could muster at this time and under these circumstances. They conversed in noisy and nasal staccato bursts, only breaking it long enough to impatiently gesture some arriving passenger to move from one line to another. Waiting, we were a captive audience to a non-stop cacophony of indecipherable chatter and rubber stamps banging on passports.

The Vietnamese people—men and women alike were just skin and bones. They appeared to be accustomed to hard work and evidently not a whole lot of food; didn't see one that couldn't use another twenty pounds. Every man in sight that wasn't in a uniform was dressed the same: a long-sleeved white shirt and black trousers. And they must sell only one size belt in Vietnam—too big, because every man had a foot of belt hanging down beyond the buckle. The sound of the Vietnamese language was new to me. I was hearing it fast and furiously from all sides. Heated exchanges would rise and fall above a background of normal conversations. To my ears—at this point, the language sounded like a bunch of ducks quacking. I was not feeling bold and decided it might be wise to view the whole procedure as a drill that should be played according to their rules. It wouldn't take too long and I didn't want to sample the difficulties you could cause for yourself if you 'made a wave'. You had to be very patient, then very responsive; still and silent as a photo, then spouting answers and handing over documents on cue. The wartime activity was not close, but everyone looked as though they were taking its presence real seriously. No question about it, I felt a strange new and vibrant energy in the air. I was sure I'd truly arrived at a place where things were happening. Everything was being done with time as the overriding consideration. People were in a hurry. You could feel the urgency and sense that at least in this place, at this time, things were barely under control. It was still pouring.

The terminal—which was the only public service building on the airport, was wet straight through, from the aircraft ramp to the small parking lot out front. In fact it was raining *inside* the building; leaks everywhere. It was a long low one story building. No I take that back. Once outside and looking back I could see the front part of it supported a recently constructed second floor—probably newly necessitated offices. Evidently it was without air conditioning, since all the windows were swung open and the curtains were tied back. Perched on every casement sill was at least one individual, sampling the cooler outside air and eating non-descript morsels of food out of pieces of newspaper and drinking what could have been iced coffee or a cream-colored soup (out of jelly jars). *Whew.* For once, I was glad I wasn't alone; content to be just one of a group undergoing the same doubt-filled situation.

I GUESS I JUST WASN'T THINKING

Our New Duty Station

We knew we were supposed to be met by an Air America van (and from our stay in Bangkok, were familiar with the blue and silver paint scheme). But no such vehicle was in sight. I don't know how he knew, but one guy said that the Air America ramp was located adjacent to the airport parking lot; just on the other side of a vine-entwined chain link fence—which contained a small and all but hidden gate. Heck with the van. In spite of the rain and puddles to be encountered, we set off on foot to cover the short distance; a band of strange-looking American gypsies lugging their Samsonites. Our travel orders were enough to get us past an elderly Vietnamese guard stationed at this apparently rarely used side gate.

Once through the fence I had my first view of what would be my workplace for some time to come; an almost level, pot-holed, puddled and patched tarmac parking ramp that boasted a wide variety of single and multi-engine reciprocating (propeller) aircraft—perhaps 20 or 30; most with tailwheels (the old fashion type); a few with the newer tricycle (nose wheel) landing gear. There were several types of aircraft I didn't even recognize. However (thankfully) all of them appeared to be well maintained, or at least they were highly-polished aluminum with white and blue trim. Each had the words *Air America Inc*, emblazoned on the side; good-looking to my eye. (I was beginning to feel a little better.)

There were Oriental workers in dark blue coveralls everywhere. I was to learn that while all the mechanics were Filipinos, the men cleaning the planes, sweeping the ramp, and doing odd jobs in the area were Vietnamese laborers. We and everything we were carrying were really soaked by now. In addition to my three-suiter and gym bag full of neat other items (including a bunch of 45 RPM records), I was carrying a plastic bag of special letters from several of my European female acquaintances. To our right, a large two-bay maintenance hangar spanned the runway side of the ramp. Attached to one side of it was a two-story, white wood building that we guessed was the administration building. We started towards it.

The entrance was on the second level. We struggled up the steps of the narrow outside stairway to a door that said "Operations." Inside the Chief Pilot's office we met Les Stroud, sitting at a desk with a sign that said "Chief Pilot." He was young—about my age. He did not appear sufficiently experienced to be behind that desk. He had a high, neatly combed pompadour and was smoking a cigar (which to me did not help him make the transition). In spite of the fact that I did not consider him to be the manager here, he commenced to give out information and instructions without faltering and with complete confidence. There appeared to be no doubt in his mind he was qualified. To me it still seemed as if he was doing this while the real Chief Pilot was in the toilet or on the phone somewhere (which turned out to be true). I was thinking he must have been the first pilot hired, to have worked his way up to Chief Pilot already. (Or he was as qualified as he thought he was, age notwithstanding.) All through this meandering, off-the-cuff introduction to Air America and Saigon, the corrugated metal roof kept up a fierce drumming under the hard rain. I began to feel a chill. At one point I asked a question about our work schedule: *How often did we fly?* One of the captains passing through overheard the question and responded over his shoulder, "Every day." *Say what!? Every day?* I was going to have to ask more about that.

A Ride to Town I'll Never Forget

About six o'clock Les was running out of things to tell us and sent us to the transport shack. There we crammed ourselves into one of the familiar vans for the trip to town. Just as we were about to pull out, we were joined by a burly Captain who had just finished his day of flying. The driver set off on what would be a wet and sloppy trek to downtown Saigon. We were wide-eyed taking in all the sights as we made our way towards the airport gate. There was a lookout tower and guard station every hundred yards. Roll after roll of concertina wire lined the road and every building was behind a wall of stacked nylon-mesh sand bags (ripped and leaking). Behind the bags were Vietnamese soldiers manning mean-looking automatic weapons. We were now in the midst of it. Prepared or not, we were likely to be part of a chapter of history.

Stan Armbrook—the barrel chested Captain who was riding with us the first part of the journey, was an outspoken red-neck from somewhere in Texas; huge forearms, dark hair and dark eyes. One would learn he had strong opinions on any subject that came up, especially the Vietnamese people. There was no love lost between Stan and the locals, I can tell you that. He continued to warn us about this and then that, discounting this and then that. No doubt in his mind about where everything stood around here. Later I heard he had been the personal pilot for Billy Sol Estes when Billy's financial scandals came to light and he chose to escape the country. Stan had flown him to Cuba and then Venezuela, with the FBI in hot pursuit.

I GUESS I JUST WASN'T THINKING

There was however, one thing which Stan said, that I had occasion to reflect on many times in the years to come. We new guys were talking about where we would domicile our wives when they were cleared to join us. (I didn't know if the others—like me, had no intention of having their wives join them here in Saigon.) We spoke about the common practice of locating wives in Bangkok, where they would stay—safe and out of harm's way. This made sense in view of the dangers here in Saigon. The flight schedule was such that pilots would fly their ass off for twenty days, and have ten days off to visit their wives and kids at the chosen safe haven. Not too bad. Stan overhearing our conversation, turned and growled, "Show me a guy who won't have his wife here in Saigon with him, and I'll show you a guy who doesn't love his wife." Hearing this I thought, *what a ridiculous statement!* And a couple of the other new guys outright challenged him on it. But he didn't renege. As the months and years went by I found out that old Stan was right as rain. The whole case for keeping your wife 'out of harm's way' was in almost every instance, just a smoke-screen for some middle-aged guy to have a chance to do some experimenting. (Unfortunately—like me.)

An incident occurred on the way to town that demonstrated Stan's lack of regard for the Vietnamese (who he persisted in mispronouncing as the "Viet-ma-nese"). The streets were choc-a-block with all manner of two-wheeled vehicles. Bicycles, motorcycles, and mopeds, whined and sputtered along as best they could. Vietnamese of both genders and all ages were guiding these spindly, vulnerable vehicles in a masterful way in and out among the bigger traffic. Mostly they hugged the side of the road, slowing down then lurching ahead to keep their balance in the rutted and puddled edges of the silt-covered pavement or soft dirt. Most of them had large bundles precariously lashed on the backs of their scooters, as well as a bulging plastic bag hanging from one wrist, and a section of newspaper held over their head with the other hand as a rain shield. A difficult and dangerous journey even without Stan. As we approached one such poor soul on a moped—barely succeeding in negotiating his way in the narrow area between the passing traffic and the weeds and rocks at the edge of the pavement, Stan—with some snarling words of contempt, waited until our van was abreast the moped, then swung open the door, slamming it into the driver's side, sending him cartwheeling over into the refuse along the side of the road. We were shocked speechless at this, glancing back and forth at each other in disbelief. Our trip to downtown Saigon was arranged so as to be able to drop off Stan at his house. His dutiful Mexican wife was waiting outside (in the rain) to meet him. *Good riddance.*

Saigon City

It was quite a sight when we finally descended into the steaming, smoky, drenched and bustling city center. Under low hanging clouds and through the fog and lingering drizzle we were able to make out all manner of vehicles jammed together bumper to bumper and door to door. Pedestrians of all sorts and ages were dodging between them, each carrying a variety of bags, boxes, or even large car parts. Three out of four cars were taxis— Volkswagen Beetles; every one painted bright blue with yellow fenders. In front of every other storefront was an outdoor cookery under a makeshift canvas awning. From each one smoke was drifting up about ten feet, then spreading and hanging there. All kinds of smells were making their way into our van. The sidewalks were lined with hawkers who had set up low-rent places of business: soup stands, tea stands, noodle stands, rice stands, and miscellaneous tables spread with wallets, sun glasses, belts, ivory-carvings, and 'you-name-its'. These were edge to edge the whole way down every street. And small children were everywhere—more than half of them taking care of even younger children. What appeared to be six or seven-year-old girls were carrying their infant brothers or sisters in an interesting fashion; one hip stuck out—almost to the point of dislocation, and the infant sitting astraddle this bony perch.

Chapter Four
A HOTEL CHECK-IN TO END ALL CHECK-INS

I Swear To You, Every Word of This Is True

We turned onto the famous Nguyen Hue (street of flowers). It was the Las Ramblas of Saigon, making its way to the harbor; a bricked promenade with a wide grassy medium, lined with mahogany benches and shaded under huge elms. It was a once-tranquil and pleasurable sight designed for French families to lounge about, but at the moment appeared to be taken over by inebriated US troops—using it for settling arguments and propositioning local girls (in the middle of a downpour). It was on this street that Air America had gotten us reservations for the first night. *It would be a hotel check-in that none of us would ever forget.*

The driver stopped in front of a narrow, stand alone, three-story, building. On each side of it was an empty sand lot. It looked as if each lot had previously borne older structures that had been demolished for more profitable businesses. In no way did our building resemble a hotel (other than the brand new red plastic sign above the door that said *Catinat Hotel*). We tumbled out of the van and into the pelting rain, each of us looking left and right for what must really be our intended lodgings. But no—as difficult as it was to believe, this was it. The driver continued vigorously pointing at it and nodding. The whole building was only about 20 feet across and I wondered how it could contain multiple rooms—it was too narrow; at best maybe two small rooms on the second and two on the third floor, one to the front and the other in back.

Based on the appearance of its ground floor, it was a recently-abandoned store, perhaps with the owner's apartment above it. The window cases on either side of the entrance no longer contained any merchandise. There were a few hand-scrawled messages on pieces of yellowed paper, atop a faded, dust-laden silk curtain, draped over a pile of boxes. It appeared the building had just recently been converted into a makeshift hotel to take advantage of the thousands of Americans streaming into Saigon daily (with no place to stay and willing to pay handsomely for a bed—anywhere).

Inside the hotel, along the left wall of the lobby (which had to be the actual exterior left wall of the building) there was a long row of straight-back chairs. Stark. No doorways, no windows, no hanging pictures; nothing on or against the wall. Along the right side (which also had to be the exterior right-side wall of the building) was the reception counter. Just past it on the same side, was a door (which according to my calculations would have opened up onto the vacant sand lot next door). However, surprisingly, it was marked *Ascensor* (elevator in French). Not surprisingly there were no rooms here on the ground floor. Standing where I was, on a badly worn, dyed straw rug, whose colors had long ago run out of their assigned areas, I could only think: old, musty, damp, dark, and for me, *temporary!* The walls were maroon and the floor was black, and both done with a high-gloss paint! *Geez!* No Hilton here I can tell you. No restaurant. No bar. For sure, no exciting, eligible, international businesswomen were going to be hanging around here. Only one hotel employee in sight; the only person in sight.

The (Long) Trip to Our Room

The five of us (without much conversation and avoiding each other's darting eyes) signed in, gathered up our soaked possessions and followed the concierge. He ushered three of us into the aforementioned *Ascensor*. Even before our full weight was on the floor I wondered if it would be up to the task. I got in with Bob and Rob, filling it to absolute capacity. Rob wasn't small and Bob probably weighed 240 pounds. The three of us rode upwards in silence, eyes downward, praying that the creaking and swaying was not a forerunner of total failure. One couldn't help noticing the deep scarring of Rob's pock-marked face. He must've had terrible acne as a kid, and I would later learn, bore a lot of complexes; not very polished. He had taught himself to fly and had done a damned good job at it. Rob I discovered had his finest hours in the cockpit. He felt sure of himself there. Another psyche took over outside an airplane—not at all refined; certainly not someone you would introduce to your sister. (Ten years later, after Air America, he would die of lung cancer in a Mexico jail.) I liked Rob, in spite of his cynical and uncouth attitude. Almost everybody liked him, at least some of the time.

The elevator went up one floor and stopped. That made sense—the second floor. But then a big surprise! The *back* wall of the elevator motored open! (which according to my calculations *would have spilled us out into airspace two stories above the sand lot to the right*). However it did not. We were in a small darkened area with no windows. The other two joined us momentarily (with similar looks of dismay on their faces). I could only conclude we were standing in some type of appendage attached to the outside of the building. The concierge broke the trance by motioning us to follow him, ten or fifteen steps further away from the building. I was forced to conclude we were suspended above the vacant lot in some enclosed, fragile, swaying, airborne walkway that would take us across the void below, and into an adjacent building on the other side of the lot. With no doors or windows in this passageway our suspicions were not alleviated. We all exchanged glances indicating a similar lack of conviction. For the moment we'd forgotten about the war and the Viet Cong and satchel charges.

Stepping out of this tunnel (into what I was praying was the building on the other side of the lot) we made a left turn, and proceeded rearwards down a long hallway. It ended with three steps up, through a door and onto a flat, open-air roof. We were on the top of the building; outside—in the elements, and it was still raining. Three long planters were on the roof top, with trellises rising above them, supporting a network of grape vines. Peering around them and scanning the horizon, we could see the tops of other of the city's buildings, poking into the gray wet clouds that were low and motionless. We faltered at this location, trying to get our bearings and plot our whereabouts from the narrow building we had originally entered.

Our concierge—noticeably affected by the rain, vigorously motioned for us to turn right and follow him, towards a three-foot high concrete block wall. We followed, wondering what more of a journey could possibly remain beyond this wall. Lo and behold, as we stepped through a cut in the wall we found ourselves *balancing on a narrow walkway around a rooftop swimming pool!* We were standing, loaded with luggage, hair plastered to our foreheads, on a two-foot wide ledge that went completely around the pool. If we took one step forward, we would have been treading water with our luggage. We shared precious foot space with dozens of kids sitting on the ledge; who anticipating our passing jumped into the pool (which was a sickening yellowish-green). Single-file, non-too-assuredly, we followed the concierge all along one side, gingerly placing our feet, to avoid crushing fingers and hands. We turned at the far corner and made our one-foot-in-front-of-the- other, tenuous way across the far side. We turned at the next corner and began returning up the third side (back towards the grape arbor.).

Halfway down this last side our leader disappeared into a door. It was a two step up entrance that we followed him into, entering what had to be a fully operational Chinese laundry! Through a maze of hanging laundry I spied four or five old men sitting cross-legged on wood tables, ironing and folding. Oriental music screeched from a radio with no exterior case and a hanger stuck in it as an antenna. A large mechanical device was cycling and steaming with archaic sighs and wheezes. The occupants did not take much notice of our intrusion, only examining us for a few seconds; the way out being through a door on the opposite side from our entrance. Out of the laundry and into *another* hallway. We were just about for giving up on this hotel right now. But a chance: At the end I could see a set of glass-paned French doors, with tied-back lace curtains behind. The best looking thing I'd seen since entering the hotel. *That could be our room.* We might have arrived! Up three more steps, through those doors, and we were there.

We computed our travel to have taken us out the side of the original hotel via an elevated passageway, into an adjacent building, completely through it front to back, out of it, onto the roof of the building behind it, off that building, and onto the roof of a fourth building (further to the right) where we went around the swimming pool, into the laundry, which must have been a fifth building behind the pool. We figured we must have made our way completely through one city block, front to back, and were now in an upper story of a building which fronted on a completely different street. (It was I would learn later, Tudo Street—the "street of bars.")

As grateful as you'd think we would be—to finally be in our room, it was nothing more than a large cell. It was only fifteen feet deep, but at least thirty feet wide, and completely empty. The only light was from one small window on each of the two exterior walls. And they were small windows—about a foot vertical by two feet wide, and worse—located almost to the ceiling; too high to look out. A real "Birdman of Alcatraz" space. All four walls appeared to have been recently poured; the cement not yet even cured—still that dark, grayish-green color. The whole floor was the same rough gray concrete as the walls. No rugs. No tile. Not a stick of furniture other than five metal cots (with no mattresses)! No tables. No lamps. A demoralizing queasiness overtook us all. There was an enclosed toilet and wash basin in the far right corner. The whole left side of the room was a shower area. A row of ugly showerheads lined the wall (like it was intended to be a locker room). A three-inch-high cement curb spanned the center of the room—ostensibly to keep the shower water from running into the right half of the room (where the cots were positioned). I was having serious misgivings about the viability of this Vietnam experience to be. The five of us sat on what support was available; not talking, heads in our hands, listening to the street sounds, each to his own thoughts. I could smell smoke, and fish, and other strange smells. It was still pouring. I was a little nauseous. *This may be gonna take everything I got.*

A new and frightening thought

As I sat there perusing the bleak surroundings, as well as my similarly stunned new comrades, and the soaked clumps of our belongings, my eyes came to rest on my stuff: the suitcase, the gym bag, and the plastic bag of letters. It was that last item that caused me to shudder. For the first time, I had no alternative but to look full face into another critical personal shortcoming, in addition to my impotence (which had already dictated my every thought and action since I was twenty). This new realization was of my perhaps genetic inability to make a commitment, to make a wholly permanent decision. The thought of doing so struck an overwhelming fear in my heart; that I would be quarantining myself from other activities, other people, and other possibilities, for the rest of my life. Of course, admittedly, I had no idea what these possibilities might be (most likely some yet unmet female partner whose aura would do it for me). My inability to perform, combined with this at last recognized second deficiency had plagued my marriage with Sara—a perfectly good woman (and now evidently persists even after having met wonderful June). Here I was with a collection of letters from June, Ardith, Paulette, Ingrid, and Erica! *What kind of true partner could I ever be? Don't most men settle on and become satisfied with one woman; one woman—special or not.* If I have this "commitment" deficiency, in combination with the real killer (which Europe convinced me of), even if I were blessed to find that one woman who would unlock my manhood, is there a chance I could still be doomed? Is it possible I am lacking the ability to love? Or love *one* woman—sufficiently to be able to exclude all others? (It was still truly my belief that if I could ever achieve sexual prowess with a woman—any woman, it would extinguish this second disturbing flaw I am at last owning up to.)

I did stay there that night. I did not stay a second night. I think Rob stayed there a week, but I don't think Rob was used to a lot of comfort. Ed quit the following day, was on the first plane out and was never seen again. The "Baht Kid" spent most his time picking up Vietnamese bar girls and therefore did not spend much time in any one room. The two other guys moved into an AAM boarding house run by one of the pilots. Me, I found a room in a small hotel, and would move on many times in the weeks to come, before finding suitable living arrangements.

Chapter Five
MY NEW DUTY STATION

At Last, Getting the Real Lowdown

The van arrived right on time and we were on our way to our first day on the job. The ride to Tan Son Nhut was about twenty minutes (with no stops). Today would be our 'in-country' indoctrination; another briefing, but this time of a confidential, revealing nature, and given by the Air America Station Manager. For the first time we would be told what we would really be doing here. We learned that in addition to MACV (the US Military Assistance Command Vietnam) that was arming, training, and fighting alongside the ARVN (the Army of the Republic of Vietnam), there was a large complement of CIA "case officers" working with members of the Vietnamese civilian population to assist in acquiring intelligence and in the actual fight against the NVA (North Vietnamese Army) and the VC (Viet Cong). These case officers were here in Vietnam covertly, assigned as staff at the U.S. Embassy or employees of USAID (the benign "U.S. Agency for International Development"). In both entities they were supposedly experts in fields such as agriculture, livestock, water supply, medicine, local law enforcement, etc.; here to mentor and supervise Vietnamese village leaders in those areas.

Air America was actually owned by the US government, so it was our State Department that got the Vietnamese Minister of the Interior to approve our operation in-country—under the guise of providing the multitude of humane airlift missions that would be required. And our capabilities did allow us to make those essential contributions, such as bringing in tons of rice to areas suffering from drought or floods, resettling thousands of Vietnamese who had been denied their villages, and delivering medical personnel and supplies to needy areas inaccessible by road. And while it's true we did do a lot of that, a more important mission was being responsible for all the airlift requirements of the previously mentioned CIA case officers. Day in and day out we would support their covert country-wide effort; delivering weapons, ammunition, food, water, and actual armed troops to wherever they were needed; often being asked to land within 100 yards of live-fire activity, and evacuate wounded Vietnamese soldiers. The briefing was finished up with a caution to never use the word CIA. If we absolutely had to refer to it, we should use the word "*Company.*" And if we ever had to refer to the case officers publicly (whether they were carrying powdered milk or an automatic weapon) they were just to be called "*The Customer.*"

An Early Note to Explain an Omission in This Part

The subject of the CIA role in the Vietnam War (and Laos) has spawned many questions and books (such as *Honor Denied*) about who and how high up, knew about it, ordered it, or supervised it—from the White House to the Secretary of Defense. However this complicated and politically sensitive explanation I will claim to be 'above my paygrade' and thusly in the following chapters I will not venture to explain Air America's relationship to the Department of Defense or the CIA. Rather *I will just hopefully provide interesting and entertaining anecdotal stories of one pilot's haphazard and sometimes unnerving escapades—on and off the field of play, as a member of what has been referred to as the "CIA Secret Airline" in SE Asia.*

The Air America Fleet

In Saigon we had a diverse assortment of aircraft. For heavy cargo and parachute drops there were a few WWII C-46's and C-47's (stalwarts that flew the "hump" between India and China twenty-five years ago). For carrying six to eight executive-level staff from the embassy or USAID, there were several smaller but nicer twin-engine C-45's. For direct support of the missions of the CIA case officers, there were two types of single-engine aircraft designed to land and takeoff from short and unprepared dirt strips—the Porter and the Helio Courier. For getting into and out of small jungle clearings, there were a bunch of Huey helicopters, just like the ones being flown by the Army here in Vietnam (except ours were polished aluminum with white and blue trim). *The big question was, what type of aircraft were they going to put me in?* After examining my military records and seeing I had flown highly maneuverable, small, single-engine jets, they assigned me to fly the single-engine PC-6 Pilatus Porter. An aircraft designed in Switzerland and designed to fly into unprepared areas (like rescue work in the Alps). It was flown by a single pilot. No copilot. After my check out (if I passed the Captain's Flight Check) I'd be flying it solo.

Checking Out In the PC-6 Porter

Unfortunately, there was no ground school or any printed training syllabus. I was told to be at the airport at 0700 the next morning and get in Frank Reynor's Porter, and do so every day for the next week. He would show me how to fly it. I noticed right off that the power control levers in this aircraft were physically much different and operated in a very different way than the single engine military propeller aircraft I had flown. In the Porter they were in the center of the console, instead of on the pilot's left. And instead of having the standard three vertical levers which added gas, increased the prop pitch, or enriched its mixture, *the Pilatus Porter had but one lever!* A weird looking small red "T" handle, sticking horizontally out of the middle of the instrument panel. The plane had a French jet engine called the Astazou, that drove a prop *that ran at full RPM all the time— even when taxiing.* The pilot just tapped this small, weird-looking red "T"-handle forward to increase the pitch of the propeller, and thus increase the thrust of the engine (more fuel was automatically provided). Frank said

Pilatus Porter

this would take some getting used to; not so much for take-off, since you just held pressure against it until a gauge on the panel indicated you had attained maximum pitch (take-off power). Landing was more tricky—had to make repeated small fingertip pulls to decrease the pitch and thus the thrust. He admitted that after months of flying it he sometimes became confused with the "T" handle. He said maintaining it was an interesting drill. Being Swiss-built the aircraft had Swiss manuals. The engine being French had French manuals; and all the maintenance was being done by Filipinos who at best spoke broken English.

Frank looked just like Gary Cooper and talked just like him (on the rare occasions when he spoke). I showed up at the plane in my Levis and a Banlon shirt and introduced myself. (Air America had not yet issued me a uniform.) I was told that Frank had already been told I'd be there and that he was supposed to 'check me out'. What ensued was five days of breathtaking flying; skimming low through driving rain across rice paddies in the Delta, buffeting through teeth-jarring thunder clouds, wing-tipping around mountain peaks or slicing through a fifty foot-wide cut in a karst ridgeline, and finally diving through low hanging clouds and fog to put the aircraft down on a tiny, rutted, well-disguised small pasture that was going to be our runway! To say the least I was wondering how anybody could do this type of flying on a regular basis.

I also learned from Frank that South Vietnam, stretching over 400 miles from the Delta in the south, to the DMZ in the north, required the Customer to have hundreds of remote areas of operations—many far from Saigon; locations that couldn't be supported from here. Air America therefore had two other satellite bases that pilots would be sent to for a one week tour—to fly out of that location every morning. One in the city of Nha Trang—200 miles north of Saigon, and the other in Da Nang—375 miles north of Saigon. At both these bases we had maintenance facilities, permanently assigned personnel, and hostels for the pilots.

Thank God for Small Breaks

What mostly surprised me, sitting next to Frank in the copilot's seat: not once—not once in five days, *did he ever let me take the controls!* And my captain's check flight was going to be in two days! I finally got up the nerve to suggest that *me trying a takeoff or landing might be a good idea.* This suggestion was met with a quizzical look. Turns out Frank's briefing had not been that thorough; me being in civilian clothes, all this time he thought I was a newly arrived case officer and his job was just to give me an 'in-country *area* familiarization', *not* show me how to fly the airplane! The last day of scheduled training, Frank was sick and I was told to fly with a Captain Wogman. *Thank the Lord for small favors.* We had about twenty short flights, none with passengers—all just cargo. Ron told *me* to fly them (while he sat on the fold-down back seat reading his Zane Gray paperback). I viewed his decision as potentially hazardous, but knew I couldn't pass up my one last chance to master this critter. I got in about twenty landing at a wide variety of strips.

My Captain's Flight Check

The Manager of Flying who would normally administer my flight check was on leave, so they assigned a chief pilot ("Tachikawa Fats") from our very different 'commercial airline-type' operation up in Japan. Instead of examining my potential captain's ability to navigate the countryside, recognize enemy held territory, and land and takeoff at the short, ill-prepared landing strips, *he had me tape brown paper all across the windscreen, and show him I could fly just by reference to my instruments, complying with the latest stateside FAA procedures.* (All this to be done using the single navigation aid in the country, which was rarely even on the air.) It was as useless a check ride as ever could have been designed! What's worse, after vocally differing with him about the correct way to turn in a 'holding pattern' he became upset and did not want to pass me. Fortunately, Les Stroud (the young Chief Pilot I'd met when I arrived) who was well acquainted with the actual type of flying we did, was aboard as a safety pilot. He recognized my command of the aircraft, and convinced Fats to sign me off. *Thank God for Les and that one day with Ron Wogman.*

Someone Who Wasn't as Lucky

The same week I was being trained by Frank, another new hire—Bruce Klark a retired Air Force Colonel, was being trained in another type aircraft by Stan Armbrook. (Remember, the burly Texan from my first day's van ride into town?) Bruce had his captain's check flight the same morning as mine. After it, while I was in the Chief Pilot's office getting my critique, in comes Stan, who had just *failed* Bruce on his check flight. Stan was ranting and raving about Bruce *having no more idea of precision flying than the man in the moon!* I was to find out later, that Bruce's last assignment in the Air Force was as the captain of the "Thunderbirds"—the Air Force's precision aerobatic demonstration team! In any case, I was now on my way. As of tomorrow I'd be checking the flight schedule for my name.

My First Flight as a Captain

Arriving at the aircraft on my first solo flight, I find an Australian Warrant Officer (with a large tattoo that said *Malaysia, never again*) already there waiting for me. He told me we were going to "one of the worst strips in Vietnam." (Not comforting to hear on your first flight.) Arriving at our destination, he began pointing at a sufficiently straight but maybe too-narrow oxcart path, paralleling a fence that ran alongside a large adjacent pasture. The general area was safe enough to allow me to make a couple low passes over the oxcart path, examining its suitability. Unfortunately the edges of the raised dike-like mound were only a few feet wider than my landing gear. It was bordered by the pasture fence on the left side and a deep canal four feet over the right side. (Probably where they had dug up the dirt to *make* the raised path.) The most crucial thing here was to make sure neither wheel slipped off the edge of the flattened top. If it did—to the left, the wing would be torn off by the fence bordering the wide grassy field. To the right—we would end up mired in a muddy canal. Either way there was an excellent chance that in sliding down the embankment the spinning propeller would strike the ground, tearing the engine from its mounts. If we weren't injured we would be stuck there until a helicopter airlifted us out (and I would most likely be fired after my first flight).

After two fly-bys, reasonably sure I could keep the wheels on the path and stay centered, I dove at it, yanked off the power, plowed onto the hard dirt, hit the brakes, threw it into reverse, and finally brought the airplane to a shuddering stop, without going over either side (though I doubt there was 30 inches to spare outside each wheel)! Stopped, I looked over at the Australian officer who was aghast, his face ashen, his eyes and mouth wide open. He points across the fence at the open pasture and shouts "That's the bloody strip! That's the bloody strip!" I couldn't believe he would have told me earlier, that the large, wide, flat area paralleling where I landed, was one of the country's worst strips. That pasture, to this day is still one of the least challenging landing sites in the country. I never considered it as the intended landing area, and he didn't realize on my initial low level passes, that rather than checking the pasture, I was checking out the oxcart path running alongside it. The bad news is, when I reached the end of the oxcart path, it didn't have enough width to swing the tail around and point it back for take-off (which I should have realized would be the case). We had to corral a dozen Vietnamese to help us lift the tail, and hold it up while we splashed a half circle through the canal, to place it properly for take-off, reversing the wrong-facing position of the aircraft.

Getting Some Wheels

I spent the next month experimenting with and learning as much as I could about my Porter and especially its STOL ("Short Takeoff and Landing") capabilities. This provided a good many 'heart in the throat' occasions. And, I received ground fire a few dozen times (but just about all the holes were through the tail or aft fuselage). I decided I'd be able to do the job, even indefinitely. The first month I lived in three different hotels and used my time off searching for suitable permanent digs. I finally located a tiny top floor apartment in an upscale and reasonably safe downtown Saigon area. Needed a car and got one, but through a strange occurrence. One day—unable to arrange a pick up by an Air America van, I was hitch-hiking out to the airport. Halfway there I was picked up by an Air America pilot in a light green Datsun. He was on his way (rapid way) to the airport to board a flight out as soon as possible; his Vietnamese wife had tried to kill him and had just hired a team of local hit men to do it. He accepted a stateside check for a thousand dollars and gave me a hand-written note that said he had sold the car to me. After my business I drove home in my new wheels.

Maybe Saigon IS Dangerous

A few days later—being the sun tan freak I am, I carried a lounge chair up onto the roof, planning on getting some rays. The only downside was the roof was paved with a black tar that got soft and hot as hell. I stretched out contentedly in the piquing bright sun. Not bad. Dozed. Was brought back to consciousness by a fluttering sound of what I thought was a bird flying by. Sat up. Nothing unusual around. Lay back down. A minute later something that sounded like snapping a taught cord. Looked around; still nothing or anyone near. Laid back down. But it wasn't another minute before another crazy sound—this one a warbling whistle. *What the hell is going on around here?* I stood up, turned a complete circle, scanning all around me. Above the trees I could survey the top floors and roofs of the surrounding buildings. About 500 yards away, on a glinting slanted metal roof, was a guy with a rifle, down on one knee, *shooting at me!* Needless to say this ended my sunning.

A Female Introduction

Several days later (evidently not having learned much) I was back up on the roof getting more rays, when as my good fortune would have it, so was a reasonably attractive Caucasian woman (who I had learned—over here, were referred to as a "round eyes.") Her name was Mary Margaret; an occupant of my building, about my age, and single! She was a Department of the Army civilian and assigned to MACV downtown. Although reasonably attractive, she was not stirring to me and for sure was not going to be the woman who would rescue me from my plight. However, in this town and at this time, the 'convenience' aspect of any female partner (especially an American) was not lost on me; dinners together, evenings of Scrabble (no TV), but other joint activities that would make Saigon a much more livable place. And of course, for her it meant the advantage of having a gentleman escort, and I did take her out to some of Saigon's many French restaurants (which at this time—with the influx of US troops, were able to sustain a profitable business). After several weeks it became clear to me—surprisingly, since she didn't show any signs of such, she was (and had been) ready and eager for a more physical relationship. And it did finally occur. However, as you might imagine—knowing my embarrassing bedroom deficiency, the one thing I remember most about Mary Margaret is her exhortations: *"You can do it! You can do it! I know you can do it."* And perhaps on occasion I did—at least to a passable extent.

Chapter Six

FIVE MONTHS IN AND BRINGING THE FAMILY OVER

We Were Not Without Losses

One crash of many

I'd only been in Vietnam four months, and already we had lost several aircraft; some due to enemy action, some due to bad weather, and some due to pilots just trying to accomplish that which was beyond his or the aircraft's capabilities. When these crashes occurred our Air America common radio frequency would be buzzing with comments the rest of the day, and upon returning to Saigon, the pilots would gather in animated groups sharing their opinions of what had happened. For the next month or so the crash would be under investigation, and finally—be the subject of an official report. That is until an accident a week ago at Bao Tri (a strip not far from Saigon). One of our twin-engine C-45's crashed while making its approach to landing there. Both our crew members, one Customer, and a Vietnamese general were killed in the fiery crash. For reasons never quite known, beginning the next day there was little or no discussion about the accident, a hushed investigation, and no published report. Rumor had it that the Vietnamese general was under investigation for double dealing, and that at least one of the crew had been shot *before the crash.*

I told you that while in Bangkok we heard that Air America had a secret base in Vientiane, Laos, where supposedly another unreported war was going on, *and the flying was much more dangerous than here in Vietnam.* Well maybe so, because word came down that a pilot flying out of there—Ernie Brase, another former Marine, had landed his STOL plane at a tiny grass strip in a valley in northern Laos (only about 50 miles from the North Vietnamese border). On exiting the aircraft he was captured by North Vietnamese soldiers who had taken over the strip the night before. The villagers later said the soldiers took him and were marching northeastward. Though we didn't know it then, he would never fly another flight for us and would spend the next seven years in the "Hanoi Hilton" (with John McCain).

Bangkok Again

The flying activity out of Saigon was almost the same—day in and day out. We'd launch out of Tan Son Nhut at 0700 and reposition at a tiny dirt strip maybe fifty or more miles away, to work out of that site all day, for the assigned case officer. This usually meant at least twenty flights a day; loading our plane with weapons, ammunition, food, water, medical supplies, and delivering them to a nearby area of active enemy contact, and on almost every trip bringing back the wounded. (The sight of some of these wounded troops was enough for me to become a proponent of outlawing of land mines. Not a pretty sight.) This was the schedule for about three weeks, and then we got our 7 to 10 days "Scheduled Time Off" to visit our families in whatever safe haven city we had chosen. Since I had recently completed my 120-day probation period (when my family would be cleared to join me), I used my next STO for a trip to Bangkok. My mission: find a good home for Sara and the kids (especially after all the buildup I'd given them about what they could expect).

Temperature-wise Bangkok didn't let me down; stepping out of the airplane was like stepping into a sauna. I got transportation to town— to the Erawan Hotel, bargaining with the driver to rent his cab all the following day, and possibly the next day. This turned out to have been a good decision, based on the delays caused by traffic, road construction, and terrible directions. During the next few days I found and discounted many dwellings for many reasons. Spent most the time cruising the areas I knew housed expatriates, and especially neighborhoods where American citizens lived. Discouraged and on the verge of giving up, thank God, two days before my scheduled flight back, I came upon the perfect abode. It was large and new, on a quiet street where two other Saigon pilots had their family's houses (and only a half mile from the American School). Mission luckily and gratefully accomplished I returned to Saigon.

Flying for "Juliet Bravo"

Some of the case officers got to know and trust certain pilots more than others. I had been adopted by Jack Benefield. Don't know what his specialty was (as an ex chief of police from Richmond, Virginia). He was the case officer in Ban Me Thout—a rugged plateau of red dirt in the Vietnam highlands (where Teddy Roosevelt had a still-standing large hunting lodge). There between the ridges almost all the flat land was a French Michelin rubber plantation; a thousand tall trees in razor sharp lines. (You could crouch down in front of the first tree, and sight down the line past another hundred without seeing even the edge of one following tree.)

One day Jack had about a dozen re-supply missions planned for me. I was to take boxes of charges and fuses to a small Montagnard village (the occupants of which were on "our" side). As a small rarely visited village—a cluster of about fifty thatched huts, there was never a need to install a radio beacon there to help find it. One got there by visual pilotage. There, I'd land on a tiny (400-foot-long) PSP (pierced steel planking) runway that had been parachuted in: 6' piece by 6' piece, and then hooked together on top of the almost always wet ground. (The military name for this PSP is "Marston-Matting.") The runway was laid in an east west line abreast of and just fifty feet from the first line of huts. On the trip there from Ban Me Tout I held exactly 165 degrees, flew exactly 120 knots, and held it for exactly 19 minutes. At which time I was over the middle of a swamp. From this point, a ninety degree left turn to a heading of due east would have me on line with and pointed at village. I noticed that about a mile or two on the other side of the village (and coincidentally, exactly on line with the runway) was a single, tall limestone pinnacle, which if someday I had cloud cover under me, turning left and seeing it directly in front of me would confirm I was heading directly towards the strip. I noted that after my left turn, this leg to the end of the runway took exactly 25 seconds. Moreover and importantly I noted that the touchdown end of the strip was only a hundred yards past the edge of the swamp (in which—today, a herd of elephants had been splashing around). On the landing rollout my altimeter read an elevation of 1,760 feet above sea level. (They called this area the "highlands" because within this elevated plateau, Pleiku was over 2000 feet, and the not-to-far town of Dalat (the lettuce capital of the country) was at almost 5,000 feet above sea level.

During the morning hours I didn't need all these heading and times details, or the elevation of the strip. It was a beautiful day and I could see the village when I was still five miles away. However about noon, with four trips under my belt, the weather made a sudden change for the worse. Taking off from Ban Me Thout I was now entering dense clouds at three hundred feet of altitude—leaving me with no visual reference to any terrain in any direction (what pilots call "solid instruments"). No landmarks available to guide me to the village and runway. *But no sweat,* I had had memorized the precise headings (to the degree) and the exact leg times (to the second). About three in the afternoon Jack comes walking out with a distinguished looking, white haired, uniformed Army Colonel. "Hey Rog, Colonel Dawkins is going with us on this trip. He wants to check out the village and see the readiness of my guys."

I got in the plane and they wedged themselves in behind me. The Colonel sat directly behind me. The weather was worse—we entered the gray nothingness at just 100 feet of altitude! I used the same angle of bank while turning south to assure the same radius of turn on the way to the 165 degrees heading. Mentally went over it: *Time now 15:04, plus 19 minutes, I should be over the swamp at 15:23.* I could sense the Colonel's understandable apprehension, not being able to see anything—*it was as if we were inside a milk bottle.* He knew I had nothing to navigate by and that we were surrounded by mountainous terrain *that was above our flight altitude!* On this southerly heading I let down to 2,300 feet MSL (which I knew from previous trips to still gave me good ground clearance). At 23 after the hour (the 19 minutes having expired), knowing I should be over the swamp, I glanced 90 degrees to my left, and sure enough, there it was—a blurred image of the limestone peak. I quickly turned left ninety degrees to a heading of due east, pointed at the peak, which I doubt neither the Colonel nor Jack even noticed. (But I knew it meant I was now headed directly for the runway.) The end of the runway will be 25 seconds on this heading. 10 seconds gone. Started a let down to 1,960 feet MSL (which

45

would level us at 200 feet above the runway), still completely engulfed in grayish-white, wet clouds. Out of the corner of my eye I could see the justifiably worried Colonel rising up out of his seat, straining his eyes ahead through the water-streaked windscreen and into a blank wall of white nothingness. While he was doing this, I tilted my head to the left and sneakily took a peek straight down. Though I could barely make them out, I knew the gray blurs I saw were the elephants in the swamp. 20 seconds elapsed. Pulled the power back and continued down. Three seconds later, at 1,850 feet (90 feet above the runway) we broke out of the clouds—and two seconds later slammed down on the metal planking that had suddenly (to my passengers—miraculously) appeared directly beneath us. The Colonel looked at Jack, shaking his head in amazement, and said, "Jesus Christ Jack, your fucking pilots *really* know this country!"

"Juliet Bravo" Again

For a couple weeks, I did routine flying out of Saigon. Then one morning the Ops Manager hailed me and told me to forget my scheduled assignment, just get up to Ban Me Thout as soon as possible. Jack Benefield had requested me again. No problem. Fired my Porter up and made the run to Ban Me Thout. Got Jack on the radio, landed, and parked on the red laterite ramp. Jack's hooch was only about a quarter mile from the strip. Wasn't five minutes before I spied his jeep careening around the last turn and speeding towards the aircraft (in fact so fast I feared he was going to be unable not to ram the plane). Thankfully he slammed on the brakes just in time and skidded to a stop not six feet from the fuselage. The thick cloud of dust that had been following the jeep, passed it and layered on me. Jack got out—wearing "cammys," an M1941 Field Marching Pack, carrying an Armalite 15 rifle (magazine inserted), and with a .45 strapped to his waist. *Whoaa*—he'd hinted as much on the radio when I checked in. Now I could see this *was* going to be a special mission. I was soon going to need my Swiss-built turbo Porter to demonstrate all its touted STOL (short takeoff and landing) capabilities. "Here's the plan Rog. You're gonna take me about 40 miles west of here, to the Cambodian border, and across it"

"*Say what? Across it?*

"Right."

"Jack, not two weeks ago we got an Ops Order saying under no circumstances were we to let our case officer talk us into doing just that."

"Well today you're gonna make an exception." He motioned towards a small oriental guy getting out of the jeep with a PRC-25 (portable radio) on his back. "You're going to take me and Nguyen to a critical recon location." What's more I was to learn we weren't going to a strip. We were going to land on a short but supposedly straight stretch of a dirt or gravel road inside the country. It ran northeast off the more well-travelled north-south Cambodian Route 76. Jack briefed me using a large scale map (as I remember called a "1 to 12.5"). It had been re-creased and folded along the intended route (that someone had marked with a red ink line). The exposed map showed an area just a couple miles either side of the route—which included all the terrain features I would be able to see or need to get us there. No sweat.

They boarded, I fired up the 750 HP Garrett 331 turbo-prop engine, swung onto the strip, jammed the throttle full forward and we were airborne. (Forgot to tell you, we switched from the original French Astazou engine to this stateside-built powerhouse.) Well accustomed to recognizing and picking out the smallest landmarks, navigating was no problem; a small stream, a slight terrain rise, a crooked ridge; all I needed. I gotta admit it felt a little eerie once we crossed into Cambodia. Although Pol Pot and the communists would not officially take over the country for a couple years, the rural areas were already supporting many of the vicious Khmer Rouge (which meant there were probably a couple hundred under me right now). We arrived at the designated, and thankfully—presently deserted, stretch of road I was to land on.

Unfortunately I couldn't circle overhead first to verify its acceptability. Loitering overhead could draw a crowd, and if so we'd be captured (or shot) as soon as the airplane came to a stop. But I wouldn't be able to assure myself that there were no holes, stumps or other obstacles that could disable the aircraft, marooning us there for certain capture. I picked a spot where the road went straight for 500 feet, racked it around, yanked off the power, dove in, and touched down on the road—which could not have been more than fifteen feet wide (and my main landing gear were ten feet wide). This only left thirty inches clearance outside each main gear, before a wheel would slip over the edge of the raised road, causing the whole airplane to slide down the embankment into a canal on each side! Utilizing full reverse I brought the plane to a stop (while wondering how many ears were hearing and questioning what was that noise screaming through the previously silent jungle). Soon as we were stopped, Jack grabbed me by the shoulder with one hand, pointed the index finger of his other hand in my face, and told me in no uncertain terms, "Three days from now—Wednesday! Wednesday at exactly 4 PM, be here! Not at 3:59 or 4:01, but 4 PM exactly! And I may be on a dead run—I may be being chased, so for God sakes, keep the engine running. We matched watch times. Soon as the door was shut I knew I had to get out of there ASAP! Any minute the Khmers or pissed-off armed civilians could come bursting out of the woodlands to either side, and I wouldn't stand a chance.

But my heart froze! As I peered ahead—down the road, I saw with horror that the trees grew closer to the road; to the extent their foliage was touching overhead. I couldn't make a takeoff from where I was. *The wingtips wouldn't fit up between the brances!* Okay. Okay. Stay calm, they may not be here for several minutes. The Porter has a reversing propeller. *I'll back it up 400 feet and takeoff from the same stretch I just landed on.* Tried to back up once. Tried it again. Big problem: Sure, I could back up using reverse, but the tailwheel kept swiveling about ten degrees right. So the result was I was angling off the roadway, which would have caused it to go over the side and slip down the embankment. I jumped out, ran back to the tail, crouched down under the horizontal stabilizer, put my back up underneath it, put my hands on my thighs and then raised up—lifting the tail wheel off the ground, and hefted it back to the middle of the road! Ran to the cockpit and gave another try backing up. Damn! Same thing—the tail canted and the rear of the plane was on its way off the road again. *Backing up isn't gonna work!*

I had no choice but to just start taxing down the road—as long as it would take to find a stretch where it was still straight and the trees were further from the edge of the road, giving me enough clearance to get the wingtips through between their upper branches. *I must have taxied for three miles, and spent ten, loud turbine-whining minutes doing it!* And I must be the luckiest man alive (or we were in the most unpopulated area in eastern Cambodia), because miraculously not once did a single person come into sight. I poured the coal to it and was outa there!

The Family Arrives!

The following ten days were my Scheduled Time Off and guess where I was: in Bangkok to meet the family! It was a little after one a.m. at the Don Muang airport; not at Sara's arrival gate, but right by the door out of Customs—the first place one would be able to see arriving passengers, and where she couldn't miss me. Gotta admit I was nervous and anxious to see her and the kids. They were coming with a minimum of baggage—mostly clothes. We had opted to ship no furniture; the home I had leased was mostly furnished. What furniture we needed we would just buy here (since the least expensive and most beautiful rattan furniture in the world was made and sold here in Bangkok). *There they were!* A bit bedraggled but okay. She spied me. The kids saw me. For the next few minutes we all stayed locked in a big embrace and in reserved anticipation of the family's new life.

The cab ride to town was enlightening to me in one respect: instead of four months older, the kids seemed four years older; quieter, only asking a few good questions, but then again they had just finished a series of grueling flights halfway around the world. In spite of their fatigue a cautious interest was aroused by the sight of the moon glinting off the shining wet backs of the huge water buffalos lining the road. Once in town, we went right by the American School and I pointed it out but don't think the kids were sufficiently conscious to take note. Got to the house (two of the kids asleep), and Sara 'all eyes'. Thank God for small favors—even in the limited light I could see an expression of pleasant surprise on her face as she looked up at her new ultra-modern, two-story white home. Inside she appeared equally pleased, seeing the glistening teak floors and the modern rattan furniture which was accented by brightly colored plaid Thai-silk cushions. Needless to say, after a long day we all bedded down in a matter of minutes, leaving further investigating to the morrow.

Next morning, Sara made a list of all the food staples and other cooking ingredients she thought she would need (not yet believing we were going to have a cook, who would take care of all this). She persisted in examining all the drawers and cabinets for dishware, pots and pans, silverware, etc. The kids—after a prolonged joint discussion on the bedroom arrangements, and to my gratification, seemed as if they were settling in already; maybe even looking forward to this new adventure of which they had no idea. There was a large side yard and they were joyously exploring it and apparently (thank you God) showing what I took to be an optimistic excitement. Just before noon, I walked the whole family down the street to meet Mrs. McInerny and her two girls (Sandy was the wife of one of my best Air America pilot friends.) *Miracle of miracles!* Sara and Sandy became instant friends, what's more—one of Sandy's daughters was Donna's age, and the other one was Stacy's age.

I GUESS I JUST WASN'T THINKING

It was obvious Sara and Sandy and the girls, were going to be immediate (and as it would turn out) lifelong friends. And the boys made a discovery: at the end of this little travelled dead-end street was a small hotel, and it had a neat swimming pool with surrounding (artificial) rock cliffs, as if it were in a jungle cavern. Mark and Kevin asked if they could run back to the house and get their swim suits. Though I surely did not deserve it, all indications were the family would have no problem adapting to this new life. I was much relieved.

During the week, using the readily available cabs we explored Bangkok from end to end (which was about five miles). The city was brand new—gleaming white; in the process of adding shopping centers, huge glass office buildings, beautiful new hotels (and more jewelry shops than any city in the world)! Combined with what the city had to offer (especially to the bachelors), with its mostly undiscovered and luxurious beaches just an hour south, Thailand was becoming a prime destination for European vacationers. So in addition to meeting and knowing the wives and families of other Saigon pilots, Sara and the kids were daily being introduced to English, German, Swedish, and other European nationals. It was new and exciting! I took Sara and the kids to the American School (currently in session) and enrolled the kids. The school was only a half mile down Sukhumvit from our house, and it appeared the kids were pleasantly surprised. Sara had made a list and picked out several pieces of furniture—all made from the thick blonde rattan so common over here. There was no need to consider purchasing a car; cab fare was nothing. And why risk an accident, in which the foreigner was always at fault, no matter what. (The Thai word for "foreigner" was "farang," which it turns out was a bastardization of the word "*francaise*;" the French having been here first.)

We visited the famous Bangkok zoo (even its renown "Snake Farm"), and took the 6 a.m. Floating Market boat tour (a bunch of tourists in long dug-out canoe-type boats) that motored past all the fruit and vegetable vendors in their boats, clogging up and stopping all waterborne traffic. In Bangkok there was no excuse for not eating your share of fresh fruit, especially pineapple, mango, papaya, kiwi, and a bunch of other delicious and readily-available fruits. Sandy told Sara that her cook, a very pleasant Thai woman, about 30, had a younger sister (that Sandy had met), and that she was looking for a "farang" to cook and clean for. Sandy arranged a meeting, and Thalee was a hit—a smiling, gracious girl about 25. Not yet sure how she could cook, but the comfort level was so high, Sara hired her on the spot. (All the houses for rent in Bangkok have a small cottage behind the main dwelling, where the cook would live.)

A couple nights we all went to a movie in one of Bangkok's giant theaters. They all had two or three tiers and must have sat a couple thousand viewers! (There were none of those small, multi-screen establishments we are now familiar with.) To top it off, Sandy bowled, and although Sara was not an avid bowler Sandy asked her to be on her team and even got her a monogramed shirt. Once again, although I certainly didn't deserve it, things could not have gone better. After a few days Mark and Kevin were making regular stops at the food stalls (two-wheeled wagons), of which there was one at every corner in town (including our street). They all seemed to be run by a guy in a white and black plaid sarong, no shirt, no shoes; busy cooking a variety of seafood or pork or some other braised meat served on a skewer. Of course there was always an ample assortment of fresh fruit. Irrespective of the kid's confidence, Sara was justifiably worried about the cleanliness of the food.

When I boarded the plane to return to Saigon I was relieved and happy that my family's transition to becoming "expats" had gone so smoothly. My renewed presence with Sara and the kids had been genuinely pleasant, and surprisingly satisfying. My dilemma, the search, the resulting longings, and wonderment, refreshingly took a back seat that week, though unfortunately I knew it could not be permanently side-lined.

Chapter Seven
COMPLETED A YEAR AND GUESS WHAT

Promoted

I hadn't been flying the line for a year when I got called up to the "Manager of Flying" office. Shook George Calhoun's hand and sat down. Les Stroud was already sitting nearby. George spoke: "Rog, you ready for some more responsibility?"

Not knowing what was in store, but knowing the expected answer, I responded, "Sure."

"Les here has been keeping track of you, and checking with the Customer on what kind of job you've been doing, and we're ready to promote you to the position of "Assistant Manager of Flying," as the Chief Pilot of the Porter program."

Wow, caught me by surprise. I knew as a program Chief Pilot, I would end up flying less daily missions, and spend the bulk of my time monitoring and sustaining the operational status of all twelve of our Porters; keeping the 28 Porter pilots in line (on and off the airport); training new pilots coming into the program; make up the daily flight schedule for the Porters (who would fly where); assume the role of Safety Officer for Porters; and perhaps most importantly, administer the six-month flight checks to make sure the captains were competently carrying out their daily operational missions. This was a serious flight check (called a "Line Check") because if they failed, they weren't just demoted, they could be sent home. My pay would change somewhat. I'd lose the opportunity to accumulate enough flight time for the generous 'overtime bonuses' we received when we surpassed 70 hours a month, but it'd be offset by an increase in base pay—almost a washout. Not sure how much forethought I gave it, but accepted.

Part Three: The CIA Secret Airline and Eureka! She Exists!

Having just been a regular "Line" captain (in spite of its calamitous possibilities) had been enjoyable to me—a real challenge and adrenalin booster. I got to know several of the case officers well and was their "go-to" guy when the chips were down. Although most the flying here in Vietnam was over safe areas, at least a couple days each week I would transport soldiers and military supplies over hostile areas, and take occasional ground fire (hits). I was definitely where it was happening! But I'll admit there was one phase of our airlift mission that I would not miss: shuttling the displaced villagers (which we did a lot). Watching them clamber aboard in awe and confusion, having lost all control over their lives, huddling and fearing the worst, while being crudely "relocated" by the all-powerful, irresistible foreign force (us). I'll never forget the old couples, pressed together, hollow eyes searching for some reason to all this. Frames of skin and bones bent and bowed from years of toil. After sixty years in the same village, now in two years they had been in a half dozen resettlement camps! Forget a life-time of accumulations, memories and possessions. In fact forget a lifetime. By the time they were herded on board our aircraft (perhaps their umpteenth relocation flight with no idea where they were going), almost all their worldly possessions had been declared excess by callous military loadmasters, plucked from their arms and chucked overboard in front of their eyes. For most, their total belongings now down to a small carton, a tied-up paper sack, or maybe even just wrapped in one piece of faded cloth.

As a new supervisory pilot I was relieved from most of the above, but was still tasked to achieve and maintain the respect of all of my pilots. I tried to do this by personally—whenever possible, volunteering to take the least desirable flights (for instance those that would overfly the most hostile areas, those where there was concern about having enough fuel to make it back, and those which would require an overnight in one of the least secure villages). I was gratified on many occasions to feel I had succeeded in earning their admiration and instilling a full measure of pride and esprit de corps within the Porter program. And incidentally there was no initial training syllabus until I got the job and designed one. It had two great advantages: a trainee could look it over in advance to know what to expect, and it put forth a list of required maneuvers and their acceptable limits, thus lending itself to *objective* grading (which had—I think been purposefully missing and as such, favored by the old hands who didn't want any new guys).

I GUESS I JUST WASN'T THINKING

One Memorable Official Duty

As the Chief Pilot for Porters I had many supervisory duties, one of which was taking each new hire (scheduled to check out in the Porter) on what we called Mission Familiarization flights. However the one today would be with *two* new pilots (instead of just one). They would just ride in the copilot seat observing me fly an ordinary—hopefully, run-of-the-mill typical day. This way they would get some idea of what was going to be required of them. One or two of these flights were scheduled before we put them in the pilot's seat to begin their initial aircraft training. We got paid by the hour—starting when we "chocked out" in the morning and until we "chocked in" at the end of the day. So (a little shamefully I'll admit) I was in the habit of getting out of the chocks ten to fifteen minutes early, and not chocking back in until ten or fifteen minutes late—every day. (By the end of the month, these thirty minutes added up!)

Today I was scheduled to familiarize someone with whom I would become good friends in years to come: L J Broussard, from Abbeville, Louisiana. He was a true Cajun if ever there was one, and been a crop duster since he was 15 (and probably one of the best "natural" pilots I ever knew). He was 5'2", smoked too-long cigars, and at 35 had gone prematurely white-haired. Apparently he never mastered the art of dying his hair because it would come out jet black halfway down, to the top of his ears, and snow white from there on down—all the way around! His favorite comment when you were considering buying something of debatable necessity, was *Why deprive yourself?* LJ was universally loved. However, the second new pilot, William Reacher—had been a Lily paper cup salesman, and what he was doing out here I had no idea. When he got talking about paper cups his eyes glazed over. Not I or anyone I knew considered Reacher of the sort to be in this line of work (or one of our peers).

Quarter to seven and neither one in sight! More than just a little irritated, I was pacing back and forth in front of the aircraft. We should be taxiing out right now! Where the hell were they? They should have been out here fifteen minutes ago. Finally—7:10, pissed at having already having lost fifteen minutes of pay, I decided to check if perhaps they were still sitting in the pilots' lounge. Perhaps not so smart, the door to the lounge was on one wall of the waiting lounge—in full view of the waiting USAID and Embassy personnel. Whoever decided to locate it there had not been

54

thinking of the potential downside. The door was a screen door. Being in full view and earshot of the waiting passengers the pilot group had to appear orderly, restrict their profanity, and keep worrisome comments about their forthcoming flight under their breath. The room was only about eight feet across and ten feet deep. There was a long couch on each side where the pilots sat (so close to the couch across from them that their toes touched).

Becoming madder by the second I left the aircraft and started across the ramp towards the passenger lounge. Obviously pissed but ignoring their glances, I marched past the rows of benches and waiting embassy personnel, towards the door to the pilot's lounge. Still several steps away— through the screen door I saw four or five pilots on each couch, including Broussard and Reacher! Approaching the door at a good clip I struck the frame of the screen door with the heel of my hand to shove it open; or in any case that was my intention. Turns out the Vietnamese laborer who had installed it, had put the hinges on the wrong side—*the side I hit!* Both hinges tore loose and the screen door took flight into the narrow room, landing across the feet of all the seated pilots. The momentum of my approach was such that I couldn't halt myself and ended up after two steps, standing atop the screen door. Once composed I said in a loud and obviously irritated voice, "Do you guys wanna fly or not!" Then turned on a heel and made my exit (through the opening that had previously held the screen door). Obviously my two guys followed immediately, but not before (I was later told) another shocked pilot nervously asked them, "You're not going to fly with *that* guy are you"?

Something I Didn't Deserve, but Appreciated

The day after the just described shameful screen door incident—the very next day, I was scheduled to fly a passenger flight, again taking LJ Broussard along. It was scheduled for another 07:00 takeoff, *but when I first opened my eyes and looked at the clock, it said 06:45! With a twenty minute drive to the airport!* I'd been flying for eleven years and this would be the first time I was ever late for a flight—which Air America did *not* look favorably upon! And to have this happen right after the scene I made with LJ yesterday. I dressed in a blur (a uniform but no underwear and no socks); into my Datsun and 50 mph the whole way, full of chagrin and contemplating what reprimand would be awaiting me. The PA system would have called the flight at 06:50 and someone would have likely escorted the passengers to an airplane, which this morning would be found to be devoid of a crew. God knows what Operations would have done then (or to me when they found me).

I roared into the gravel Air America parking lot, shut off the engine, leaped out and started what would probably be a useless run towards the passengers waiting area. To my surprise, halfway across the tarmac ramp I spy LJ, leading our passengers in a slow ramble past varying aircraft on the ramp, pausing to give them a verbal rundown on each one: the make and model and cargo or passenger capability, and when it was introduced into service. He was conducting a tour of the aviation equipment of Air America (which as well as it was being done could have been thought to be part of the normal boarding procedure). What he was doing was *clearly designed to disguise the fact I was late, and hopefully give me a chance to arrive!* You might now understand why I previously mentioned that LJ and I became good friends.

Couple More Things on LJ

Not long after this LJ invites me to his house for dinner with him and his wife. After I graciously accept, he says: "First we'll have our fill of a great Chateaubriand and Bordeaux, then we'll go into the study for a Brandy, and then about 9:30 I want you to say good night and thank me for a wonderful evening, because that's what time I go to bed." *Talk about getting things straight up front!* I show up at the appointed time, the Chateaubriand is brought out by his butler, and then the bottle of wine by his maid. Unfortunately LJ did a bad job with the cork screw; pulled it right through the cork—making a hole in which it could no longer grip. The Bordeaux (the real favorite) now out of the running and the two of us are pondering an alternate grape. Our contemplation was interrupted when LJ's butler appears at the tableside. He takes the bottle of Bordeaux, hustles over to the steps leading down from the kitchen, takes a seat, and crosses his legs so as to lock the bottle upright between his shins. He then pulls a shoe lace out of his shoe and wraps it around the neck of the bottle— twice, above the wine level and below the cork, and like a Boy Scout trying to start a fire by friction he begins a rapid side to side movement of his arms. The shoe lace spins around the neck of the bottle, until lo and behold, the air in the bottle, above the wine level gets hot, expands *and pops the cork out!*

LJ (Jason) was a real character—although with several quirks. A month after our dinner he's sent to Bangkok for a week of the periodically-required ground school on the Porter. He takes his wife with him. Though it will be mostly school work for him, his wife can spend the days sightseeing and jewelry shopping, and they can have a nice dinner out every night, in one of Bangkok's five-star restaurants. A few days later I'm sitting at my desk in the Chief Pilot's Office when a tough looking babe with a Louisiana accent comes barging in. I know what's coming before I hear it.

"Where's that lying little Cajun shit!?"

There was no doubt in my mind the little Cajun shit she was referring to was LJ. "Well ma'am, can I ask what your relationship with Jason is?"

To this question I considered ducking (or at least staying an arm's length away). They could have heard the answer three offices away: "What's my relationship? What's my relationship! I'll tell you what my relationship is, I'm that son-of-a-bitch's wife!"

Kheerist! I know (somehow) Jason arrived here with his wife, and she's with him now in Bangkok! Who the hell is this person? I get on the phone and call our facility on Pat Pong road where Jason is going through his ground school. I get one of the instructors to call him to the phone. "Jason, how goddam many wives you got!?"

He answers calmly, "Two, doesn't everyone?"

I won't have the space and time to describe to you the settlement of this issue, other than to say, it wasn't smooth.

Cute Bit of News From Bangkok

I was happy that Sara had settled in, and made a bunch of close friends there in Bangkok, although her almost constant companion and closest friend remained Sandy. A few days ago Sandy had come over to our house, very upset because her husband John was in jail! And it was going to cost a lot of Baht (Thai currency) to get him out. One night while they were home, there was an attempted robbery of their house. John, hearing the intruder grabbed the nearest weapon, which happened to be a two-liter bottle of Coke. The intruder, referred to as a "khmoy" (the Thai word for robber) *had a knife!* Surprisingly, John was able to strike defensive blows from a sufficient distance, causing the robber to retreat—out the rear door and over a back wall. Turns out according to Thai law, regardless of the situation, *the combatant with the largest weapon is the aggressor and guilty party!* The full coke bottle was adjudged to be more lethal than a short knife. They paid the fine and John was free. Additionally Sara told me she had been asked to join some of her friends on bowling dates, and was becoming real good—scoring 170's regularly. She was even on a team that played twice a week and had uniforms (well at least matching shirts). They had already won one trophy and she was excited about more coming!

Chapter Eight

A DESERVED COMEUPPANCE, A SPECIAL GUY, AND THE WAR

A Note in a Restaurant

In spite of the many restrictions dictating the daily life in what had been "The Pearl of the Orient," certain considerations had kept a small community of French citizens here in Saigon. Most were businessmen, but there was a smattering—not many, but a few single French women who evidently also had reason to remain in Saigon. The impossible dream of every bachelor (or geographically single) American male in Saigon, was to someday, somehow, get hooked up with one of these lithe, perfumed creatures of whom we had only caught momentary sight of— flitting into or out of one of the French stores. And you might imagine, after my adventures in Europe and associations with those Continental females (though I am embarrassed to admit it), I could be one of the above mentioned American males.

An Air America Supply Officer who had been in Saigon for many years was married to a Vietnamese woman who owned one of the city's smallest but most frequented restaurants—*La Cave*. It had a warm ambiance and served a delightful menu of French cuisine. It was only a few blocks from my apartment and so I ate dinner there frequently. Today I had left the airport about 11 A.M., found myself in downtown Saigon around noon, and decided to give *La Cave* a try for lunch. Once seated I felt a real flush. *Holey Moly, there she was!* Not just any one of those mysterious, rarely-seen seductive-appearing French women, but one in particular—an especially attractive one I had caught a glimpse of and admired several times in the last few months. On none of those occasions was there the slightest reason to approach her and I had been left with just the excitement of having briefly seen her. And even now with the two of us only 15 feet apart, I still had no reason to speak to her. It was probably just my wishful thinking, but during the meal I thought on one or two occasions *I caught her looking my way.*

Sadly, as I snuck my tenth glance in her direction, the table was empty. *Shoot!* Checking the door—there she was just going through it. She'd evidently finished her meal and was not going to waste more of her day here. While still watching the closed door behind the would-be object of my affections, one of the waiters approached my table. He was extending his hand towards me; a hand holding a folded piece of paper. He said nothing, just gave it to me and pointed in the direction of the French woman's just-vacated table! *Holy shit! She had sent me a note!* I opened it, and felt a rush of excitement as I read the English words: *"I have admired you for some time and could we meet here tonight at 7."* I was stunned! Clutching the note and not breathing while speculating on what an unexpected event this was and what might evolve tonight! (You can bet I was going to be here at 6:45!)

I was brought back to reality by a US Army officer who had been eating at a nearby table, and had now come to my table. He spoke: "That note was meant for me!" Of course I told him the waiter had given it to me, and specifically motioned it had come from the French woman, and he could not have mistaken her intentions. I don't think I convinced him, but he shrugged and walked out. I managed to hold onto the note, and even if nothing worked out it would be a fine piece of memorabilia.

You might imagine, the rest of the day I was in a state of heightened anticipation and justifiable concern about—if it were to be an overnight, would I even be able to validate it or experience the shame I now knew so well. I began sprucing up at six, shaved and even used a recently purchased cologne (something I was not in the habit of doing), and then chose what I felt was my coolest Continental attire (which did not cause me to feel any more capable). I was in *La Cave* and sitting at the bar at 6:45. Waiting nervously, swinging my head around each time I heard the front door open. 7:15 and she still wasn't here, but that didn't surprise me. 7:25—still not here. About 7:30 I heard the door again; this time being surprised to see that same Army officer from lunch, entering the restaurant and walking straight towards the bar. He took the seat next to me and spoke: "Let me tell you what *really* happened. That note the waiter gave you. It *was* meant for me! *I was the one who wrote it and sent it to her.* She didn't want to have anything to do with me, gave it back to another waiter, who accidentally returned it to you."

An Air America Pilot We All Remember

The next couple weeks I flew many hours; maintenance test flights, training flights, and quite a few standard "line" flights, affording me the opportunity to rub elbows with almost all of my pilots. Though for sure I'd earned their respect and maybe even some affection, they often did things to make me the brunt of a joke. One of my sharper bachelor pilots who made a habit of it, was Mike Seale (a justifiably storied Air America pilot). Mike was an accomplished skier—in fact, had been a world-class downhill racer. Before joining Air America he had competed in Germany and Austria, being often photographed in the company of European Super Models. Mike knew I was a former Marine ("Jarhead" to him), often asking another pilot or anyone in earshot of me, *"Do you know what the worst three years of any Marine's life were?"*

They would respond, "No, I don't know. What were they?

Mike would answer with a smile: *"Fifth grade."*

One week when I was on my "Scheduled Time Off" in Bangkok, Mike made a trip to the Philippines where he ordered a beautiful, 3-foot-wide set of Air America pilot's wings, carved out of single piece of teak. While I was still gone he hung it over the screen door to the pilot's lounge (in full view of all the waiting embassy passengers). On first glance it looked handsome and appropriate, until the viewer got close enough to read the raised inscription under the wings that read, *Our Pilots Aren't Afraid to Die!*

A few months ago he was a passenger on a commercial airline flight that at night and in bad weather, crashed while attempting to land at the Taipei international airport. When he came to his senses he was hanging upside down in a bush, a few feet from the ground, still strapped in his seat—only yards from the burning aircraft. He later received some presidential medal for making repeated trips into the flaming fuselage, saving the lives of seven passengers who would have burned to death in their seats. He himself received his share of serious burns. After this tragic Vietnam War ended, Mike returned to his cabin in Coeur d'Alene, Idaho and took up running—becoming a dedicated marathoner. One day after his morning run he was stretching on the kitchen floor, waiting for his oatmeal to come to a boil. The heat must have been set too high as suddenly cooked oats began spewing over the top of the stove. Mike sat up quickly, turning and reaching for the heat control to shut it off. In so doing he severed his spinal cord and *spent the last 20 years of his life as a paraplegic.* (We love you Mike.)

An Enjoyable "STO"

When my seven days off rolled around I did as usual, hopped aboard an Air Vietnam plane and flew to Bangkok. This time I had a surprise for Mark and Kevin: I had carefully drawn out all the plans to build an exact scale model of my Porter. This especially pleased Kevin, who was already showing an advanced interest in aviation and building model planes from commercially-sold kits. We found a shop where we could purchase all the balsa wood and glue we'd need, and set about the task. Took almost the whole week, but came up with a realistically looking Swiss Turbo Porter, that would actually fly! The propeller was powered by a thick piece of rubber we mounted inside the fuselage, stretching the length of the aircraft. The boys and I spent almost all day the last two days at Santi Chai park, that while it had a fair amount of trees, also had a large open space that we used as our flight operations area. I was gratified to be able to provide this small bit of excitement for the boys, especially since there had been no improvement in my ability to carry out a husband's most intimate marital duties.

One Big Reason the War Wasn't Going Well

One day I took a flight to a village that was regarded as "not ours." This meant US troops considered it safe to visit during the day, but "off limits" at night, likely infiltrated by North Vietnamese soldiers or Viet Cong. There, in hidden clearings outside the village or inside darkened huts within the village, the VC held highly emotional classes to explain to the villagers about the invasion of foreigners (us), and how we were desecrating their land and defiling their ancestors. This was an effective tactic, since decades of living through Chinese, Japanese, and French occupations, and now tragic everyday occurrences—proved it. In most Oriental societies the ancestors become deities and a daily decorated shrine to them can be found in every family's dwelling. Of course—truth be known, and here's the kicker: 95% of the rural Vietnamese population did not believe they were fighting against their uncles and cousins from North Vietnam. All they knew was that it was we foreigners that were blowing up their roads and bridges, burying mines alongside their rice fields, napalming their or neighboring villages, and then when we stopped in to visit (during daylight hours) our troops screened all the young male inhabitants, yanking a half dozen suspected teenage Viet Cong sympathizers out of their villages (never to be seen again). They thought *we* were the enemy like the previous invaders. In truth, most if not *all* the rural Vietnamese were VC in their head. They *all* feared us—it was just that only a few were willing to face certain death by defying us. And then when we did kill that one guy who just threw a satchel charge at one of our jeeps, we chalked it up as a single VC who had been hiding in that village, *not realizing the entire rest of his village was of the same mindset, just not as daring.*

A Matter of Numbers

The village I was going to land at (Lao Bao, about 30 miles west of Quang Tri) had supposedly been cleared of the last enemy forces the night before. My passengers were not senior embassy staff. They were US Army officers—going there to supervise another "Body Count." General Westmoreland's theory to winning the war was this: North Vietnam could only send down about 6,500 soldiers a month; so if we killed 6,501 NVA a month, mathematically we would eventually win the war. (I'm not kidding, that was our battle plan.) The objective was—everyday, to kill as many Vietnamese as possible, count em and then declare every one of them to be Viet Cong or a North Vietnamese soldier. I can tell you—to my eyes, the assortment of very young and very old, barely clothed, emaciated bodies I saw, did not look like enemy soldiers. But not important to the Department of Defense; to them, each one was a hard statistic numerically proving we were on our way to winning the war.

The Real Reason So Many Soldiers Returned with PTSD

I landed at a little-used strip at a recently decimated village, let out the passengers, and resigned myself to a day's wait at the aircraft while corpses were gathered, stacked and counted. Surprisingly to me, the officers— accompanied by one young corporal, motioned me to follow them (something I was not keen on doing). We journeyed single-filed down a narrow path, about 100 yards, to what little remained of the village. There were craters everywhere; evidently before the overwhelming ground assault by US and ARVN forces, it had been pummeled by repeated airstrikes and then artillery barrages. It was now a lifeless, devastated area (and probably already was when our troops made their assault). Not one in ten huts was still standing, and everywhere you looked, there were bodies (of all ages and both genders). I was not feeling well, watching while the bodies were assembled and counted. Several hours later, the task completed, an Army helicopter landed and then left with my officer passengers. I would be making the flight back to Saigon with just the corporal who looked too young to even be in the service, and appeared to be yet unsettled about our mission here in Vietnam.

Together we left the village center and headed for the same narrow path we had used to get to the village. It was a dirt path about three feet wide. Two abreast, the jungle foliage on each side brushed our ears as we made our way down it. About halfway to the airplane, we hear a strange creaking noise a short distance behind us. We both whip our heads around and alongside the path see what appears like a picnic basket lid swinging upward out of the ground; a lid that had been covering a small underground hiding place. Also visible was the head of an emerging person. My young corporal at first stunned into inaction by this, as a result of his training and everything he'd heard, reflexively points his weapon at the figure and lets go a burst, after which there is an audible gurgling sound and the person sags back into the hole. The corporal is visibly shaken, his eyes full of wonderment at what has just happened, or more particularly—what he himself has just done. I'm sure a soul-shocking 'first' for him. Together we slowly approached the dugout. The splintered lid is still wide open and splattered with blood. We look into the hole and are sickened at the sight of what appeared to be a 75-year-old Vietnamese man, disfigured by the bullet entry points. And then we see it, and hear it crying—a couple month old baby in the old man's lap! One could easily conclude he was its grandfather or some village elder, *just trying to hide the baby from the carnage until everyone was gone.*

The corporal was mostly incoherent, but one could not miss the effect his actions had on him. He looked left and right (as if for someone to question or give him approval of his actions). He tried to speak to me, but even though I understood the words, they did not arrange themselves into understandable sentences. He leaned forward as if to pick up the baby, but then stopped, unable to get closer to his own handiwork. He didn't get sick, but gagged and appeared on the verge. I told him I'd been to these apparently wiped out villages before, and every time at least half the residents were in hiding nearby. The baby's mother or family members would likely be here within the hour.

We were the last two Americans in the village, with no alternative but to hurry to the airplane and just get out of there. We knew organized special mission troops would soon be arriving. Needless to say the flight back was without a word of conversation or any sound, other than the almost constant moaning from the corporal, and his indecipherable utterances. Sitting on the aircraft floor, his back against a side bulkhead I could see him trembling, the whole way back. He was indeed a shadow of the 18 year-old blonde, blue-eyed, farmer's son from Iowa who had come to Vietnam just three months ago. This day would no doubt forever live with him.

Chapter Nine
AN EXTENDED STO AND FAMILY VACATION

The Sexiest Shoes Ever Made

Each time I travelled to Bangkok, the final walk to my house took me past a shoe store that displayed the coolest European shoes ever made. Being a shoe freak, I couldn't pass it without a short look-see inside. Today was no exception, and in doing so my eyes fell upon a pair of shoes like I had not seen since Cannes or Rome! They were lace-up, but—and here's the great part: they were low-cut like loafers—only having three rows of laces instead of the normal five. This kept the top edge of the instep real low, exposing a major portion of one's foot. And since they were surely made to be worn without socks this extra skin exposure was regarded as sexy. (Remember me sheepishly observing all those cool dudes on the French Riviera in their red moccasins *"sans chaussettes."*) Well these were some shoes! There was a one-inch-wide strip of smooth tan leather that ran down the top center of the shoe to the point of the toe. Bordering it on both sides and down to the soles was a light-colored, taupe suede. It was love at first sight.

The pair on display was a European size 41. I tried them on, knowing I was a size 42 (if not 43). I got them on, but not without considerable difficulty. Once on I experienced excessive pressure everywhere (especially on the back of my heel). *This size was not going to work.*

"Paithoon, (By now I was on a first name basis with the owner.) I'm going to need a 42, maybe even a 43. Can you check in the back?"

"For sure Capin Yanki. Just a moment."

A moment turned into several—a delay that caused justifiable concern on my part. And with due cause, because when Paithoon did return, it was empty-handed; meaning there was no bigger sizes, but he had a plan B.

He pointed excitedly at the size 41 on the floor in front of me and began a twenty-minute treatise on how soft the shoes were, and in no time would stretch and fit me nicely. I grimaced—not that convinced. Still, it was killing me to imagine leaving without these beautiful "running pumps." And yup, you guessed it: While he didn't convince me his stretching theory was a certainty, I couldn't abandon them. I bought them and continued on home to a wonderful greeting from my wonderful family.

Turns out there was a new American film playing in Bangkok, one that the whole family wanted to see—tonight. Only problem was, it was in the Dusit Thani theater on the other side of a large and busy city; a good five miles distance, of which the bumper to bumper traffic would turn into at least a thirty minute drive. No one here tackled that trip across town often. But not insurmountable, the cabs are cheap and not too uncomfortable. *And it could serve a purpose*: what better way to check out my new shoes, than just to sit with them on for two hours; without doing any walking. Just sit there and let them stretch; see how my feet felt. But just in case it would turn out they really were too tight, I had to be sure not to scuff the soles; had to keep them looking unworn, in case I had to return them tomorrow.

We called a cab and it arrived. To keep the soles unmarked, instead of using the concrete walk to the street, I walked the whole distance in the grass alongside it. I then had the driver reposition the cab so I could make one giant step from the grass into the cab, without stepping on the gravel at the side of the road. Upon arriving at the theater I had the driver park directly in front of the ticket window. No way to avoid it though, I was going to have to traverse about twenty feet of concrete. I'm sure I was a sight, picking up each foot and then laying it down flat, making sure on each step that the undersurface did not twist or drag; keep the soles scuff-free. Once inside— no worries about sole damage; the whole place was carpeted.

We all took our seats (in a six-seat glass-enclosed box for those willing to pay an extra few baht). *But uh-oh, big trouble*: After thirty minutes of sitting there, the back of the shoes felt as if they were seriously cutting into the back of my heel. I reached down, undid the laces and adjusted the back edge of the shoe to a place a bit lower on my heel. *No luck*. I was only able to bear the pain another twenty minutes before I had to pull my heel up and out of the shoe. I was now convinced, there was no way I could keep these shoes; would have to take them back tomorrow morning. So leaving the theater I was even more careful with each stride I took (whenever possible putting my foot down on a stray piece of cardboard or discarded plastic bag), until I was safely in the cab.

Up early, I inspected the hopefully barely-marked soles. And they weren't too bad; a few more dents than I would have expected, but small. First thing I did was find some clear shoe polish wax, and spread it over the soles; then, and this took some experimenting, ended up using the bottom of a soup spoon to flatten out the detents and polish the soles. *Not bad!* But not perfect. I found an aerosol can of "Pledge" furniture polish and gave both soles a thin layer of spray, then buffed it with a wool sock. *Perfect. Glistening!* Finished, I put them back in the box, side by side, reversed direction, and fold the tissue paper over one and under the other—just like I had picked them up in the store. Got Sara to give me an old shopping bag, dropped the box and the receipt in it, and was on my way.

Paithoon saw me as I entered the front door and called out to me, "Capin Yanki, how you like that movie last night. I saw you at the Dusithani theater with your new shoes."

A European Vacation with the Family

Something I never told you; one tremendous perk being an Air America employee stationed in a war zone: a full month off each year! Obviously almost everyone used it to return to the states and visit family and friends. This "Home Leave" was besides our regularly scheduled STO's, which themselves provided enough time to go to exciting tourist destinations worldwide. And that's only the half of it; somehow—God knows how it got approved, but Air America was able to be classified an International Air Transport Association carrier. We became a card-carrying member of the world's respected airline community (including British Air, Air France, Lufthansa, and other similarly known airlines). Moreover and of the utmost importance, this membership made us eligible for significant airfare discounts on most airlines. Generally these discounts fell into two categories: pay 50% and get firm reservations; pay 25% but go "Space Available." This latter category meant if the flight was overbooked or additional paying passengers arrived at the last moment, *you could get bumped.* You can probably tell (being the cheap screw I am) which one I utilized for our first family vacation during this "STO."

Bound for the French Riviera

As you remember my questionable but exciting adventures ashore while aboard the aircraft carrier in the Mediterranean, I decided to share (what of it I could) with the family. At least some of the places I had visited; starting with the French Riviera. Unfortunately, on our TWA flight there we had to go through Bombay, India—about midnight, and endure a two-hour wait while we changed planes. I had gotten us "Space Available" tickets, but things were looking good. Surveying the number of people waiting at the gate, I could see we were in good shape. At best the plane would only be about three-quarters full. A bit tired and worse for the wear, we were glad to hear our flight called. We exited the building and entered a bus that would take us out onto the ramp and to our aircraft. Halfway out to the plane, in the midst of what appeared to be an urgent call on his hand-held radio, the driver slowed to a stop. He then made the announcement we were going to momentarily return to the gate.

Once there, to say confusion reigned would be an understatement. One ticket agent ran onto the bus and started *counting.* My heart sank. She ran back into the terminal and another agent entered the bus. I peered through the half open terminal door and saw a group of about 15 (large) African American women, who I was to learn were part of a Southern Baptist tour on the way to Israel, and I was afraid—a sufficient number to get us bumped! *And they were.* An agent inside said we had a real good chance on a 2 P.M. flight tomorrow—lots of empty seats. Our luggage was already loaded; they couldn't get it off. We were assured it would be waiting for us at the Nice, France airport when we got there. Here we were, marooned at a dark and deserted foreign airport at one in the morning. We straggled outside onto a crumbling cement walkway, with six-foot high mounds of dirt and piles of broken concrete lining the road in front of us (the only road into and out of the terminal area), and half-built structures and motionless construction cranes in every direction. I looked around; at a loss and not sure what I would do next. As I lowered my gaze I saw four sets of eyeballs on me that said, *"I hope you have a plan Dad."* I did—not so bright, but just about the only one possible: Get a cab and ask the driver to take us to a reasonable hotel.

Mercifully, ten minutes later a lone cab (who knows why) comes down the street in front of the totally dark and deserted (people-less) terminal. Got him, and he spoke almost perfect English (which of course is not unusual in India). I told him what we needed and was surprised by a return look of disbelief if not outright fear. He didn't say anything, just let us climb in and pulled away. The first part of the ride was on a straight but unlit, poorly paved, remote road bordering unending fields of trash. I could see we were headed for a glow on the horizon (that was hopefully the city).

Once in the city we spent the best part of an hour being turned away from hotel after hotel—all evidently full. At the last one the driver begged the concierge to suggest a hotel that might have a vacancy. He did and even drew a crude map for the driver. I don't know the quality of the map, but we must have gone down every street in Bombay twice, before pulling up in front of our destination hotel which supposedly would have vacancies. It did, not being even a quarter finished built! Nothing but a first level of concrete blocks, and steel girders from there on up; a completely see-through hotel!

It was then that the driver was apparently struck with a great idea. His face lit up and he held up a forefinger. He drove us fifteen minutes to a halfway hospitable appearing building with a couple lights on. He ran inside and in two minutes was back outside urging us to follow him in. We did, went to a nearby desk, and got a room—a big room with only one bed, but the largest bed I'd ever seen; at least two feet wider than a King size. We were going to spend the night in the Bombay YWCA (the Young Women's Christian Association hostel). I'm not sure—*even with five of us in it,* any bed ever felt that good! This experience caused the kids to coin a chant I would hear during the rest of the trip (and at mirthful times in the future): "We go Dad's Way. Space A. Bombay!"

Finally, the Cote D'Azur!

Got the 2 P.M. flight okay. Got to Nice okay. Got our luggage okay. Got a van to town okay. Things looking good! Checked into the Le Negresco hotel (right on the waterfront, but not a cheap overnight). Got two rooms, one for the kids and one for Sara and I. We were just beginning to unload our suitcases when Donna comes running in, "Mom, Dad, I got to show you something. You've just got to see it. In our room." Wasn't sure what she had seen but it sure seemed urgent. We followed her to her room and she raced to the head of the bed, pointing to a brass plaque on the wall above the headboard. Inscribed in it were the words: *"Elizabeth Taylor and Richard Burton Slept here February 12th and 13th, 1966."* Upon returning to our room, and looking above our headboard we discovered that Tom Jones and two other similarly famous celebrities had graced our room.

As a family we did just about everything you could do, even rented a car and took extended sight-seeing drives—easterly almost into Italy, and westerly almost into Spain. Much of the road along the coast was high up on the rocky cliffs above the sea. The views of the Mediterranean below us were nothing less than spectacular, and the kids were duly impressed. I was able to save some money as we stayed the nights in cheaper Bed and Breakfasts. In Monaco we took the famous Palace Tour, and in my famous Cannes, we strolled the Esplanade like we belonged there, and in Antibes we visited a topless beach! (You should have seen the kids.)

On Levelling a Table

On our Nice hotel terrace there was a first class dining area with white linen table cloths and place settings of silver and crystal. It was appealing and picturesque under a brightly striped awning. Sara and I decided to have the kids eat dinner in their room and we would sample this regal hotel eatery. We showed up at six, dressed as sharply as we could, and must admit we were shown to our table with surprising respect. By 6:30 the place was full, and I may add—full of obviously well-heeled clientele, most acting as if somewhere in their lineage was royal blood. While we certainly felt out of place, evidently it did not show. I ordered a bottle of the more reasonably priced wine and a Chateaubriand for two. They even mixed the salad and béarnaise sauce table-side. Have to admit; it was a delightfully prepared, presented and delicious meal.

Only one problem: our small table rocked. One leg was a bit shorter than the others. Evidently this deficiency had not gone unnoticed by the waiters. Next thing we knew one was at our table, grabbed the cork from our wine bottle, whipped out his handy little Le Theirs paring knife, cut a quarter-inch-thick disc off the top of the cork, stooped, and shoved it under the short leg. Mission accomplished he gave us a quick smile and was off. We were to soon discover he must have cut too thick a piece, because that leg now being longer than the others, the table still rocked, albeit the other way. Once again our dilemma did not go unnoticed. Another waiter was at our table side, grabbed the same wine cork, whipped out his paring knife and cut another disc off the top of the cork, stooped and put it under another leg. Another smile, which we returned with a "Merci," and he was gone. Hate to say it, but while I don't know the exact cause, the table was still rocking. Yup, you guessed it. It was noticed again. Sara and I sat through the same routine two more times, until there was no cork left (and our table was still rocking).

Sticking In There No Matter What

We had such a wonderful meal we decided to do the same thing again the next night. Our only concern, the skies were threatening and there could be rain. Of course the eating area was under that lovely awning. Just before dinner was served a light rain began. We felt reasonably safe under the awning. Felt adventurous tonight and ordered Duck a l'Orange, but just as it came out, it started raining hard! I could hear it pelting down atop the awning, and fearfully saw the awning deeply sagging— the seams straining to hold under the weight of the pooled rain. While we were considering jumping up and taking refuge inside, we noticed a well-dressed and distinguished appearing French couple sitting two tables away, who in spite of an impending waterfall, refused to take any notice of the dangerous extent of the sag in the awning—*almost directly above their heads*. While it was far from the worst thing that could have happened, a few stiches in the awning seam directly over the French couple's table, gave way, causing—while not a steady stream, repeating large drops of water to come down—landing not only on their food, but also right on top of their heads. Do you think they got up, or complained, or reached for a napkin? No. In fact they completely feigned to be unaware of anything awry. His coiffured hair was soon matted down and her mascara was painting black tracks down both cheeks. Still, neither displayed the slightest reaction to the condition besetting them. The height of it was when each one of the lady's false eyelashes popped loose at the inside corner and swung out, perpendicular to her face. She gave no sign she was aware of this and continued to eat, finishing her meal so altered. When we walked out, barely able to contain our laughter, it was through an inch of water.

At Least To Me, One of the Funniest Things I've Done

In spite of the heavy rains and leaking awning last night, and threatening sky at the moment, we decided to risk our luck by once again taking our evening meal on the terrace (under the porous awning). Sara was in the bedroom finishing dressing, and I was in the bathroom doing the same. When she was ready she called that through the bathroom door. I opened the door and emerged properly dressed but wearing a mask and snorkel and swim fins instead of shoes! Of course it was just done for a joke and after a good laugh I dressed properly and we went to dinner.

A Great Success

Things went well enough that I could almost imagine aborting the calling dominating me, think for a moment that I could cast it off, and just savor that which is so desirable in a proper family arrangement. All of us were sad to see out time in Europe come to an end, but we had done as much as anyone could in seven days.

Back in Saigon, and Alex Webber— the Smartest, Kindest Man I Ever Met

Though I didn't mention it, about a year ago Air America discontinued using the French "Astazou" engine in the Porter, and began test-bedding a new and powerful engine manufactured by Garrett AirResarch in Phoenix, Arizona. To assure the pilots and mechanics would properly operate and maintain it the manufacturer sent an engineer to Saigon to help us. Most often these tech reps work primarily with the mechanics. His name was Alex Webber, about 50 years old and never married, although he had a lady friend (Pat) who visited him here every three or four months. His gray hair was always a military-style crewcut, and he was never seen wearing anything other than a khaki shirt and trousers. Although Alex never told us, he had a Ph.D in physics, and thirty years' experience as a tech rep working with Air Forces around the world, including a year with the Royal Navy aboard a British aircraft carrier. Here, he (correctly) thought that educating the pilots about how to operate the new engine was more important than helping a filipino mechanic turn a wrench on a brake housing.

One night each month I scheduled an "All Pilots' Meeting. In these meetings I would share with my pilots new information about our current operations as well as what I had learned about operating the new Garret engine. To make this second part even more accurate and beneficial, I invited Alex Webber to speak at these meetings. He jumped on it enthusiastically. I can't tell you how informative and revealing his talks were (replete with drawings and diagrams). He was an expert on a physics law called "The Conservation of Energy," and knowing this he gave revealing and detailed information on how the pilots could compare the state of power produced, by comparing the BTU's available from the incoming fuel, the exhaust gas temperature, and the resultant torque produced. Understanding this ratio a pilot could see an engine becoming less efficient. The end result:

a pilot could predict an engine failure many hours before it would fail! Surprisingly to all of us, that equation could easily be worked out by just comparing three engine instruments on the panel. Not only were my pilots duly impressed, but I felt like a kid in a candy store; learning more about operating engines by listening to Alex, than I had in the past ten years in military aviation.

Something entirely unwarranted: As a result of Alex spending more time with the pilots than the mechanics, the head of Maintenance (Boyd Messinger, a generally not especially well-thought-of, but long-time manager) was jealous and felt that Alex was under-appreciative of Maintenance's role in dealing with the new engine. He wrote to Alex's company (Garrett AirResearch) bad-mouthing him and recommending that he be recalled, if not terminated! When I heard about it I was incensed; a rank injustice! I immediately wrote a letter to Garrett, praising Alex's knowledge and extensive contribution, including his efforts in educating the pilots and make sure they were operating the aircraft in the most efficient manner. His lady-friend, many years later told me that Alex (being such an introvert, and being so much smarter than the people he did come in contact with) never accumulated a wide circle of friends, and always carried that letter in his back pocket. When the head of the maintenance department continued to press Air America to back up his request to Garrett to get rid of Alex, I informed Air America if they didn't oppose Boyd's request, I was going to quit! (A week later I was able to give Air America a letter signed by 28 of my Porter pilots, saying, "If Roger quits, we're quitting!")

Chapter Ten

TWO SHORT PERSONAL TRIPS

A Memorable Moment at the Temple

Several pilots had visited Angkor Wat, an old temple in Cambodia (sometimes referred to as the eighth wonder of the world). Since all our Porters were grounded for at least three or four days (there had been several failures of the metal shaft driving the fuel pump). I decided to do something worthwhile (for a change) and take a short (educational) trip there. This required a flight to Phnom Penh and then a short flight north to Siem Reap where the temple was located. On this second flight a pamphlet about it said it was one of the largest religious monuments in the world, spreading out over 400 acres. It was originally constructed as a Hindu temple but transformed into a Buddhist temple in the 12th century, and represented the highest class of Khmer architecture. And—I had never known this: its silhouette is the symbol in the middle of the Cambodian national flag.

Got a taxi to a local hotel, but based on the deserted streets and empty hotel, had a hard time believing I was in the vicinity of what in 20 years would be a world-renown tourist destination. I got to the temple about two in the afternoon, and while I was of course, mightily impressed by this gigantic walled structure, what added to its uniqueness and the effect it was having on me: *there were only two other people there*; only one other couple was visiting the temple! I could just make them out a hundred yards away, meandering along one of the upper walkways. There was not another human being in sight. No guides, no vendors, no locals—no one! Nor surprisingly were there any information booths or kiosks of any kind. *Eerie.* This expansive stone structure (built on a giant, half mile-square swamp) and the surrounding grounds, on all four sides—as far as the eye could see, didn't hold another moving being. I was the sole pilgrim encroaching upon its apparent sanctity. I felt uncomfortable, even irreverent, and could not shake the sense I was violating some ethereal boundaries.

The temple itself was a centered attraction completely surrounded— on all four sides, by a tall and richly engraved stone wall. From inside one facet of it was a long, straight as an arrow, ten-foot high and banistered stone walkway leading to the temple itself and a flight of stairs that appeared to be the main entrance. I felt unjustified to be on the premises; as if I were not authorized or even qualified to be there. I took the long walkway and entered the interior of the temple, weaving my way down one narrow stone passageway after another. Everywhere, the walls chock-a-block with three dimensional carved animal monsters. (Homo sapiens-type monkeys with big heads and whose faces bore what could only be called evil-intentioned expressions). I was no longer merely uncomfortable, but now as the sole visitor—was beginning to think the attraction may no longer need my presence.

After twenty minutes of navigating twisting passageways, I found myself at a tall, arched entryway. I went through it (almost as if I was called to do so), and then down a flight of stone steps. I was in a chamber, the likes of which I had never seen, nor would experience again. This sunken stone-floored room was about 25 feet wide and 50 feet deep. At the far end were several six-foot-wide steps (like I had just come down) but leading up to a huge stone throne. Ten feet in from the near wall (that I had just come in through) and ten feet in from both side walls, were a line of stone pillars. The ceiling was not an arch and there were no truss-like members spanning it; made you wonder what could be holding up twenty tons of stone. Outside of the pillars, on three sides, were inclined rows of benches (bleachers) carved out of the existing rock. Just inside the three rows of pillars, also on all three sides, cut down into the floor, was a one-foot-wide, one- foot-deep, channel—appearing to have at one time been used to hold water or perform as a drain. One thing unusual about this sunken channel was the exactitude of its measurements. If it had been cut into the floor with lasers it could not have been straighter or more consistent in width and depth. (God knows what kind of tools they had 800 years ago.) There were no windows in the room. The only light entering was through the door I just came through, and a small rectangular cut in the ceiling—about six inches by a foot, through which I could see a few wisps of clouds drifting by.

Alone and not unaware of a palpable sacred aura of the room, I crossed the expanse of the room and began up the steps of this grand ancient cathedra. (Or perhaps felt I was drawn to it). At the top, I surprised myself by sitting in the throne! Within seconds of doing so I felt warm and somehow comforted, my thought-process seeming to elevate, maybe even moving into a strangely more peaceful state. Suffice it to say it was an experience like never before. Scanning the room and the floor in front of me, I noticed at the foot of the steps to the throne, there was a rectangular patch of light from the opening in the ceiling. Perhaps due to its brilliance or creeping movement towards me, I couldn't look away from it. In so doing I noticed it was now moving up the steps, exactly in the middle of them—towards me. I'm realizing that at this time of the year, and at this time of day, the westward descending arc of the sun was causing the bright rectangle to continue eastward—up the steps. I couldn't move. In about twenty minutes the light was on my feet, then my knees, ten minutes more, on my chest, and finally it was hitting me full-face, and I was looking straight into the sun. Whatever this room had been for, *that occasion must have been scheduled for this exact day of the year and this time of that day.* I was moved to a point of reflective wonderment.

That night I had an itching for a good meal of Chinese food, and entered what appeared to be a suitable place. The thin, gaunt waiter, with the typical black trousers and a white shirt brought me a menu with European cuisine. I called him back and explained to him I was here for Chinese food, and would he please bring me a Chinese menu. Though I could not understand every word, and for who knows why, it was for sure he didn't want to. I insisted until he gave up and left—evidently to get one. In a minute or two he returns, and with a look of disdain handed me a menu all written in Chinese.

The Next Day, Shopping at the Morning Market

Back in Saigon I had recently had begun letting a guy room with me; not permanent, just temporary while he was transiting Vietnam. He was working as a free-lance journalist and had a contract with TIME magazine. His name was Sean Flynn (the son of the famous movie actor Errol Flynn)! While Vietnam was the headline-earning line, Sean was hung up on Cambodia; unusually concerned about recent political developments within the country. In fact that's how I met him—trying to hitch a ride with me to a small strip a mile from the Cambodian border.

In any case he had told me before I left for Angkor Wat, that anyone could buy marijuana (the raw stuff)—no sweat, in the 'morning market' in Phnom Penh, and he'd sure appreciate it if I could bring him back a bag. Remembering this, the day before I was to fly back I decided to visit the market and give it a try. In every city in the Far East there's a morning market. Before sunrise, hundreds of vendors, peddlers, and especially farmers (or it appears—their mothers or grandmothers) migrate in from outlying districts and open up their flimsy stalls in this huge, shanty-like flea market in the city square. It can be a quarter-mile by a quarter-mile, open for business at first light and mostly closed down by 11 a.m. There is nothing you cannot find in these markets. Although most of it is meat, fish, fruits, vegetables, nuts, and other very strange looking edibles, there are stretches of stalls that sell nothing but pots and pans, or articles of clothing, or any number of apparently hand fabricated but useful household devices (but absolutely no Angkor Wat tee-shirts or souvenirs of any kind)!

Not a solitary vendor was speaking English. No way to know where the herb or tobacco stalls were. It was going to be a matter of traipsing the line; just keep plodding along till I found one. Aha! I came upon a stretch of tattered canvas cubicles, whose back walls displayed rows of single packs and cartons of every known brand of American, European, and Chinese cigarettes. These stalls—like all the others, were manned by a pair of betel-nut-chewing, 90 pound, 90-year-old women. Everyone over 50 years of age—with no exception, chewed this betel nut, which permanently dyed the teeth and lips a dark red and produced an almost purple spit. It was some type of opioid plant that kept these aging creatures active throughout their long days. I bounced back and forth between several stalls, making repeated inquiries in pigeon English, and supporting them with any motion or gesture I could add that might clarify my quest for marijuana. I was totally unsuccessful in getting even one of these old women to understand what type of mind-altering product or cigarette I was trying to buy. Finally in the midst of silence and blank stares, as a last ditch effort, I picked up a loose cigarette, twisted it under my nostrils, simulated a deep inhalation as if breathing in its aroma, and then rolled my eyes crazily—hoping this might set the tone. Immediately, a tiny aged woman (with no teeth) sitting in front of the rack of cigarettes, jumps to her feet, points at me and in perfect English shouts: "Menthol!"

Hawaii, the Hard Way

When I returned to Saigon, the required parts had not yet arrived and my Porters were going to remain grounded another three or four days. If I'd have known it was going to be this long, I could've taken a free STO in Bangkok! Under the guise of being a pilot on an "International Carrier," with some vague claims Air America pilots could occasionally get themselves a free ride aboard one of these independent cargo planes. The captain would let us sit on the "jump seat" in the cockpit. Every day—at least twice if not three times, cargo-only air freight operators who had acquired military contracts would come into Saigon loaded with pallets of military supplies. One such company was Airlift International out of Miami. Months ago I had written a letter to their chief pilot requesting free passage on their aircraft, and I had been surprised to receive a letter back with his approval.

I knew they stopped in Hawaii coming and going, and with several more days to waste I thought that might be a good way for me to spend a day or two there and see Honolulu. My new roomie, Sean heard about my plan and asked if there was any chance he could come along. I told him that since I was 'sort of' an airline pilot I was able to get written permission; and it was doubtful he could get on board without some authorization. But who knows? "The captain might be a good guy and approve you as well." The day of my hoped-for ride I was at Tan Son Nhut airport when the Airlift flight landed. I was not thrilled to see that on this day, they were using an old four-engine propeller plane—a DC-6 (originally designed in 1946). Within five minutes of parking, there were a half dozen puddles of gas, oil and hydraulic fluid under the fuselage and wings. I approached the captain (Captain Mountain). He was craggily-faced and about 5' 3" (understandably wearing high-heeled boots) and with shocks of white hair poking out under his "50-mission-crush" hat. He read the letter I had received, nodded okay and motioned me to the airplane—without me showing any identification. At his urgings I introduced Sean and asked if he could come along. I was surprised when this appeared to be no problem. Captain Mountain nodded okay immediately (making me think my letter wouldn't have been necessary).

As was the procedure, Captain Mountain had dropped his full load and the return trip should be empty. It was dark by the time we took-off (and I was pleased to hear all four engines start on the first try). Inside, the raw hull was visible to us; just olive drab aluminum—no carpets, no sidewall covering, or any composite ceiling (thus exposing all the ribs, stringers, rods, cables, and electric bundles). Plus, it was configured to carry cargo and therefore, there were no seats of any kind. But it was not entirely empty—there was a long row of empty pallets down the center of the cabin. It was poorly lit by three or four dim incandescent bulbs hanging from a single electric cord that was strung the length of the cabin, swaying just inches above the tops of the stacked pallets. By rearranging some of the pallets and weaving our arms through the tie-down straps, Sean and I were able to fashion ourselves some reasonably tolerable places to sit for the grueling low altitude flight ahead (which including a refueling stop at Wake Island, would take all night and most the next day). The age of the airplane was not lost on us as there was a constant creaking, snapping, reliefs of pressure, and other sounds similar to something breaking or about to break.

I'd like to say "just when things were going fine," except out here over the middle of the ocean, in the middle of the night, and in an airplane almost as old as I was, shivering in the dark—things really never felt fine. At about two in the morning, cruising at 15,000 feet, we entered just about the most God-awful weather I'd ever seen. It was a squall line with blinding flashes of lightning and crashes of thunder, a deluge of loud pelting rain, and boiling, violent cumulus clouds, that we pilots refer to as "thunder-bumpers." The airplane was being tossed around like a ping pong ball in a lottery tumbler. I can assure you, flying in our modern jets at the high altitudes they use, you would never have experienced the ride Sean and I went through. We were being thumped and bruised—hanging on to the tie-down straps for dear life. Our aircraft's flight path was so radically up and down, that peering out the small windows, the wingtips would arc so far down as to go out of view, and then be yanked back upward—now so high as to again be out of view. How they kept from breaking off I'll never know. Every single one of the light bulbs hanging from that electric cord had smashed themselves against the tops of the pallets. We were now on a roller coaster in pitch black, and I think I could say—justifiably concerned.

Mercifully, thirty minutes later we emerged, intact, and mightily relieved. We were in the clear and the ocean surface beneath us was glinting with bright moonlight. Finally, everything seemed right with the world. Sean recognized we might owe a debt of gratitude to Captain Mountain and the copilot, so we made our way forward to the open cockpit, where we relayed our thanks for getting us through such a dangerous stretch. Sean said to Captain Mountain (not too brilliantly): "So you're a pilot, eh."

To which Captain Mountain, shucks of white hair still sticking out from under his hat and one high-heeled boot propped up on the instrument panel, responded, "Yes son, I am indeed."

As many people who had accumulated their forty hours of flight time, and gotten their "Private Pilot's" license do, Sean could barely wait to add, *"So am I!"*

The Captain responded, "Son, one thing you might want to remember: Picasso was a painter, and so was the guy who did your house."

There is one other thing I remember about that Airlift crew: The copilot wore a large silver ring, set with a shiny blue and white stone I couldn't recognize at first, but when I got a closer view, was surprised to note it was not a stone at all, but *an artificial glass eye—looking back at me.*

A Disheartening Event in Bangkok

By now Sara had won quite a few bowling tournaments and received her share of trophies; you know—those cheap plastic-coated brass plaques and bowling figurines. Proud as she was of them, she wanted to display them so passersby could see them. The corner of our house facing the street had a floor to ceiling glass window. It was there on a standing cabinet she placed them all. The afternoon sun shining against the exhibit reflected back a brilliant shining golden glow, as if we had our own Fort Knox stacked in that corner. Sadly, one day when the family was out, the khmoys, having evidently seen the brightness, and thinking it was from a horde of gold artifacts, broke in and stole every last one of her trophies!

Chapter Eleven
DAY TO DAY OPS AND AN
ENTREPRENEURIAL BLUNDER

A Line Check to End All Line Checks

I was running a "tight ship" and was gratefully aware that the Porter program was well regarded by upper management, the other program managers, and even more importantly—the Customer. I was lucky because in addition to me trying to set the example, all my guys were born and bred "Get it done" guys. Still, once a year, every captain has to go through a ground school on his aircraft, and then take a "Proficiency Check" and a "Line Check" in it. The Proficiency Check was administered by check pilots from the company Flight Standards Office in Bangkok (who we jokingly referred to as "the experts from the home office"). While the Proficiency Check was important, it dealt mostly with dotting the "i's" and crossing the "t's." *There was a more important flight check administered every six months.* On it, the captain had to prove to his program Chief Pilot (me, in the Porter program), that he could fly a long, hard, frustrating day; determining and selecting what might be the only safe routes; loading and unloading the airplane himself; fueling it while it was still running, and make it into and out of the most unlikely landing sites. This was the "Line Check." The program chief pilot would ride in the copilot's seat (often the whole day) trying not to make suggestions, just evaluating the captain's flight decisions and control of the aircraft.

Today I was going to fly all day with a guy named Jack Smythe, making sure he was up to and willing to do whatever it would take. (Frequently I would give no warning this check was coming, and surprise the pilot by just meeting him at the airplane at 0630.) But not today. Jack and I were good friends, and I already knew what kind of job he was doing, so anticipated an uneventful day. We were scheduled to go to a strip about 40 miles southwest of Saigon; safe, you'd think—being that close. But no, the strip at Bao Tri was famous for changing hands; controlled by friendly forces at sunset and held by the enemy at daybreak. And even the village—a mile from the strip, would be in enemy hands one week and ours the next. This being the situation at Bao Tri I was keen to see from what direction, and at what altitude Jack would approach it, and how he would determine if it would be safe to land. (These were the types of things I would grade on these Line Checks.) We would have to check the strip and surrounding areas carefully, from high above—before committing to a landing. Today (fortunately) we wouldn't be on the ground long; just long enough to unload about ten wooden crates of metal .45 caliber ammo cans onto the ramp. Full, the metal containers weighed about 30 pounds each. Empty—no longer useful, they became "collectibles." Handy and sharp-looking, with two neat latches, almost every pilot had one or more somewhere in his house.

The strip was an east-west oriented strip and we would be landing to the west. As we overheaded it (once again—me in the copilot's seat monitoring Jack's decisions and actions) nothing appeared especially abnormal on the ground, minus the fact we couldn't see a single soul within a mile of the strip. That *was* unusual, but not a definite indicator of enemy presence. Once again, this strip was a Marston Matting strip; made up of those hundreds of perforated steel planks hooked together end to end and laid over otherwise unsuitably soft or wet terrain. Being only 500 feet long, just the Porter and two or three other "bush" planes could land and take-off from a strip of this size. Halfway down the strip was a short PSP taxiway coming off the runway to the south—leading to a small, basketball court sized parking ramp. Proceeding from the south edge of the ramp was a straight dirt path that led about 100 feet further south to a small sentry's kiosk (in which a Vietnamese soldier was usually sleeping). It continued another 100 yards, meeting a more frequently traveled east-west road.

Landing and Unloading the Cargo

Jack made a tight spiraling descent, landed and got the aircraft stopped in half the runway. This enabled him to turn off midfield and take that short taxiway to the ramp (saving us two minutes taxiing back time had he rolled out to the end of the runway). On the ramp Jack spun it around and put on the parking brake. He stayed at the controls—engine running. Before the plane had come to a stop I was out of my seat, through the cabin, ready to swing the doors open and begin my job of unloading. If the Viet Cong had observed our arrival (which they likely did) we might have just a couple minutes before they rushed the strip. Uh-oh—not good; glancing at the sentry's station (100 yards down the path to that nearby road), I noticed it was unoccupied—not even a sleeping guard. Got the ten crates off and stacked on the ramp in just a couple minutes. Jumped back in the aircraft and locked the door. Sweating and out of breath I flopped into the copilot's seat. Unfortunately, instead of moving straight ahead towards the taxiway leading to the runway, Jack locked the left wheel and began turning the airplane, which caused the tail stabilizer to swing around and become wedged behind the nearest pile of ammo boxes. We were snagged.

I was out of the aircraft in a second, grabbed the problem wooden crate (by its neat rope handle on top) and walked backwards, dragging it away from the aircraft. Positioning it far enough away from the tail I started back to the aircraft, when two yards from my feet, several rounds hit the PSP— loudly, tearing it and ricocheting who knows where. While stunned in the realization that I was being shot at, several more rounds went singing past my torso. As I was preparing to jump back in the aircraft, Jack having seen what was happening decided (for some unknown reason) to jump *out*, with our one M16 rifle. It was loaded with a single magazine of 20 rounds, which I can tell you from experience, if you don't know how many enemy there are, or exactly where they are, and you're scared enough, you can use all twenty rounds in the first ten seconds! (True, I had my .38 Police Special revolver, which might have been useful if I was a security guard at Kohl's.)

Just a matter of yards from the west edge of the parking ramp was a round, water buffalo pond, about fifty feet across. (The natives dug these next to every tilled field so the water buffalos could cool themselves during the day, which without doing they would die later that day). Jack and I amid the snaps of the passing rounds, quickly covered the distance to the pond, and jumped into the dark and slimy water. Once in and upright we found our feet mired in goo and the water level halfway up our backs. We plastered ourselves side by side, chests pressed into the black mud bank that faced the incoming fire, and stuck our heads up just high enough to peer over the edge of the hole. In so doing, we were able to see—about a hundred yards past the east end of the strip, from within a hedgerow, the muzzle flashes as they continued firing. Must just be a few of them; could only see four muzzle flash locations. Probably a rag-tag group of untrained VC. Their rounds were going by either high or wide. And (thank God) it appeared they had not thought of *disabling the aircraft,* which was still parked with the engine running. We knew the VC always had a limited supply of ammunition, and would most likely run out in the next few minutes. *Please God they do and don't rush us!*

Luck was with us. The shots became less frequent then stopped altogether. Jack and I tried to talk ourselves into making a break for the airplane, but couldn't get the nerve, deciding to just hide in the hole for a little while longer. We waited about ten minutes and decided it was now or never; time to make a break for the airplane. We were still lying there on our chests against the upsloping bank, side by side, staring to the east, when before we moved—about the loudest noise I ever heard! Fired from somewhere *behind* us, a single bullet slammed into the mud between us! In the six inches between us a single round cracked into the black mud. While frantically scrambling out of the water and up the black mud bank, we turned our heads to look at the far side of the pond. There, standing on the west bank of the water hole, silhouetted by the late afternoon sun, were four VC firing at us! *Thank God one lousy marksman fired too soon.* If they would have waited and all fired together, this story would not be being told. And God knows how, between the rounds passing us on both sides, over and under us, we got to the aircraft without being hit! In a second we were in our seats and moving to the runway. Besides the scare the water hole situation had given me, I got another when Jack—instead of taking the metal taxiway out to the runway, chose to take a shortcut straight across the soggy wet grass. (You never do this because of the chance the tires will bog down and you'll become permanently stuck.) But we made it! Onto the runway with only half of it to use for take-off. He crammed the throttle full forward, and we were on our way out of there, barely becoming airborne by the end of the runway; our wheels ripping through the foliage where the VC had first begun firing at us (*before they walked all the way down the north side of the runway, crossed the west end of it, and advanced up our side to the edge of the pond behind us)!*

Saving A Good Man's Job

In a previous chapter I went over the varied responsibilities of a program chief pilot; one of which was administering the just described, much-too-realistic Line Check. But there was another responsibility I had (although

Air America would later hire specialized personnel for this task). I would act as the "Safety Officer" for any accident involving one of my Porters. This meant making the official investigation of the crash and submitting recommendations, which could, and did from time to time—sadly result in the fining of, or even the severance of the concerned pilot.

One day at my desk, Jim Kwigley comes running in from the Operations Office and tells me that 58F with Al Case at the controls had crashed at a dirt strip near Binh Lam, about 50 miles north of Saigon. He's okay, but from what Al radioed back, it sounds like the aircraft is finished—for good. *Shit!* Al had joined Air America after two Marine Corps combat tours in helicopters, but with us—instead of flying rotary wing, he started as a First Officer on a C-47 (a fixed-wing aircraft). When his seniority allowed him to do it, he bid for a captain's position within my program. Al was at least ten years younger than me but had already turned more than prematurely gray—we're talking snow white. He checked out easily and we became good friends. Based on his intelligence and ambition, I predicted good things for Al. He had a lot on the ball and could assert himself when he thought he was right, and later became a very successful businessman. He checked out at least six months ago, and had been flying the line almost daily since then. I wolfed down a sandwich, grabbed a camera, a fifty-foot tape measure, and a folder of forms, found a Porter not being used and departed for the crash site.

When I arrived overhead I could easily make out the bright red laterite strip. (Laterite is a common clay found throughout Vietnam—usually hard, but can easily become either mud or breath-choking dust.) There was no mistaking the strip as its color was sharply contrasted by lush green on both sides. Of course I couldn't land on it since Al's aircraft was disabled right in the middle of it. Hard to figure out what could have happened. The Porter is a "high-wing" plane (meaning the wings extend out from the top of the fuselage), and looking down I could see both were disjointed— angling sharply downward, both wing tips resting on the ground. For sure this aircraft would not fly again. I couldn't see the gear (wheels or struts) since they were under the wings, but for sure they were collapsed. I had no radio communication with the customer so had to just visually try to find an acceptable landing area.

I did then what I always do before landing: examine the intended landing area for any possible obstacles, reasons to make an unusual approach, or decide not to land at all. In so doing I saw something unusual—in fact seriously unusual. At most of our barely discernable landing sites, to better outline it, the Customer placed a row of white-painted boxes along both sides of the strip. Here, I saw that while there was a row of white markers on the left side of the red laterite runway, *there were none on the right side.* I knew there should be. This being unusual, I scanned the area and noticed something new: On the far left side of the weeded field to the left of the red laterite runway, was a long row of white markers. Obviously now meant to mark the left side of a new landing area—*the wide grassy field!* I could only assume these were the runway edge markers that had previously been on the right side of the laterite strip, but moved to their new location after Al's plane closed the laterite strip. (So while this new side-stepped location made sense, it did nothing to explain why Al crashed.)

I landed uneventfully (in the grass field) and was met by the Customer. I was greatly surprised to hear what he had to say: The furthest left row of white markers in the grass field were indeed the ones that had previously been on the right side of the laterite runway. But, they were *not* put there because Al's airplane closed the laterite runway. They were put there last night because yesterday afternoon a mortar had come in and blown a six foot deep crater, in the middle of the runway—*the hole that Al had rolled into when he landed (without checking the location of the new left side runway markers).*

Unfortunately for Al, this put a whole new light on the accident. The red laterite strip that we were in the habit of landing on was of such a contrasting color compared to the green fields on each side, Al didn't bother to question the fact that there were no markers on the right side of the strip. He was just sucked in. If he had he questioned the absence of right-side markers, and looked around, and seen them moved over onto the grass field, he would have realized—they were outlining a newly relocated landing area, and even if he could not make it out from altitude *there had to be something wrong with the original laterite runway.* (And at midday, with the sun directly overhead, there would be no shadows to show Al the mortar hole.) I glanced at the deconstructed aircraft (which was painful to do) and saw Al walking towards me. Of course I queried him regards him not checking for two lines of runway markers. Surprisingly he shook his head, made some gesture with his hands and said, "Rog, if I came back in here again, I'd do the same thing!"

"Al. Say anything, but don't say that! How in the hell do you suspect I can get you off with that attitude. You've got to have learned something here!" I stood there wondering, how could I make Al's poor decision-making appear less culpable? It was true that the depression he went into was not markedly evident from the air. And now, with his airplane over it, I couldn't get a photo which would convince upper management that the crater was not obvious from the air. My only way out, was to somehow make the newly marked landing area—the grass field, appear even less suitable as a landing spot. One thing we could 'hang our hat on' was that the grass was about two feet high, and could well have been hiding tree stumps, big rocks, or even 55 gal oil drums, or any other object that would disable an aircraft.

I took Al over onto the grass field (where I had just landed), and had him stand in a spot (that did not show my aircraft in the background). I had him stand upright, hands on his hips, looking into the camera—with the top of the grass midway up his thighs. While this amount of growth did look as if it might be sufficient to discourage a pilot from attempting a landing, it was not all that damning. Then it hit me, I had Al continue standing there, with his hands on his hips, looking into the camera, *but had him kneel!* The photo I then took, and one that became part of the official accident report, *showed the grass above Al's waist!* It was sufficient for the Board to conclude no one would attempt a landing in that overgrown field, and Al escaped, going on to be a storied "Black Ops" pilot with Air America (and today's historian for Air America).

Another Example of No Forethought

Of all the stupid things I have done, none equal—at age 16, having gotten my German girlfriend's initials tattooed on my forearm. Now fifteen years later I made an almost equally ill-considered decision: to join in with two other Air America pilots, *and buy a downtown Saigon nightclub from a wizened old Chinese business woman.* It was the whole top floor over a flea market across from the railway station (and visible in the background of that notorious photo of the Vietnamese general shooting that suspected Viet Cong in the head). Our plans were grandiose: to hire the city's top rock band, and fix it up as the "in-place" for GI's to drink, listen to the latest heavy metal, and pick up bar girls. Problem was, all the tables and chairs—designed for 115 pound Vietnamese soldiers, wouldn't come close to holding up under the weight of U.S. GI's. We therefore declined to include the furniture in the transaction; incurring substantial wrath from the previous owner (and her son, a colonel in the Vietnamese

Army). When the purchase went through, all three of us were out of town, flying up country. When I returned Tom met me at the airplane. "Roger, you're not gonna believe this. The fucking roof's gone! They took it off to resell the galvanized metal sheets. The place is a goddam open-air bar in a monsoon! Unless we put on another roof, we don't have a club! We did, substantially increasing our investment in Saigon's newest club, "The Whiskey A Go Go."

The Chinese grandma (who somehow still ended up as a part owner, used to show us the electric bill each month, and collect the Piastres from us to pay it. One month I noticed a familiar amount: the precise number of Piastres *as three months ago!* Couldn't be. Thus did I learn grandma had been screwing us monthly—showing us copies of old and substantially larger bills from her dress factory. Of course you couldn't come out and accuse her of that, without inviting someone to find your body in one of Saigon's garbage strewn alleys. (Her son had his own Vietnamese Mafia that employed the same tactics as ours.)

One night the band (our main attraction) didn't show up. Grandma informed us they were on strike. It was no contest, pay em what they demanded (no bargaining) or close down the club. There was no other comparable group in Saigon, had to do it (and there went at least two weeks profit). About a week later their sound equipment that I had purchased in Bangkok on my last STO, ceased working. We found out that members of the band were in the habit of setting their cokes on top of the amplifiers, the spilled coke seeped through the cooling vents and hungry ants did the rest. Our investment was again increased.

But of all the tricks contributing to the downfall of our entrepreneurial spirit, none surpassed the following in its brazenness. One day two Frenchmen in suits and two policemen (always dressed in white from head to toe, and therefore referred to by everyone as Saigon's "white mice") came marching into the club. Lo and behold what I learned then was that there had never been the first electric bill sent to the club! Grandma had the main electric line for the whole club spliced into an exterior neon sign on the outside of the building. *A French soft drink company had been paying our electric bills since our opening!*

But let me tell you the coup de grace in making me give up on this short but futile business venture, and turn all my attention back to my real job: One night, as well as our almost exclusive crowd of U.S.GI's, there was one table of Vietnamese soldiers who were doing a lot of drinking, and becoming more and more boisterous. The group was beginning to worry Joe and I. (Joe was third Air America owner.) Next thing I know, the big guy is away from the table, up and standing behind the bar, obviously inebriated and groping the bar maids. It was obvious he had no thought of being called out for his actions. I don't know what his rank was, but he evidently was not accustomed to any signs of disapproval.

I had no choice but to approach the bar (from the customer side) and hope I could jokingly get him into a conversation and back to his table. But it did *not* go well! While he did speak some English, we were not on the same frequency, and in half a minute his attitude went from bad to worse—mean! Before I could come up with some peace-making gesture, and with no provocation on my part, he began shouting and appeared as if any second he would attack me. And true enough, a few seconds later right there, in front of my eyes he reached inside his jacket, towards his belt. I thought, for a knife, and being only two feet in front of him, leaped backward, out of arm's reach, *only to see him withdrawing a pistol!* As (another) example of how poorly I think ahead, I took off running, but *away* from the exit (and steps down to the street), instead—towards the other end of the club where there was a solid wall with the two restrooms, and no way out! I was just smart enough to run in zig zags, while he emptied the cylinder, missing me with every shot! (Five or six.) When I smacked into the far wall (between the men's and lady's rooms) I turned and to my great thankfulness, saw that his three buddies had accosted him and were dragging him towards the exit. I made it to the nearest chair, and with a pounding heart, collapsed into it. I was out of breath and soaked, and definitely finished with this misguided experiment as a business owner.

Chapter Twelve
TWO YEARS NOW AND THE STATUS OF THE WAR

Got Everybody Out (Except for One)

Although it didn't happen frequently, we would sometimes be contacted to divert to a strip that was under imminent attack; a strip where the Customer had operatives he needed to get out before the village fell to the NVA (or perhaps VC)—we rarely knew which till afterwards. The NVA had uniforms (with backpacks) and sometimes even wore bandoliers of ammunition, while the VC were usually in rags, their footwear often just rubber shower shoes, and they only carried one rifle and not much ammo (ammo that some North Vietnamese laborer had carried hundreds of miles from the DMZ).

I was flying west of Da Nang and got such a call—instructing me to switch to a discrete Customer frequency right away. I did, was able to make contact with the case officer ("Mule") and give him my position. He began shouting the "Victor" number of the strip to go to, where his people would be waiting for me. (The strip names were so hard to pronounce, the company assigned a "V" number to all 200-plus of them.) I was to go to the rarely used strip at Dac To in the A Shau valley—where *nothing* good ever happened. While I had never landed at this strip, I had once flown over it after dropping off medical supplies at the Special Forces camp just north of it. It was right alongside the Ho Chi Minh trail, a valley that hundreds of North Vietnamese soldiers traversed daily. We never held any territory within ten miles of it, for more than 24 hours. He said he had several Vietnamese operatives there that he absolutely had to get out. I told him I'd be there in about 25 minutes, and asked him when was the village supposed to be overrun? He answered, "Not till noon if we're lucky!" Checked my watch: 10:25! *Geez.*

I GUESS I JUST WASN'T THINKING

When I was still a mile out I heard two or three loud snaps, as small arms fire penetrated the skin of my aircraft. Overhead the village I saw hectic activity below me; individuals running in all directions, lugging bundles of who knows what and even small pieces of furniture. I knew if I dallied over the strip it would tip off the villagers, and when I rolled out to the high end of the strip, there would be a hundred of them already there waiting for me. So I stayed low and did a tree-top approach—hoping that most of the panicking villagers in the basin wouldn't see me approaching, and those few already up on the strip would see me coming and get out of the way. (In the past this situation had resulted in villagers running right through the prop.) Whoever got to the plane first would yank the door open, and in he and a dozen others would explode. If Mule's guys didn't get to the plane first, there may not be an inch of space left inside when they did get there. I landed (missed the ones wandering on the strip), threw it in reverse, and brought the airplane to a stop. As I had suspected, here they come. *Please God, make the first ones my Customer's guys.* Today, the aircraft (that normally has six passenger seats), had them all removed; and I had been carrying ten or more passengers on most flights—curled in balls or sprawled on top of each other (which was about to happen again).

The first guy in looks at me and says, "Good job. Good job. Mule said you'd be here!" *I lucked out*—the first villager to the plane *was* the Customer's guy. He pushed his wife on board, and then handed her two large bundles of something. Thankfully he took over the loading, yanking some individuals into the plane and roughly shoving others backwards. Within a minute I had 12 persons on board, including wives, kids, pigs, and a dozen of those huge bundles. Ready to go, *but the door was stuck open!* I had no choice but to vacate my seat, claw my way over the mass of bodies, leap out, release the latch and pull the door closed behind me (during which time a couple bodies tumbled out and a couple more wedged themselves in). That done and while struggling towards the cockpit over the damp, malodorous, pile of humanity, I saw a villager *sitting in my pilot's seat!* With considerable effort I succeeded in raising him high enough to drag him back over the top of the seat, unceremoniously plopping him on top of the other bodies. I reclaimed my seat, poured the coal to it, and was roaring down the runway (dodging dazed villagers still wandering across the strip).

Ever since I closed the door—during the take-off roll and especially while lifting off, I could hear one guy in the back screaming and shouting at me in a desperate (and what sounded like a considerably demeaning) tone, that I could not interpret or understand the reason for. I heard a couple more rounds snap by, which must have missed us, since there were no screams inside (minus that one guy way in the back who was going ape shit). Going through 200 feet and starting my turn towards Da Nang I (first) became aware of a notion that something was suddenly wrong with the world; an overwhelming awareness of something (not sure what) but real bad. Next (second) I heard the shot—which inside this small cabin, was loud. Then (third) I saw my left hand was no longer gripping the stick, and my arm was lying across my thigh—bleeding; though I still felt no pain. I then became aware of the commotion in the cabin as *a couple of Shep's guys overpowered the soldier who had just shot me!* On the instrument panel in front of me was a splattering of what looked like pink oatmeal; which I realized was pieces of bloodied cartilage. Still didn't hurt—just numb; and my whole hand as well. On course for Da Nang. Not bleeding badly. I noticed a hole in the instrument panel where the bullet had gone through the center of one of the gauges. Cabin quiet now. Another twenty minutes and I'd be at Da Nang, where there were several medical facilities. Please God, let it just go okay, *not have the feeling come back or me pass out.*

I got there and landed. Mule was there to meet me and off-loaded his guys—including the crazy one who had shot me (which I learned was because in evacuating the strip, *his son did not make it onboard)!* In the clinic at Da Nang ("Charlie-Med") I was treated respectfully—for a civilian sometimes erroneously viewed as a mercenary or worse, a drug runner. (Don't know who started those damned stories that seem impossible to squelch.) On closer examination my wound was declared minor and was easily cleaned and dressed. The bullet had just creased the end of my ulna bone. According to the doc, the small chip of bone that was missing was on the outer side and not in a place that would ever bother me. (Good thing since it was out in my plane stuck somewhere on the instrument panel).

A Mounting Concern

After an extended time 'in-country' and especially after today's flight—us in the process of losing another village (and maybe a whole province), I was more and more concerned about how the war was really going. For two years, on a daily basis I had flown the length and breadth of the country; from the southernmost towns in the Delta to the mountain villages bordering the Demilitarized Zone. But I was now realizing that many strips I had landed at, and villages I had stayed overnight at—two years ago, *were no longer ours*. Even with US military units just about everywhere we weren't acquiring more territory from the enemy, or even holding that which we had occupied a year ago, or coming close to appeasing the general population; not by a long shot. It was my conclusion that this thing was not going our way. Not such a brilliant deduction, as this same conclusion was held by many others, such as Daniel Ellsberg (the "Pentagon Papers"), and would ultimately prove to be the case.

Looking Up Old Friends

While at Da Nang I finagled a ride to the Marine Helicopter base at Marble Mountain, just a few miles southeast. A couple of my old Marine Corps buddies (that were now flying helicopters) were there and I might be able to locate them. It was a primitive base, uncontrolled mud, lots of tents, outhouses, trenches and sandbags everywhere. It was dark when I entered the compound; being in my Air America uniform, my shirt bloody, and my arm in a sling, the Marine sentry (standing in a four-foot-deep hole, with just his head and shoulders exposed) immediately waved me through the one opening in a wall of piled sand bags. Three or four steps inside, behind me I heard the sentry calling me *by name,* "Captain Yahnke! Captain Yahnke!" Of course I was more than just a little surprised to hear my name being shouted. I turned and he was running towards me, holding something out towards me. "Look, look, you signed my ID card!" Somehow the guy had remembered my face since I was his Company Commander at Parris Island Recruit Depot four years ago.

I found a hooch with a wooden sign "Officers Club" over the door. I searched the whole place but no Bernie or Don; however—surprise! I *did* see two old buddies—Rich and Chili, who I had been in a photo-recon squadron with in 1959. They were not flying helicopters. I think they were flying F-4's or Crusaders for an attack squadron stationed at Da Nang. Don't know what had brought them here to Marble Mountain. We stayed there although one of them kept insisting we take a jeep back to Da Nang, where the Officer's Club was air conditioned with tile floors, better food, and even a bunch of nurses.

So Many Young, Wounded or Dead

The moving part of the evening—whose stories I have not yet been able to forget, was meeting an H-46 helicopter pilot named Martin. As much as I thought I knew about this war, I really had never computed the scope of the ultimate sacrifices being made by our young Marines, every day and every night—especially up here in what they call "I" Corps. It was the furthest north sector of operations in Vietnam (Quang Tri province) and went right up to the Demilitarized Zone. Instead of rag-tag Viet Cong (such as commonly encountered 300 miles south in the Delta), up here there was battalion after battalion of well-trained and well-armed North Vietnamese soldiers who had only left the comfort and security of their own garrisons a day or two before!

"Grunts" is a term used by aviation Marines (with utmost respect) to describe the back-pack-wearing, rifle-toting, hand grenade-carrying officers and men slogging through waist-deep rice paddies or hacking their way through six feet high elephant grass; the ones actually doing the day or night, face to face or hand to hand combat with the enemy—the real veterans and true heroes; NOT clerk typists in some safe headquarters. And if you needed a better idea of why these battles were so ferocious, remember this: *the enemy were born and raised here and held the absolute conviction that it was their homeland, and that we were the invading foreigners attempting to occupy it. They were—to the man, ready and willing to die defending it.* Martin had just finished a physically debilitating and soulfully disheartening week; up close and personal with the ultimate sacrifices made by these grunts (as well as the numerous injuries and fatalities suffered by his fellow helicopter pilots).

The generals (hopefully the generals *in* Vietnam, not the Pentagon) had decided we should occupy a certain burnt-out, bombed-out, artillery scarred, bald hill (hill number 208), not far from Dong Ha and the Cam Lo river—only 7 kilometers from the DMZ. It would be a choice lookout post to monitor the North Vietnamese troops making their way southward in the ravines just below and alongside it. Martin's job—everyday, was to bring the new grunts in and bring out the ones he dropped off the day before (be they alive, dead, or wounded). He said, almost every one of them looked 18 years old. Bringing them in they just sat in muted silence with the proverbial 1000-yard stare, in no way able to comprehend what the next 24 hours would hold for them. And the next day on the way out—even more demoralized, having just witnessed things they'd never imagined.

Day after day he'd do these drop-offs and pick-ups as quickly as possible; before the NVA mortars started raining down on his aircraft—about 60 seconds (you could count on it). Though he didn't dwell on it, many of his fellow chopper pilots did not return from these missions; killed when their aircraft was demolished by incoming mortars, or shot to death in the cockpit when their aircraft was delayed on the ground or for some reason unable to take-off.

Martin never once straightened up in his chair or even looked up, or made any type of wise crack—his gaze fixed on his shoes. It was apparent that he had been, and was, part of a too-little publicized, deadly and ongoing tragedy. What was new to me was the *extent* of the casualties. *If the American public would have known the level of this youthful sacrifice, then—in 1967, we would really have had protests.* Consistently when the NVA launched their advances on the hill (two or three times every night) the best estimate was the marines were out-numbered 7 to 1 if not 10 to1! Martin said yesterday, he had left off the new grunts at 4 pm, and in picking up the 18 Marines he had left off the day before, seven had been killed, and of the remaining marines, half were seriously wounded—dying. And he had been doing this day after day for the past several weeks—witnessing the same amount (or more) casualties on every trip. Three days ago after landing atop the hill, and while under a mortar attack and taking constant small arms fire, the platoon leader—God bless him (a 22-year-old First Lieutenant) would not let Martin takeoff until he had personally gotten every last one of his dead and wounded (that outnumbered the living) on board. When he finally did, the lieutenant stuck his head up in the cockpit and gave Martin a "thumbs-up." It was then Martin saw that evidently during the night the young officer had taken a round through his left temple that exited where his left eye had been! He had done this last minute gathering up with just one eye! Needless to say, I was awed and deservedly humbled. What seemed to bother Martin most was that after several weeks of this carnage, today the powers to be (whoever and wherever they were) felt we no longer needed hill 208, *and it was left to the enemy.*

Chapter Thirteen
HE WAS RIGHT, THE NRA PRESIDENT, AND A VISIT FROM JUNE!

How Could Anyone Believe Such a Thing

Just a couple miles north of the Saigon airport was an Army Supply Depot; situated on twenty-acres of table-flat ground that appeared to at one time have been about six side-by-side soccer fields. In addition to a dozen warehouses and row after row of stacks of pallets, it housed several hundred American troops, living right there in tents and various sized prefab buildings. Any time of the day or night, you could find officers and enlisted men crisscrossing the area.

Today, before walking out to the airplane my passenger said he had to make a quick stop at this compound before we left. He invited me along. There—while my passenger was taking care of business, I passed the time just surveying the area. While in the midst of this, a sergeant nearby recognized me as a civilian and perhaps deserving of some startling news. He came over to me, looked me in the eye and pointed down at the trampled grass between our feet and said with all conviction and certitude, "Right now—while we're standing here, just five feet below the surface there's a mile of tunnels and hundreds of North Vietnamese soldiers." I was dismayed that someone (anyone) could have heard some far-fetched rumor like that, and believed it! *All the Army would have to do is just give a guy a shovel.*

Fifteen years after the war ended, I couldn't avoid taking a trip back to Vietnam; to have one more look at the place I had spent so much time. In the lobby at the Continental Hotel in Saigon I saw a tour advertised and decided to take it. It was titled: "the NVA Underground Complex."

The van took us—yep you got it: right to the same athletic field that had held the supply depot. Within twenty feet of where I'd been standing with the sergeant, there was a yellow plastic ribbon stretched between three stanchions. It marked a five-foot deep hole with a squared entrance at the bottom. I ventured down the carved steps into a hollowed out passageway, and entered what must have been a thousand yards of passageways, with areas that were rooms to eat, rooms to sleep, and other discrete spaces— five or ten feet under the surface! It gave me goose pumps to realize that years ago while that sergeant had been talking to me, in spite of me completely discounting it, all kinds of activity, *was in truth, occurring right under our feet!*

Chance Meetings with Visiting Celebrities

One of the occupants in my apartment building was a young man; not a military guy, but a Department of the Army Civilian—assigned as a Director of Special Operations. While this title could mean something vital and dire, in actuality his job was to schedule entertainment for the troops. A key part of this effort was bringing in Hollywood actors and professional athletes to talk to the troops. At this time so many people were flooding into Saigon daily, there was a critical shortage of hotel rooms. (Even high ranking generals were being forced to stay two and three to a single hotel room.) This being the case James would often ask me if I could put up the likes of Georgie Jessel, Hugh O'Brian (from the Wyatt Earp TV series), or some other person of note. One afternoon, in the midst of painting the interior of my apartment, James shows up at my door with a tall guy carrying a suitcase. Not only did I put him up for a couple nights, Charlton Heston helped paint my apartment!

I Can't Believe She Pulled It Off

While in Saigon I received mail there and was able to continue corresponding with June. The Spanish vaudeville tour was over and the Stafford Ballet was now with a huge German circus—*The Circo Magico Tihany*, which was currently performing in Jakarta. She said of all the countries they'd been in, Indonesia was the poorest and most primitive. The girls were brought from the hotel (which they were locked in) to the theater in a large tractor-drawn cart. In addition to still being the Ballet Captain (the mother hen for the twelve girls), June herself appeared as the female centerpiece in acts with jugglers, clowns, elephants, and even one with lions! As the main attraction in several acts and known as one of the more senior and level-headed employees, she was the unofficial spokesman for the artists, and was well listened to. I was astounded to read she had convinced the owner that since they were already in the Pacific, and there were 500,000 American troops in Vietnam, he should try to schedule performances in Saigon, pull in a bunch of revenue in just one week. She succeeded! *The circus was coming to Vietnam in the middle of the war.*

She didn't know exactly when they'd arrive or where they would find a suitable venue, but did know the name of the hotel that would be putting them up. I at least had that. Waiting for the circus's arrival I checked out the address of the hotel and discovered another not-yet-completed wet concrete structure that (if it could get some furniture, running water and electricity) was going to be their hotel. On my drives to and from the airport, I noticed a fenced-in empty lot next to and owned by the Cercle Sportif (the French sports club in town). It was being cleaned and raked, and having rows of chairs set up on it, and I was pretty sure I'd found the future venue for the circus.

I don't know what chartered airliner they used, but the whole circus arrived (minus the elephants). I forget now how I got their arrival time, but managed to be at the terminal when their plane landed. When Customs and Immigration was through with them and I could finally greet her, I was taken aback—thrilled (and humbled) at the unbridled joy and enthusiasm she shone with just to be looking at me. She ran all the way to me and of course I got one of those long and rib-crushing hugs she was famous for. "Roger, Roger! You look just great! Oh, it's been so long. I'm so glad to see you"! And so on as she introduced me to all the girls—half of which I knew from the European tour. Wendy and Laurie seemed almost as happy as June to see me (and once again see their captain with what anyone would have considered her true love). In Spain the other artists repeatedly seeing me at the Artist's Entrance waiting for June referred to me as her "*novio*" (fiancée in Spanish). During the bus ride to their hotel the girls kept the excitement at a high pitch. June held one of my hands with both of hers, and appeared to never stop looking at me (although I have seldom if ever felt less worthy of such a show of adulation).

Most of the senior members of the Company, including June—spent the first few days directing the setup at the performance site. The male performers worked day and night building a large wooden stage and back drop. I was impressed by the motivation, effort, and skill of acrobats and unicyclists utilizing power saws and drills. Of course the girls' hotel was 'off-limits' to guys, but for their captain the girls made an exception for her *novio*. Though I never stayed overnight we had late-night joyous parties, with French tarts and ice cream, and plenty of café au lait (which is not great to drink at midnight). I felt privileged (and guilty) as I was made a natural part of each evening's festivities (usually held in one of the girl's rooms)! Each night—ten minutes after they arrived all their makeup was off and their faces covered with white skin cream. With this facial covering and in their loose fitting, wild patterned flannel pajamas it was as if I was in a room full of clowns. Throughout these evenings there was never the slightest hint of flirtation, nor even of me being of the male gender. The one thing I do remember about these visits is the bedspreads being strewn with 45 RPM records, and that every other song they played was "Reach Out, I'll Be There" by The Four Tops.

I am truly saddened that the details of this short week have mostly escaped me. I can remember no romantic trysts with June. If so, they must have been at some other hotel because I'd gotten the word that Mary Margaret (my American girlfriend here)—knowing the circus was in town, would station herself on the roof of our building, just waiting for me to try to sneak June into the ground floor entrance. I have hated myself ever since for having let this current but temporary relationship with Mary Margaret, throw a monkey wrench in much more warm and serious plans I could have had with June—a person with whom I had such a history, and who had done so much just to arrange a way to see me! It was surely true that I had never been able to forget her, and had her on a deserved pedestal; in fact, maybe even grown to where I could say, I loved her, deeply and unselfishly—even without the expected sexual unions; a genuine respect, indebtedness and affection. (Being once again nothing more than heavy petting due to my damned problem.)

One evening (when Mary Margaret was out of town) after the circus performance I threw a barbeque on the roof of my building for all the cast; jugglers, acrobats, lion tamers, fire eaters, trapeze artists, unicyclists—you name it. Before the meal was half over I was dear friends with almost every one of them, and I must say I was greatly impressed by their stories and their devotion to their art. I became especially close to one performer—Arnaud ("ar-no"). He did several acts, one of them being that act you've seen many times: the man running up and down alongside a table, just barely able to keep six plates spinning on the top of six three-foot wooden dowels. After teaching me all the tricks one afternoon, he convinced me to do the act that night. I had been able to fairly well master the technique and the farcical display of panic you had to show when you almost didn't reach one in time. (The art was: seeing how far you could let the dowel lean and the plate wobble, without letting it fall.) I was extremely nervous by show time. I managed to get all six up and spinning, and make my several dashes to rescue one. Perhaps fortunately for me, I didn't get to complete the act. A U.S. Army helicopter flew over too low and the downwash from the rotors sent the plates and dowels flying in all directions! There was one act that I have never since seen played out so perfectly. One of the artists was an older man; a slight-of-hand expert. He would come down off the stage, mingle with the crowd, introducing himself and asking questions of the attendees. When he returned to the stage, his jacket pockets were full of watches, wallets, eyeglasses, etc., *that the attendees had never noticed had been taken!*

When the circus pulled out (and it did all too soon) I realized my time and intimacy with June had been terribly insufficient; sadly non-committal. (For which I despised myself!) In spite of June maintaining her wide and constant smile, I sensed a slight disappointment in her eyes; like an opportunity had been missed, like it should have been a much better time together, with some mention about a future. And she was definitely right. Still, like all our greetings and salutations, our good-bye included a massive hug by her, a kiss that actually hurt my lips (and lets you know the person on the other side means it with all her heart). She told me they were bound for Singapore and were going to be there for at least a month. You can bet I had my next mission! *Get to Singapore at my first opportunity! Regardless of what strings I had to pull.*

A Reunion like Never Before

That meant I knew my next "STO" (the 7-10 days scheduled time off each month the married guys got to visit their families), was not going to be a trip to Bangkok. Shamefully I wrote Sara that I was not going to get my time off next month. (Had to do it by letter. Making an international call was a real hassle.) Certainly not proud of myself, but this was the most urgent deviation I could imagine. I could see no alternate. Of course you know my plan was to use this time to visit June in Singapore, and show her the consideration and affection she deserved, and that I somehow failed to demonstrate in Saigon! Unfortunately my STO did get delayed—almost a month! But the day it started I was Malaysia-bound.

I GUESS I JUST WASN'T THINKING

Unlike the acrylic and stainless steel megalopolis it is now, in the late sixties Singapore was still the sleepy, palm-fronded town that one could cross in a ten minute cab ride. And I did, plus some—visiting every theater and several stadiums, in an attempt to locate the circus. *No luck anywhere.* Nor did anyone I asked seem to know the whereabouts of a German circus. It was nine at night and I decided to make the rounds of all the big clubs, on the outside chance the ballet was performing on their own. One club after another; and finally—in one, my heart leaped! On a big stage there were several scantily dressed dancing girls, and one in the middle of the stage, in a bubble bath, apparently naked, *and it looked like June!* I think I was more relieved than disappointed when I realized it was not her or the Stafford Ballet. (I should have known. They never did any routines like that.)

I plopped myself down at an empty table, head in hands. No explanations and no ideas; tired and perhaps a bit nauseous. Out of my doldrums I realized a waitress was standing alongside my table, obviously waiting for a drink order. I was thirsty and to give me five more minutes to rest (and come up with another plan), I did order a citrus alcoholic beverage. When she returned, she appeared friendly, even ready for some small talk, so I decided, *why not, ask one more person.*

"Let me ask you young lady, are you by any chance aware of a German circus in town?

"I haven't been to it, but I heard about it."

"What! *You have?* Where? *Where is it?* "

"I think out at the old armory."

"The old armory? What's that? Where is it!

"You know, up past Yishun, at the old Brit base in Sembawang."

"Sembawang you say, Sembawang?

She nodded an okay. I could've hugged her, but just paid for my drink and hurried (ran) out of the club. The one time I really needed a cab, none were in sight. Finally one came by and I was successful in waving it down (frantically—in fact so much so I'm surprised the guy even stopped). Head in the window and with an urgency I doubt was lost on him, I shouted, "The old Air Force Base. The one at Sembawang! Do you know it?" He didn't answer but nodded I hope affirmatively. I was in and we were off. We stayed northbound, a long time, out of town, less populated and lots of shanties. Finally, a mile or so ahead, against the night sky I could see a control tower with a circling beacon, and then as we got closer, other buildings which appeared to be hangars, and finally parked airplanes! *This has to be it.* Only thing was, I didn't see any parking lot filled with cars, or any people coming or going. The place looked deserted. The driver, at first not sure of our whereabouts, located the main gate and got us over there. As soon as he stopped I jumped out and approached the guard on duty (a very proper appearing Royal Air Force Airman). "The circus! The circus, where's it at?"

"The night before last was its last night. There's nothing left, not even a pallet. Everything was taken down yesterday."

"Where are they staying! Do you know where they were staying?!"

"No, but let me ask the sergeant."

It was now almost eleven. He disappeared into the small building for only a few minutes. When he came out he was holding a scrap of paper—with an address! Impressed, I thanked him profusely, and almost trembling with anticipation jumped back in the cab and shoved the paper at the driver After looking at the address he did not seem certain of the location or pleased about it. After just sitting there studying it for several more minutes he responded to my urgent requests to *get this frigging cab moving.*

I would have thought the circus company would have been staying real near to the venue, but no. We drove for some time, winding our way into other less and less populated or comfortable surroundings. He finally slowed to a stop in what I would call the 'middle of nowhere', in front of a single, isolated four-story building. (It's only neighbor was a 20 acre fenced-in lot with two gravel piles as high as the hotel, glinting in the full moonlight.) The complete lack of activity was causing me to consider a terrifying thought. Only two windows in the whole place were lit. I leaped out of the cab and ran to the ground floor entrance, which was unlit and bore no sign. There appeared to be no rooms on the ground floor and I bounded up some nearby stairs. I raced down the second floor hall, past one empty room after another. Up another flight. The same thing on the third floor; every room was empty. The place was deserted. No—wait. I hear voices coming from a room at the end of the hall. I was down there and into it. What I saw was not encouraging: a starkly empty small storage room with two old guys—one of them maybe Tihany himself, playing cards at a rickety table (it and their chairs being the sole pieces of furniture). I gushed out my mission and dire question. The skinny guy smoking looked up at me and said, "No mate. You missed em. The whole lot took off outa Paya Lebar airport at three this afternoon. Going to Sydney."

Chapter Fourteen
1968, STARTING WITH A BANG

The Year of the Monkey

It was 30 January, the Chinese New Year's Eve; nothing to us, but a really big deal here in the Orient! By mid-afternoon it seemed two minutes did not go by without the sound of fireworks from some nearby neighborhood. From all quarters of the city the population was having a go at it. In the streets surrounding my building the little kids were lighting off bottle-rockets, cherry bombs, and those long strings of fire-crackers that snapped and leaped like a crazed snake until the last one had gone off. I could see that New Year's Eve here was not going to take a back seat to anything I'd seen stateside. Unfortunately it kept up (and me up) through the night (and I had to be up at 0-dark-thirty). And I wasn't going to be driving to the airport alone, I'd promised Mary Margaret I'd take her friend Ann with me—who also lived in our apartment, and drop her off at her workplace on the way. Ann—all 5'2" and 180 pounds of her, was ready and waiting for me in the lobby at 5 A.M. We walked in the dark to my faded green Datsun parked less than a block away. During this walk I was surprised that instead of the normal pre-dawn silence, there was still the sound of those damned fire crackers, distant celebrating or shouting, and even this early, the sound of cars 'peeling rubber'.

We started via the normal route which would have us, after rounding the first corner, going down the street behind the new US Embassy (a gated, well-guarded monstrosity of a building). Rounding that corner—at this ungodly hour, I was almost run over by a large truck, careening on two wheels and whose back was filled with ARVN soldiers, wide-eyed, and firing in all directions! It was then I noticed beyond the truck, dark figures by the side of the road and others running across it, carrying rifles! *Something was definitely amiss.* Never yet had I seen any activity at this hour, much less what I was now seeing (and feeling). As I turned down the street that would take us past the back side of the embassy, I could see more people crossing the road with rifles! And once again, firing in all directions, including ours. The car had not been hit but it looked as if a couple of the men with rifles were shooting at it! Uniforms were not recognizable, so I was not sure if they were Vietnamese soldiers or civilians. (I could see they weren't Americans.) No idea what in the hell was going on. I braked and pulled over to the right edge of the road, next to a five-foot high wall in front of a well-appointed home. (The embassy was in an exclusive area of the city.) Across the street from the home was the back wall of the embassy.

Quick as I could I shoved Ann out of the car and then pulled her through the gate in the wall in front of the home. I manhandled her (not easy) along the inside of the wall, until we came to a small alcove in it. I plopped her down in it, while sounds of gunfire were ringing out from just down the street from where I had parked. "Stay down in that corner and stay there until you don't hear any more firing, and that may be noon! But don't get up until you're looking at an American!" I was banking on the fact that whatever was going on, the US military headquarters downtown would have been notified of it by now, US troops would be here in the next few minutes, and it would be all over within an hour.

In what turned out to be a bad idea, I decided to try to go over the back wall of the embassy and if they didn't already know, apprise them of the situation just behind their property. Running quickly and bent over, midway across the street I realized getting over the high wall may not be possible. Halfway across the street I noticed that about twenty feet to my right, the top three feet of the wall, as well as the wire, was missing. This breech, combined with an ambitious leap, would allow me to get over the wall. I hauled myself to the top edge, and leapt the eight or so feet down into the grassy back lot of the embassy. While still airborne—on the way down, to my horror—instead of an empty space I saw a bunch of raggedly clothed Vietnamese with AK47's, which I then realized, were Viet Cong! They were already in the Embassy grounds, and now finding themselves being joined by an unexpected flying foreigner coming over the wall. Fortunately, they were as surprised as I was. I made perhaps the fastest U-Turn and exit of the US Embassy ever made. They didn't get a shot off until I was atop the wall. I crossed the street and joined Ann, and we did have to wait until almost nine, before the last shot was fired and we heard commands being shouted in English, and knew the US military had the situation under control.

Assuming the disturbance was over and had been just a small and unsuccessful attack on the US Embassy, we got back in the car and resumed our trip to work. We were both shocked, exchanging glances of disbelief when each time we rounded a corner and began down another street, we saw it strewn with dead bodies, *lots* of dead bodies. And while there may have been some bodies of North Vietnamese soldiers, they were mostly Viet Cong, which is to say—Vietnamese civilians who had arisen at three in the morning, retrieved their hidden weapons, and taken to the streets! On almost every street, US troops were dragging bodies to the curbs. I dropped Ann off at her building and continued in amazement to the airport—all the way there witnessing the same street scenes. Inside Air America operations it was abuzz with stories and explanations of what had happened. As is well known now, it wasn't just a local attack on the US Embassy here in Saigon, or even the whole city. It was country-wide—part of precisely planned and timed attacks on US Military installations, Vietnamese Army garrisons, and U.S. supported police headquarters—*beginning at the same moment, in every city and village in the country!*

Now, while I don't deny this was planned in Hanoi, the unavoidable and hugely discouraging take away from it is this: To have carried it off, *half the population of the country had to have known about it,* and known about it for weeks if not months! And with thousands of Vietnamese working closely—often one-on-one with their US counterpart—on a daily basis, *not a single Vietnamese clerk or laborer or translator or military assistant ever uttered a word or even a hint about the upcoming event!* This single fact will give you some idea of what esteem we were not held in by the general population, and the actual extent and numbers of what could have been called the enemy.

A Plane Stuck in Hostile Territory

The country-wide coordinated uprising gave the US Military (and we civilian pilots) a whole new perspective on things. As you might imagine our attention to our surroundings—in Saigon and especially up-country, was measurably increased. In spite of the "Tet Offensive," Air America's aviation operations continued basically the same, although the further north we flew, the more concern and 'hurry up-ing' (minimum ground time) was in place. Perhaps the biggest win for the North Vietnamese Army (and the Viet Cong locals who assisted them) was the capture of Hue Citadel. This small city (about 90 kilometers north of Da Nang) was almost sacred, being the revered religious and cultural capital of the country. The city had a reasonably sized macadam strip, which up to three days ago was used on a daily (if not hourly) basis by Air America aircraft.

This strip of course was no longer available, but there remained an urgent need to get supplies to the retreating ARVN forces and our own troops, who were mostly worried about being pursued (but also worried about receiving orders to try to retake the city)! Forty-eight hours later they all—including many wounded, were holed-up in and around a small hamlet about ten miles south of Hue. To have another resupply and medevac landing site, we helicoptered in two Air America engineers and a translator, to hire villagers to hack out a strip. They fashioned one in record time. Three days later it was done and I was sent in for the first trial landing. I made a tight spiraling descent to the strip; knowing if I flew a normal pattern (extending a mile or two from the strip) I would've been shot down for sure. After a couple bouncing, careening rollouts, I radioed back that while it was rough as hell, there were no protruding stumps and it was okay for "short take-off and landing" aircraft. An hour later two Porters arrived, and to my surprise, a large cargo plane—the Canadian De Havilland DHC-4 "Caribou." It was undoubtedly sent because it was our only "STOL" cargo plane.

A Caribou with both main landing gear down and locked

I GUESS I JUST WASN'T THINKING

Perhaps being a bit 'up-tight' regarding a new strip (and in close proximity to thousands of enemy troops) the Caribou pilot was late in lowering the gear handle (the wheels) and the struts did not have time to lock down, before they touched the ground. As the wings lost lift on rollout, the fuselage settled onto its belly and the struts stuck where they were: not yet locked down. No damage anywhere, but mired here for who knows how long. The pilot was Stan Armbrook (the guy from that first van ride to town the day I arrived). He, two of my Porter pilots, a few helicopter pilots and a couple "kickers" put their heads together and came up with what would have to be called an overly innovative plan: a way to raise the airplane just high enough to be able to lower the landing gear that last foot. Time was of the essence because it was more than likely that the building of the strip had not gone unnoticed by the NVA (and even at this moment we were probably being observed from a not too-distant hill).

Here was Stan's plan: Among the items he had brought in were large (8-ft by 15-ft) empty rubber bladders which would soon be filled with aviation fuel to sustain our operations here. Although not without considerable manual labor, one of the bladders was wedged into a couple-foot-wide trench dug under the fuselage. Then an air compressor was hooked up to the bladder's filling valve and turned on. And glory be! As the bladder expanded, it pressed up on the bottom of the fuselage and started to raise the whole plane; only a few inches, but it was on the way up! Seeing this initial progress, Stan shut off the compressor and sent the copilot to the cockpit to wait for his signal: when the wheels would reach a sufficient clearance above the ground, Stan would give him a "thumbs-up" and the copilot would turn on the hydraulic pump that would lower the wheels, which then would continue their movement to the fully locked-down position. Once the aircraft could stand on its own two feet, they'd crank the engines, taxi out and take the hell off! *Get outa Dodge before big trouble came.*

Sounds good, right? Well the best laid plans of mice and men sometimes go astray, and in this case they did—prohibitively (and hilariously) so. Before the belly of the aircraft reached even one foot above the ground, the whole plane tipped to the left until that wing tip hit the ground. *The bladder wasn't exactly centered under the fuselage.* Quick, turn off the compressor! Let it down. Drag the bladder a foot to the left. Here we go. Second try. Yup, you guessed it: as the fuselage reached a foot off the ground, the plane rocked over the other way—onto the right wing tip. Turn off the compressor! Let it down! Drag the bladder back to the right about six inches. The third try resulted in the same tilting outcome, but this time again to the left.

Back to the drawing board, but not for long. Stan had a fix! The Caribou was a high wing aircraft—meaning the root of the wings was not low near the belly, but lay straight across the top of the fuselage. The wings were a good 10 feet above the ground. Stan had four guys climb up on the fifty-foot-wide left wing and four guys up onto the fifty-foot-wide right wing. *And here was the plan:* Stan would stand in front of the nose of the aircraft, his arms spread wide from his torso, horizontal to the ground, simulating the present wings-level position of the aircraft (like a "Landing Signal Officer" on an aircraft carrier). Stan would signal the men on the wing by the position of his outstretched arms; for instance lowering the arm of the wing that was descending. Seeing this signal the men on that wing were to quickly shuffle towards the fuselage to lighten that wing and allow it to rise. Were the situation to correct itself, Stan would level his outstretched arms. If the situation reversed and the opposite wing started down, Stan would lower that arm, and those men would shuffle towards the fuselage. *Well, that was the plan.*

That which ensued was a tragically comical scenario. It started out as planned. *Started out* that is. As the bladder inflated, the left wing was not coming up so Stan lowered the arm pointed to that side, signaling the men on the left wing to start moving towards the fuselage. That shifting of weight did correct the situation, but the men must have moved too far towards the fuselage because now the right wing started down. New signal! Stan's arms switched to the other way! The guys on the right wing started their move towards the fuselage. Almost immediately the left wing started down again. The arm signals were reversed and the first group again began running towards the fuselage. Oops! The right wing went down. Stan's arms were flailing like a hawk's wings with a heavy fish, and then the funniest ("keystone cops") part: the men on the wings had given up on their directed shuffles and were taking it upon themselves to break into full runs, but out of sync, *passing* each other in *both* directions! For safety of life and limb, a desperate series of screams and profanity mercifully curtailed the operation. The Caribou was there for three days; the rescue operation required jacks and additional pieces of heavy equipment.

One Brave Little Guy!

While living in Bangkok, Sara had made friends with another wife being safe-havened there. But not just any wife; *she was the wife of the Australian ambassador to Vietnam.* They had met because of the boys; our son Mark and her son were in the same class and best of friends, Somehow these two ladies decided—in spite of the recent "Tet Offensive" (or because of it) to make a weekend junket to Saigon, get a feel for their husband's safety—and bring their sons along!

The day arrived and—believe it or not, even I was excited. They arrived safely (on perhaps the first 727 ever made) and now operated by Air Vietnam. Turns out a plan had already been firmed up: Sara and I and Mark would take the evening meal with the ambassador and his wife and son at their distinguished residence. The idea of what level of formality might be included in this caused me to feel somewhat unprepared, and to instruct Mark on a series of "dos" and "don'ts," as well as an earnest request that no matter whether the food was to his liking or whatever other awkward situation might develop, he would hold his tongue and maintain a reverent silence. I was determined our family unit would show refinement.

Shortly after the meal the two boys were excused from the table and migrated to the other end of the dining hall where they commenced to play with some toys, and engage in some apparently harmless roughhousing. A moment or two later when I happened to glance in their direction I saw a look of horror on Mark's face. No utterance, but a wide-eyed, mightily painful grimace. He stood up (shakily) and walked as if (almost) nothing was wrong—without a word, silently toward me. When he got alongside my chair, with tears in his eyes, but not a single utterance, he raised the hem of his shirt, turned sideways, and displayed a set of teeth marks that had not just left a depression, but had drawn blood!

Chapter Fifteen
IT FINALLY HAPPENED, A TRIP,
AND A TOUGH DECISION

January 31st, 1969

Remember those "Line Checks," and the overly realistic one I took with Jack Smythe (ending up in the water buffalo hole). Well this morning I was scheduled to administer another one, to one of my bachelor pilots that I flew with in the Marine Corps—Chet Falk. We who knew him back then were greatly saddened when the Marine Corps passed him over as a Regular Officer, and relegated him to the "Reserve," basically ending his career in the Corps. He loved the Marine Corps with all his heart, and till the day he died the greeting on his phone was the Marine Corps Hymn. We knew he was passed over because "he just didn't *look* like a Marine." He was willowy tall and somewhat flabby, with narrow shoulders, wide hips, and a flat ass, and was never seen carousing at the Officer's Club with the other rowdy Marine Officers.

Being familiar with his consistent good work here and having just flown a whole day with him a week ago (and not having flown that much myself recently), I decided that we'd pull a sly one on this check flight: While I would write it up as a standard "Line Check," I would sharpen my own skills by doing the piloting duties, and let *him* sit in the co-pilot's seat (where I would normally be on one of these checks). Chet had a nickname here in Saigon: "Black Cloud Falk," that he earned regularly. If something was going to go wrong, it went wrong with Chet. He never took any STO's, until a bunch of us finally convinced him to treat himself to a week in Hong Kong (as many of the pilots did). Chet does so, but in stepping out of Baggage Claim at the Kai Tek airport, he's hit by a cab and spends the whole week in the hospital. His first year in Saigon he didn't buy a car, just took cabs. We finally convinced him to join the rest of us with his own transportation. Instead of buying a car he chose to purchase an Italian motor scooter. His first day on it—riding a little too close to the edge of the road, his toe catches on the curb, radically twisting his foot and breaking his ankle. Acquiring a personal vehicle yielded him three months on crutches. And those are only a couple examples. Perhaps these type things should have been a signal to me.

Early in the afternoon, we were dispatched to a strip in the Delta, with an airplane full of money (the payroll for hundreds of case officers' Popular Forces located in that area). We pilots would turn a blind eye to the fact that these money-hauling trips always had the airplane several hundred pounds overweight, and occasionally out of C.G (the center of gravity) limits. The flight down to Cao Lanh was uneventful, and except for some Army helicopters in the area, no reason not to land. I racked it around (as much as you can rack an overweight airplane around). All was clear when I got abeam my intended landing point and I began my descending left 180 degree turn to final approach. I was carrying out the standard landing pattern flown by all fixed-wing aviators (and is as well known by helicopter pilots)! On short final, lined up with the centerline, a hundred feet in the air, and a couple seconds from touchdown, one of those Army helicopters (obviously not looking around) swoops in from the side of the field, to land *right on the runway touchdown zone* (a "no-no" for helicopters). His action caused me to have to abort my landing, pour the power to it and struggle over him. The heavy aircraft plowed ahead on this—what we call a "Wave off" in the Marine Corps (or a "Go Around" in the Air Force).

By the time I reached the far end of the runway I had climbed to about 500 feet of altitude, and was just about to begin my left turn into another downwind leg, to repeat my landing attempt. I say "about to" because I never did get to start that left turn. There was a loud ping, a gushing sound, and then terrible vibrations, followed by silence. I'd been hit and had lost the engine! I was not only at a low altitude, but with the nose up, and having suddenly lost all my thrust, I was rapidly losing critical airspeed! Chet was hollering "Watch your airspeed! Watch your airspeed!" I had to shove the nose over immediately—and *way* over, just to *keep* the airspeed I still had and avoid a fatal stall. Nose down, even without an engine a plane will gain airspeed, but of course, you lose precious altitude!

(If I had been a second later lowering the nose, we'd have lost another three or four knots, stalled, spun, *and gone in upside down*!) I had nosed over so steeply, that looking through the windscreen—there was no sky visible, just the ground! I held it as long as I could, diving almost vertically towards the ground, and gaining the airspeed necessary to make the flight controls effective. At what I judged to be the last second I could hold the nose down—about 100 feet above the ground, I yanked the stick back to arrest our plummeting descent. We must've hit flat, or at least I think we did. There is no memory of the impact.

When I came to, I was still in the cockpit, but when I opened my eyes I saw only a totally gray screen. And worse, the wings had disjointed from the top of the fuselage, and the fuel they had been carrying was now pouring down on the top of my head. And, at the same time I felt the JP4 gas drenching my body, I heard the loud "snap" "snap" of the 8,000 volt emergency igniters sparking in the engine—30 inches in front of me! (The first step in an engine loss is to turn these igniters on, and I had done it automatically when the engine quit.) But right now—still firing, they were perhaps seconds from causing the fuel to ignite, and Chet and I to be enveloped in flame! Although I could not yet see, I knew where the igniter switches were located on the panel, and had them off on my second swipe! Still blind and numb, I heard voices. And though I could see nothing, I felt rough hands all over me, and then dragging me out—not through a door, but over the jagged edges of the windscreen which had been broken out in the crash.

I lay in what felt like warm mud, listening to voices around me—all in a different language. I was to find out Chet and I had been hauled out of the aircraft by members of a nearby South Korean platoon. My eyes were open, but I still couldn't see. (We'd hit so hard, I was later told that I'd driven the legs of my pilot's seat, right through the bottom of the airplane.) I was fearful I might have damaged my spinal column, and was afraid to try to move my arms and legs—particularly my legs. I tried first with one hand. It moved. Then the other. Success as well. The big test: try to move my feet. Great, one at a time I was able to slide both heels a few inches forward and back. Think my vision was coming back; could now see patches of sky through the gray. I spent another hour in a Korean Army field hospital tent getting stitches. When that was completed I boarded the Air America helicopter that was sent to bring us back. On the way to the chopper I got a look at the airplane, and it reminded me of that phrase in the Jim Croche song: *Leroy Brown looked like a jig saw puzzle with a couple a pieces gone.* For sure it'd never fly again.

It was several days before I realized the extent of at least one injury. I was about 20/400 in my left eye and likely to stay that way; a huge hunk of cornea having been gouged out. I managed to stay on flight status by obtaining an eye chart and memorizing the letters. I made a few appointments with US Army ophthalmologists here in Saigon, and one to a renowned eye doctor in Bangkok. I learned that if I wanted to regain anything close to 20/20, I needed a type of total corneal transplant only done by two doctors: Ramon Castroviejo in NY Presbyterian Hospital, and Joaquin Barraquer in Barcelona, Spain. Castroviejo had a waiting list in excess of eight months, so I discounted him. Perhaps Barraquer would be less busy. I thought that before learning he had *invented* the operation, and people from all over the world traveled to his clinic for this surgery! But then again—another factor: the Stafford Ballet and June were now back in Madrid, just 45 minutes from Barcelona. *I'll bet you can guess where I chose to go.*

Embarking on another Adventure, via London

Took leave from the company and embarked on my journey. (Not sure how I explained the choice of the location of my medical treatment to my wife.) I first had to fly to London to see if my 'Loss of License' insurance company would conclude my flying days were over and agree to a settlement, or—if they would demand and pay for possible corrective surgery. It was late at night when I landed at Heathrow. Hailed a cab and flabbergasted the driver when I admitted I had no hotel address for him because I had no reservations. In spite of his surprise he commenced an earnest search for a hotel with a vacancy. After several tries he found a nice upscale hotel in Knightsbridge—the Eden Hotel (where all the bell hops were tall Swedish girls in mini-skirts)! He told me to wait in the cab and he'd check the hotel's suitability. I told me *no worry, don't bother*, thanked him, and struggled dog-tired up the steps. Inside attempting to register, I realized with a jolt I'd left a leather packet with all my money and documents, on the backseat of the cab. I got directions to the nearest police station and ran the whole way. There, my presence was (gratefully) immediately responded to. The constable told me not to worry, I'd get it back. To myself I said *if you don't mind, I'll worry*. I asked them why they were so sure I'd get it back, they told me there are no taxi 'companies' in London. Every cab is the driver's own business, and *if in the span of one year he has more than three fares complain of lost items, he loses his license and livelihood!* I said, "Well what if the driver didn't see the item, and the next fare steals it?" The policeman told me: next time I take a cab, notice the yellow and black decal on the glass that reads: *It is the driver's responsibility to assure that the fare has not left any items in the cab.*

Back in the hotel I went into the pub where I was told a pint of Whitbread and a toasted cheese sandwich would calm me down. It was good, but didn't. While at the bar I perused the comfy confines of the carpeted room. I was surprised and excited to see—sitting in a far corner in two easy chairs, Judy Garland and the 1950's blonde actress Veronica Lake! (Judy Garland lived out her life in Chelsea—the adjacent suburb.) It wasn't thirty minutes later that the cab driver came crashing back into the hotel, apologizing profusely for—in the dark, not having noticed my wallet until he was almost back to the airport.

The next morning I hopped a cab for downtown London to check with my insurers. The cab proceeded for about ten minutes then pulled over to the curb. The driver twisted around and slid open the glass partition between he and I, and spoke: "Please accept my apologies for having been short with you when you got in. I just knew—that for you, taking the underground you'd save a lot of money and at least thirty minutes." He let me off on Fenchurch Street and I set about trying to locate 51-53—with no luck. While paused there on the sidewalk a guy passes me, stops, turns, flashes a wide smile, and starts back to me extending his hand. My mind churned, *"Where did I know him from? What was his name?* I knew I'd be embarrassed when he spoke and he knew me, but I couldn't remember him! He spoke: "Excuse me, I don't mean to butt in, but you appear lost. Could I be of help?" The people at the insurance company were equally as accommodating. They volunteered to either pay my settlement or pay for the transplant. I could make that decision. They said they knew it was a big decision, and just get back to them when I could. Based on my first twelve hours I was a big fan of the English people.

Off to Spain (Again)

Mission completed in London I flew to Barcelona, where I found the airport to be the same long, only one-story high, single-roomed, wooden-sided structure I traversed during my carrier cruise. I exited through a single set of double doors (the *only* way out). Outside on the walk I joined a very organized queue and soon enough had one of those stiff black cabs. I gave the driver the address: 514 *Avenida Muntaner*. (This was decades before the city hosted the Olympics, which unfortunately razed many historic sites and markedly diminished the culture and ambiance I was now seeing.) At last I was on my final leg to the Clinica Barraquer, and justifiably nervous; worried about what kind of reception I'd receive as an unannounced arrival, and assuming they would take me—the big question (and the one the insurance company needed an answer to) was: would I make the decision to try the vision-saving surgery, or chicken out and go for the whole settlement?

Soon enough we were approaching the Clinic; a massively built, intimidating edifice. Even from the outside it was special; all stone with gothic architectural decorations. Paid the driver and was out (lugging my single but huge suitcase). Two sets of heavy double doors—an exterior set and then an interior set. There was only one reception desk and it was directly beyond the second set of doors. I approached it and when greeted, stated my case. Shock and disbelief would be the best way to describe the expression on the girl's face. She politely excused herself, to return in a minute or two with a nurse and a stern-faced administrator. I was informed that no one—regardless of their status, arrives here unannounced! It appeared that although I was guilty of this very thing: no appointment (or even previous contact)—to them the fact that I was a United States airline pilot must have carried some weight. They left and returned with a doctor, who checked my pilot's ID. After a short conference among themselves, I was given a check-in date the following week! (Keep in mind, I had not yet come close to making the decision to actually go through with the surgery.)

I set about finding a hotel near the Clinica Barraquer and was successful in finding a not-at-all imposing, comfy, old wooden hotel—the Hotel La Rotunda. It was located on the corner where the steep funicular up to Mount Tibidabo departed. (Tibidabo was a 1,500 foot peak and popular tourist site, providing a panoramic view of Barcelona.) The La Rotunda appeared to have been a large and old residence, perhaps even a historical building—with a wide variety of accommodations. I was lucky in getting a homey, old fashioned third floor suite, with a balcony that looked down upon interesting activities in a spacious, foliated and brick-pathed back lot of a nunnery. My task here: *eight days to come to a decision: To do it or not to do it!*

Part Three: The CIA Secret Airline and Eureka! She Exists!

I am a Libra dammit (the scales) and while I had been making life and death decisions almost daily for the last few years, the days came and went without me being able to come to a decision (although I thought of nothing else). One night I decided on a plan: I'd go to bed early, get a good night's sleep, order a good breakfast sent up in the morning, and then while my mind was fresh, and the morning sun would be flooding into the room, I would make the decision—*just make it!* Right or wrong. I would likely never be more fresh and clear-headed, and thus that decision should be the most sound I could come up with. Well, I did just that, or almost just that; everything except come to the decision.

With only a day to go, I was in my room about 10 p.m. Having skipped dinner I decided to walk to a nearby bistro and have the plate June had introduced me to four years ago: the famous *"entrecote y espinaca a la crema."* In addition to the steak and creamed spinach, I ordered a bottle of Rosé wine (in a tall, unusually shaped three-sided container). I'm not sure if it was the meal, or most probably the wine, but about midnight, the sound system in the restaurant played Frank Sinatra's famous hit, "My Way" (in Spanish—"Mi Manera"), and that did it! The perhaps reckless but nostalgic melody and lyrics seemed to say "What the hell," and pushed me over the hump. *I'd do it!*

Chapter Sixteen
THE CLINICA BARRAQUER AND A LOT MORE

The Clinica

Once through the reception area I entered a large sitting room and was surprised to encounter a surprisingly out-of-character, trendy, Art Deco interior. White marble floors throughout, contrasted by black steel pipe furniture. I didn't see a single 90 degree angle in the place, everything was curved or rounded—tables, furniture rails and door archways. All four walls were spanned with floor to ceiling mirrors (which I was to find out later—for patients with impaired vision, caused them to often find themselves walking into a wall). The prominent motif looming high on the walls and circling the large room was a row of large signs of the zodiac.

I was escorted to a private room (which I discovered they all were) on the third (and top floor for patients). The whole fourth floor (top floor of the building) was the permanent residence of Dr. Barraquer. He only operated four days a week, from midnight till 6 a.m. On those days he spent the afternoon and evening studying the charts of the patients he would be operating on. During this preparatory period he listened to classical music that we on the third floor could hear well enough. While doing this, he never sat—just continued pacing his residence. His floor (our ceiling) was made of thin white marble supported by a metal grid. It allowed us—if looking up, to track the dark shadows of his feet as he walked. I also learned he was a recluse, only exiting the building once or maybe, twice a year, when he went on holiday in August or once more if he had to appear at some seminar

My room contained only four articles of furniture: a narrow bed, one of those black pipe chairs, a small chest of drawers, and a mammoth, round, black marble table. (As I found out later—so did every room.) There was no facility dining room. All the patients ate their meals in their room, delivered three times a day on a hostess trolley, by a butler in a white frock (who when he showed up the first afternoon to leave a copy of the evening's menu, I thought he was the doctor). On top of the table was a large circular crocheted doily, and on top of that, a protective piece of glass. Each meal, prior to the food being set out, the table would be further topped by an exactly sized felt table cover (bearing the room number), which was then covered by a freshly pressed white table cloth.

My First Office Visit

I was impressed on my first examination by Dr. Barraquer. I entered a room—a dark, high-walled, perfectly circular room, about twenty feet in diameter. It had a round black tower in the middle—maybe ten feet in diameter. Perhaps a dozen chairs—all facing the tower, were mounted on a track that encircled the tower. Some were already occupied by other patients, their faces but a foot from the tower wall. I was instructed to take a seat in the chair nearest the door. I did, and being satisfied the nurse left the room. A few moments later I felt a jerk and realized my chair (the track) was moving around the tower. After about five minutes there was another jerk, and I moved another yard further right. Ten minutes there and then, after the next movement to the right I was in front of an open window, and looking directly into Dr. Barraquer's face (past a device called a slit lamp). Inside the tower it was well lit and I could see an assistant behind him at a desk. *Whata place!* I learned then, that in this clinic Dr. Barraquer never used synthetic transplants. All the grafts were from previously screened donors who had just left this world hours or minutes earlier. I was therefore going to be in a 'waiting mode' until a properly matched cornea came available.

Meeting Meredith

An English-speaking nurse told me I should check out a room just down the hall. In it I'd find another English-speaking person: a young woman from England, also awaiting complicated surgery—on *both* eyes. Even totally blind she was a pistol. These chance meetings with members of the opposite sex (embarrassedly) seemed to be occurrences I always welcomed. Who knows, one of them could be that urgently awaited magical female. I found her room; knocked once and was invited in. She wasn't alone. Her grandmother was with her. Introductions were politely made and I was offered one of those black pipe chairs. Whoever gave me the steer had hit the nail on the head, Meredith spoke English and was an attractive blonde. They had that part right, *but she was only about 15 years old.* We exchanged several minutes of niceties, and then about an hour on current global affairs. I was astounded at how much this young girl knew about everything going on—worldwide. She acquired this wealth of information by reading several talking books every week (which she ordered from our Library of Congress). She was sharp as a tack and I guessed, not someone to be fooled with. And if she would have stood up I think I would have seen a shapely figure. Of course we asked each other what had caused our visual problems. I recounted my story about my crash in Vietnam and then asked Meredith to tell me about her situation. What I heard was devastating and left me feeling guilty about even being here.

"Well" said Meredith, "it began a little over two years ago. I was in the ninth grade at a private Catholic girls' school on the outskirts of Manchester. Our science class had been studying the earth's crust, mantle, and core, and an experiment was planned: we were going to build a miniature volcano—get to see an actual eruption. I was assigned to conduct the experiment. First I was asked to make a quick trip outside to collect a small heap of garden soil. Back in the classroom I was told to form it into a mound with a depression in the middle. The teacher then gave me a mortar and pestle, and three jars of powders. I was told to put a spoonful of each into the mortar and grind them. I did, while the other young girls watched expectantly. While leaning over my work there was a sudden intense white flash, and then—what felt like eons later, I heard a loud bang, and realized I had been impacted with a searing substance. I just stood there unable to move. Someone shouted 'Are you all right?' I remember replying, 'No, I don't think so.' I put my hand up to my school tie only to discover it was a melted blob. My face, hair and clothes were caked with a molten substance. Some of it fell onto papers lying on the lab bench, igniting them. Before doing anything for me the nuns began emptying flower pots on the burning papers. While the exterior of the magma was hardening, beneath the crust the acidic action of the chemicals was devouring my skin. Two nuns ran into the room. Each took one of my arms and hauled me into the hallway. A couple of my friends in the hallway cried out, 'Who is it? Who is that?' I was startled to realize I must be unrecognizable. They rushed me into a vehicle bound for the hospital. I gave them my father's work number, because my mother was pregnant and overdue, and I didn't want her to be upset. By now the lava had eaten more deeply into the flesh on my face and the pain initially absent, now became excruciating."

I was surprised by her matter-of-fact tone and almost dismissive attitude, concluding I was in the presence of someone of resolute character (or she'd been asked to relay the details so many times, it was almost old hat).

"For the next two years my family exhausted the talents of the leading ophthalmologists in the United Kingdom. I think in fifteen months I had five surgeries, none of which afforded the slightest improvement, and may have even further damaged the remaining ocular tissue. Finally, after several conferences, the UK surgeons decided that Dr. Barraquer would be the most qualified to treat me. Dad brought me here a year ago, and I've had four more surgeries."

Fortunately, unable to be seen by her—to supply more live tissue for a transplant to attach itself to, they had grafted mucous membrane from the inside of her bottom lip. When one looked at her opened eyes, instead of a blue or gray iris, *there was wet pink flesh!* Impacted by having heard this tragic story, I felt it time to switch to lighter subjects (while I could not help but dwell on this poor girl's disastrous medical history). In addition to a valiant positive attitude she could be quick with a witty response. Before they had grafted the interior lip tissue to her eyes, they had tried with some subcutaneous tissue off her thigh, to which she responded, "If you make a scar to where I can't wear a mini-skirt, I'll sue you into the ground."

Wow, John Lennon!

Something unexpected and very special happened while here in the Clinica: Meredith's father was the Director of Entertainment at England's only independent TV company and as such was responsible for producing all the programs that showcased European and American actors, actresses, singers, rock groups, and other celebrities. Each time one of these people or groups was on his show he would tell them, "If you go to the Riviera this summer, try to take a short trip west into Spain—to Barcelona, and visit my daughter in the Clinica Barraquer." Evidently her dad was well respected in the industry because we were visited several times by notable personalities or groups. My favorite thus far had been "Gerry and the Pacemakers," whose current number one hit was the nostalgic Liverpool testimonial, "Ferry Cross the Mersey" (*"We don't care what your name is boy."*) However this visit was to be eclipsed. One night while I was taking the evening meal in Meredith's room with her and her grandmother (a deliciously prepared cannelloni being washed down with smuggled-in Chianti), who walks in but John Lennon and Yoko! Not only can I say that I had dinner with John and Yoko, but listen to this: he gave Meredith a reel-to-reel tape of a song the Beatles had recorded, but decided not to release (titled "Where Do You Go To My Darling"). When she left the Clinic, she gave it to me. Much later I gave it to one of my daughters, and unfortunately it is now among the missing.

Preparing for the Surgery

Evidently Barraquer and his staff wanted to make sure I got the precisely right cornea, because over the next several weeks, *twice* (once in the middle of the night) I was rushed to the prep room, eyebrow shaved, face scrubbed, IV inserted, and my whole left eye socket painted with some bright red disinfectant, only to be soon wheeled back up to my room because they did not approve the donor cornea as right for me. When the proper donor cornea arrived (from a nine year old boy), after the prep I received a shot of what I think was a morphine derivative. From the entry point of the needle, all the way up my arm, over the shoulder, up the side of my neck, and into my skull I felt a disarming sensation of a thousand icy fingers tickling their way up; leaving a semi paralysis in their wake. This was followed by several moments of stark terror as I felt the gurney chattering over the grout lines towards the "O.R.," *and I was still conscious!* And I had guessed right. Soon there was a large blinding white light directly above me, *Whoaa, this could be trouble.* The anesthesia wasn't working! I tried to tell them but discovered I couldn't speak; perfectly alert and aware, but unable to form any words! *Move your hands, or your feet!* Let them see your condition! Yup, you guessed it, I couldn't move a muscle. Resigned to whatever was coming and waiting for the pain to begin, I woke up in the recovery room—the operation completed. *Evidently I didn't know anything about what a patient should be experiencing just prior to the final dose of surgical anesthetic.*

The Actual Surgery

The type of transplant I needed was not even done in the states (except by Doctor Castroviejo). A small—perhaps 7/16ths of an inch diameter, sharpened, hollow cylinder (like a minature cookie cutter) was utilized to remove almost the whole corneal from the donor—a plug that went completely through from front to back. Some moments after this plug arrived at the clinic, they used the same-sized tool to remove a similar plug from my eye; the donor's plug now the exact same size as the hole in my eye. This drastic 'completely front-to-back' procedure is required in cases of unusually deep corneal perforations. Stateside, only an "Anterior Lamellar" transplant is done—where a flat piece of donor tissue is layered on top of the minimally scarred surface portions (which would not have worked on my deep gouge.)

Understanding the Skills of Unsighted Persons

In London I had bought a 45 RPM record player and about twenty of my favorite records, hoping to be able to pass some of my recuperation listening to them. After the surgery in one eye—I don't know why, but they bandaged *both* eyes! I was going to go through a week or so of no vision; *be completely blind.* We've heard how sightless people elevate their perceptive abilities, eventually being able to accomplish tasks of discernment that would have been thought impossible by a blind person. In one week I would experience this myself. Just by "feel" I could select the desired record from a stack of twenty apparently identical records. You may ask 'how'? The answer: By a process of elimination: Some of the records were thicker—stiffer than others; some had a glossy label and some had a matte label; at the edge of the record, some had a long run in before the needle reached the sound track, and some had a short run in; on the records I played the most, the spindle would have enlarged the center hole. These differences and several other distinctions, would allow me to continue to narrow down the quest, ending up with the exact sought-after record.

What You Might Have Expected From Me

Meredith had a friend who often came to visit her; a comical guy from Ireland who spoke with a brogue so thick I had a difficult time interpreting it. I could barely understand half of what he was saying. When I asked what he was doing here in Spain, he replied, "Teaching English at Berlitz." *What!?* I'm sure anyone in his class would have had to send their resumes to Dublin if they wanted to get a job where they would be understood. About a week after my surgery I was in Meredith's room being entertained by Brendan's stories. The new plug in my eye was being held in place by 32 stitches, which continually hurt or itched violently. To protect the graft I wore a convex shaped, plastic guard over the eye socket. I had discovered that by pressing inward on the center of it, its edges pushed sufficiently hard into my eyebrow and cheek to distract from the irritation of the stitches. Guffawing at one Brendan's punch lines and at the same time pressing in on my *cascara*, I must have pressed too hard, because it inverted, popping from convex to concave—slapping hard into my graft! There was an immediate sensation of something bad having happened; something having been ripped or displaced.

An hour later I could feel an oily liquid on my cheek, and it wasn't tears. *My eye was leaking!* I'd pulled out some stitches. The graft could be shifting, and if not corrected would produce a bulge; an irregularity that would create a large astigmatism—reducing or voiding any benefit achieved by the surgery! *I was ill.* I needed help fast, but it was a Friday night and Dr. Barraquer was unapproachable on the weekends. Saturday I succeeded in getting an associate of his to see me. I still remember his name: Dr. Miguel Riquelme. I'd seen him several times and quickly gathered Americans were not his favorite people. The visit did not go good. He insisted the moisture was just tears, and not to worry. But I *was* worried, real worried. I was able to see Barraquer on Monday. To say he was furious would not adequately explain his reaction when hearing and observing what had happened. The new adherence of the moved segment was such that it could not be torn loose and relocated. The eye was too weak and traumatized to consider this. Even if at a later date I wanted a second transplant, this one had been so large, it was doubtful there would be enough surrounding tissue to accept another implant. He was noticeably shaken and his exact words were: "*Solo un Americano!*"

June, Still and Always

Wonderful June managed to get over several times, taking the train from Madrid to Barcelona. She was all bubbly each time and appeared absolutely thrilled to see me. I believed I was not allowed to leave the clinic, so we just found entertainment inside. Once—in between her visits, only ten days after the operation, knowing that the Stafford Ballet had a big party planned in Madrid, I unwisely snuck out of the clinic, took a cab to the Barcelona airport, and purchased a round trip to Madrid. I realized this might be a bad idea as I felt weak and light headed leaving the clinic, and while walking in the airport, twice had to drop to one knee to steady myself. When I got to Madrid (two hours before the party) I was shaking and feverish. I went straight to a hotel and got in a hot bath, hoping against hope I would experience a miraculous revival. I did not. I went to the party at 1:30 a.m., met June, and joyfully (insofar as possible), did my best to appear upright and sociable for the two hours before we escaped back to my hotel. Poor June. I doubt she was anticipating having her body ravished, since by now she was accustomed to a ton of kisses but no penetration. And that was good tonight, as I collapsed in bed feeling even less amorous than normal; not up to the type of activity, any other guy would have killed for.

Out of the Clinic

After discharge I went back to the Hotel La Rotunda to gain strength before attempting the trip back to the states. I found that holding my head upright (the normal position) caused significant discomfort in the eye socket. Only hanging my head (looking at my shoes) relieved it. This being the case, in bed at night I tried positioning my head face-down in the pillow, *but no matter how I shaped the pillow, breathing soon became an effort.* I thusly spent the next two weeks sleeping in a most unusual position: I would kneel by the side of the bed, lean over until my forehead was resting on the edge of the mattress (nostrils free), and sleep through the night in this position. After this much trauma to an eye, the worst lingering effect was a horrible case of photophobia (inability to take bright light). Before turning on a lamp I had to first get my hand on the switch, turn my head away, close my eyes, and then flip the switch. Going out of the hotel in the morning sun was not possible. I bought two identical pairs of sun glasses, popped the left lens out of one pair (threw that pair away), and glued that lens behind the left lens in the other pair. With this double-layer arrangement I could navigate outdoors during the afternoon. What I guess I should mention at this time, was that my post-operative accident resulted in my left eye vision being reduced to 20/400—*exactly what I arrived here with!*

The Moon Landing

It was now July of 69, and while recuperating in the hotel the U.S. launched its first manned moon shot. In discussing this forthcoming event with the bartender, I was amused as—with our limited language skills, he attempted to manually demonstrate his opinion of the coming event. He would hold one hand up, eye level, canted downward at the wrist, with his fingers extended to simulate the legs on the lunar landing module. He would then—while making a humming sound, let his hand descend until his fingertips settle on the polished wood bar. After leaving it stationary there for a few seconds, he would grunt and raise it an inch or two, then let it fall back to the bar; grunt, lift it, and let it fall back down on the bar. He repeated this till it was obvious, that while he thought we might land there, *we weren't getting back off!* The world watched in amazement when the video showed the lunar module settling on the surface and Neil Armstrong hop off the ladder. It was so jerky and stilted and the moonscape appeared so artificial, a large percentage of our own population did not believe it actually happened; rather that it was filmed on a Hollywood set. (Myself, I could see how many people might be skeptical of the video.) To my great surprise—there in Barcelona, watching this video with people from a wide variety of European countries, *none of them ever questioned the video!* To them it was real! The U.S. had done it!

And What's Been Missing These Past Weeks?

Any mention of my wife and kids, that's what. *What kind of person am I?* Well Sara and I *had* been in contact by mail, even a couple phone calls. But I admit, as you have no doubt noticed, I have been primarily (almost exclusively) preoccupied with my own life, rather than things of perhaps (no—definitely) greater significance: my wife and kids and their lives and day to day tribulations. Once again now (the other time sitting on the cot in that first-night hotel room in Saigon) I was provoked to take a hard look at myself, as possibly an individual—a male, who besides a devastating deficiency, may be incapable of feeling a proper and complete devotion to just one woman, and acting upon it. Shamefully—that one woman being my wife! Why could I not feel what so many other good men felt and responded to? It may have been a step in the right direction that I was at least becoming shamefully aware of this shortcoming, though I had yet to see a sliver of progress in overcoming it. A sad commentary. Well for now this wholly questionable Barcelona experience is over. Hopefully it hasn't done any lasting damage to my relationship with my family, friends, and professional career. Hopefully it will only be a single, isolated and closed chapter.

Time to Start Thinking About "What Next"

One thing this visit provoked: a love of Spain and their language. I bought a book on "Learning Spanish," would buy more books in the states, and for years to come spend twenty minutes each night studying Spanish. There would only be a few more days before I would check out of the hotel, take a cab to the airport, and board my flight back to the states. *Whew.* And then once in the states, I wasn't sure how long it was going to be before my eye was sufficiently healed to apply for an FAA vision waiver on my pilot's license, and set a date to return to Air America (and hope like hell this official limitation on my license would not prohibit my re-hiring)! Not sure where I was going to do that recuperating; maybe at Mom and Dad's house in Florida, or with my brother Hank, who was also living in Florida. And it might also include doing some fancy talking with Air America Headquarters in Taipei. In a recent communication with them, in spite of me being here because of a work-related injury, I was startled, when as most my old friends in Human Resources had quit or been transferred, the new guys there did not seem to be familiar with me and my solid reputation, or express pleasure to hear I was ready to rejoin the operation. One guy even mentioned things like he thought they were fully manned at present. *Afraid to reflect on what that may have meant.*

Chapter Seventeen
AN UGLY TIME IN THE STATES

Arriving in Florida

I made the decision to recuperate with my brother Hank. He was married with two kids and lived in Hobe Sound—a small oceanfront town midway down the east coast of Florida. It had no airport, so I flew into West Palm Beach (about 35 miles south). I was surprised when his car pulled up being driven by his wife. Based on my history of unsupervised work schedules—coming and going as I pleased, it was strange to hear from Lea that Hank couldn't finagle an hour off work. Thankfully (I think due to his heartfelt but undeserved admiration for his big brother) moving in was never an issue and proved to be harmonious. His wife and kids did not seem at all uneasy with me in their household. I immediately contacted Sara, letting her know my whereabouts and my plan to return to S.E. Asia just as soon as I could. She and the kids were living their normal (pretty much stress-free) day-to-day lives in Bangkok, which they now had become well accustomed to and understandably fond of.

Healing and a New License

I was making progress, but not a lot and not fast. It was a couple weeks before I could hold my head erect without the eye socket pain. Another couple weeks before the tears were manageable (as long as I had a clean handkerchief with me). My photophobia was still present, but now regular sunglasses worked okay (no more double layered lenses). I still was putting in a drop of Decadron every morning to prevent inflammation—which if it flared up could result in a rejection of the graft and total blindness in that eye. After about a month I considered myself ready to contact the FAA and apply for a reissuance of my pilot's license with a vision waiver.

I scheduled an appointment at their main offices in D.C. and was greatly surprised by the efforts made by all the staff. They appeared to be doing everything in their power to prove I really didn't need a waiver. Standing twenty feet from the chart, straining, squinting, and imagining (to cheers of encouragement each time I worked out another letter), I *did* do better than I had expected. But it was still way short of what would be required for a waiver-free license. One nurse (who was determined to get me to 20/20) ran out of the room, came back with a table lamp, ran up to the chart, found a nearby electrical socket, plugged it in, pulled off the shade, and pointed the bare bulb towards the chart! Even with this additional illumination I couldn't even read 20/80. After some discussion and a couple phone calls, a plane was rented and I was scheduled for a one-eyed flight check. The aircraft they secured was a small (and old) twin-engine propeller plane, the Cessna 310—not well-liked and known for its squirrely handling characteristics. With a patch over my bad eye they had me do a series of maneuvers and two instrument approaches (one with only one operative engine). I passed and received a fully operational Airline Transport Pilot's license "By Reason of Demonstrated Ability" (the 21st one ever issued). I was of course thrilled at this, but secretly wondered, *how well would a one-eyed guy do if a piece of dust blew into his good eye?* I quickly phoned Air America and informed them I was "A-Okay," and in possession of an unrestricted ATP license (which I was) and ready to return. This time—fortunately, I got a guy in personnel I had known, and who was familiar with my previous record with the company, and he cleared me to return, no problem! (Which news you might imagine was music to my ears.)

Spur of the Moment Ideas

My flight back to Taipei entailed a couple stops: the first in Los Angeles where I would have to overnight. And here's where spur-of-the-moment ideas combined with carefully constructed dialogue can turn things on their ear. (That's short for "be disastrous.") Remember my initial flight training in Saigon, and that guy Ron Wogman who though he shouldn't have, let me fly all 20 flights that one day, and thereby be able to pass the Captain's flight check? Well he had been furloughed and was now living in L.A. I thought contacting him and having a beer for old time's sake would be a fine way to spend the evening. After several failed attempts with Information, I was able to get a current number. And this should have been a warning to me: To say he sounded excited to hear from me would be the understatement of the year, insisting almost desperately that I come over to his townhouse for a steak and some libations (in fact directing me to stay put and he'd come pick me up).

Ron was a born salesman and had won awards from a dozen mutual fund distributors. If you had to describe Ron, it would be a smile from ear to ear, one hand out to shake yours loose from its wrist, and though not apparent—a brutal "closer." He was on top of the world. The ride to his townhouse was nothing but upbeat. His wife gave me a big hug, and like Ron she was barely able to contain her joy at some recent good fortune. We went out to the patio where he fired up the grill. The steak and wine were great. I could feel a ground swell all around me, but had no idea what inspired it. Ron got a bottle of champagne from the kitchen and then three glasses for an almost ceremonious occasion. He poured us each one and started.

"Rog, you can just thank your lucky stars. Just count your blessings. I've stumbled onto the greatest money-making operation in history!" I rightly concluded that this operation was somehow going to involve me. On the one hand I couldn't say I wasn't interested to hear about it, but was plenty content to at last be on my way back to Southeast Asia where I was among like-minded individuals, knew what I was doing, was good at it, and widely respected for doing so. There's a great satisfaction in that and nothing more.

"Well tell me about it Ron. What could be so great?"

"Can't. You gotta *see* it, and *hear* about it—from the guys who've already made it! And there's an 'Opportunity Meeting' tomorrow night at the yacht club. You'll hear success stories like never before!"

"Well you got to be able to tell me something. What does it involve?"

He said "There'll be time enough for that at the meeting tomorrow night," and he and his wife raised their glasses for me to join them in an undefined but joyous toast. As much as I badgered him the only detail I could get out of him was that in a year, we'd both be millionaires. I accepted their invitation to spend the night with them, *and cancelled my morning reservations to Hong Kong.*

The meeting the next night was not comfortable to me. Every one of the gentlemen he introduced to me (in sharp suits, with slicked hair and pinky rings) shook my hand harder than necessary, and would not—after much too long, let go. I believe they were establishing control and keeping me captured; waiting to see if I could or would pull my hand out of their grip. Among them were a famous race car driver and some well-endowed soap opera diva. One by one they stood at the podium and described their previous financial calamitous situation, but how now huge sums were flowing into their accounts weekly. The name of the parent company was "Bestline." It had a varied line of cleaning products that (according to the cult members) would soon be challenging Procter and Gamble. The difference: Distribution! *A series of private citizen wholesalers and retailers.* Although I had no familiarity with it and didn't recognize it at the time, I had just been introduced to one of the most egregious 'Pyramid Sales' schemes ever devised. Ron's closest associate—in fact the person who had recruited him, was Glenn from Oklahoma (geographically innocent enough), whose story about losing out in a Taco Bell franchise, almost brought tears to your eyes.

And how did one get the best start in this tremendous money-making business? By buying in at the highest wholesale level possible. This meant the transfer of a sizeable sum to your recruiter (Ron in my case). Although the following details were not carefully explained at the meeting, as a "General"—the highest level wholesaler, I would order product direct from the factory, recruit a fleet of down-and-out citizens trying to make ends meet. They would buy my inventory at an almost 50% markup, and retail it by going house to house on nights and weekends. While they did all the work, I would just sit at home "raking in the profits," which meant receiving the handsome overrides from all their sales. (I was to later learn that the most important phrase to know and use repeatedly when recruiting new members was: "just sitting there raking in the profits.")

Can't Believe I did It

I am embarrassed (sorely so) to confess to you, my next two actions. My blood runs cold when I reflect on it: I not only called Air America in Taipei, saying I may have a "few week" delay, but (and this as much as anything else exposes me as the inconsiderate familial person I am): I phoned Sara in Bangkok telling her to put all our stuff in storage, and as soon as possible, bring the family to the states. Not knowing where we would live, I had to tell her to standby for the actual arrival destination. I had been impressed by my brother's choice of Hobe Sound, a small, clean, surfer town with practically no crime and good schools, and was thus viewing it as a possible location. How I could ever have failed to recognize the extent of this disruption to my family's by now, well-established living arrangements, soulfully dismays me to this day.

Ron, Glenn and I flew to Pittsburgh (chosen for reasons I fail to recollect) to schedule an Opportunity Meeting. I'd like to tell you it went well, except I never made it. Unfortunately the second day there I began to think that images viewed through the grafted eye were becoming slightly more cloudy. I stared at the line between the doorframe and the wall, evaluating how well I could make out that line. Within an hour there was no question, it was becoming less and less distinct. I knew it was the beginning stages of a rejection! Dr Barraquer had often mentioned an ophthalmologist (Conrad Moore) at the Baylor College of Medicine in Houston. Justifiably worried, I bid Ron and Glenn a quick goodbye, hailed a cab to the airport and caught a flight to Houston. There I was rushed into an ICU specializing in eye trauma. My treatment started immediately with injections *directly into the eyeball*. I was there four days. The rejection was arrested and I was released with a prescription for more Decadron. But surprise of all surprises: I discovered Meredith (the English girl from the Clinica Barraquer) was also there, undergoing yet more surgery. For two days we had a great time. On the one hand reminiscing about our time in Barcelona, and on the other—watching amused and awed as one Baptist evangelist after another paraded into the room, and aware he had a captive audience, launched a spiel of redemption like no other! I rejoined the other two guys in Pittsburgh on the fifth day. We stayed in Pittsburgh another week, and in spite of what I'd heard, if it was any example of the success we would continue to have, I was in big trouble.

Selecting a New Territory

Whether it was because it was a good idea, or Glenn and Ron were running out of fertile ground there in L.A., after suggesting that I might locate my family in a little oceanfront town just north of Palm Beach, they leaped on the idea of the three of us "opening up Florida." I moved in with my brother in Hobe Sound and relayed to Sara that she should fly into the West Palm Beach airport. They dutifully (admirably), but obviously confused, arrived about ten days later, and we all moved into a small oceanfront motel not too far from my brother's house.

Getting the Business Going

Ron and Glenn arrived several days later and shared a motel room in the nearby town of Jupiter. Together we set about *opening up Florida*—scheduling its first Opportunity Meeting in the town of West Palm Beach. This entailed taking out a newspaper ad (vague at best) a full week in advance, announcing the location of the grand occasion, and a phone number to call to *guarantee your seat*. This phone number was then manned day and night for possible 'takers'. For whatever reason, I (the fresh "newbie") was assigned this task. One thing was made certain to me—a life or death requirement: *Do not hang up until I had their phone number.* I was told in no uncertain terms, the phone number was imperative! Glenn told me repeatedly, "No matter what they say or promise, if we don't call them up the afternoon of the meeting, and give them another pumping up, they won't show!"

As a sensitive person I felt invasive demanding the caller's phone number, in fact many put up a firm resistance, particularly the ones that wanted more details than I was allowed to give out (for instance that it would involve him getting rid of a garage-full of soap)! One day I received a promising call from a guy who said his name was Jim Vance. While I did manage to get his address, *I failed to muster the fortitude to get his phone number*. But wait, perhaps all is not lost. This was the days when you just dialed 411 and some operator in Houston or Chicago or Orlando answered. You gave her the name and address and she would give you the phone number, no sweat. I dialed 411 and got an operator (somewhere). I gave her the name, Jim Vance, and the address: 3255 Fisherman's Drive, Jupiter, Florida. She asks me, "Are you sure of that name?" I say something along the lines of *how many ways can you spell Vance?* She answers, "Well I live at 3255 Fisherman's Drive and my husband is Jim Bance—with a B."

Fortunately, Nothing Lasts Forever

The weeks that followed may have been the most unsettling of my life. The results of which was an undiagnosed but likely nervous breakdown for me, and I'm sure—a horrible time for Sara. Fortunately, the kids did all they could to make the best of things. I became more and more depressed and I'm sure a social liability when with my family. The continuing callous efforts to separate worthy individuals from their hard-earned savings quickly got the best of me. I couldn't fall asleep at night and couldn't get out of bed in the morning. While the three of us on occasions did sign up a wholesaler and pocket the upfront money, it was not at a rate that would declare any of us millionaires in our lifetime. My mental and probably—physical health, was at an all-time low, and my domestic situation—six of us, yet unsettled and cramped in adjoining motel rooms, was producing a myriad of difficult situations. (The first month was perhaps the worst because the school year had not yet started and the kids were underfoot continuously.) I finally got the courage to share with Ron and Glenn, the fact that I just could not keep it up. (Good riddance to the 6,730 bucks it cost me to "buy-in.") I listened to their encouragement and endured their recriminations, and then contacted Air America (again). Although that "couple week" delay had turned into six weeks, they mercifully told me I could continue on back. If you think the approval for my first return was "music to my ears," this second one was a symphony!

On the Way Back

Sara drove me to the airport, and I was—for the first time in three months, actually happy, in fact jubilant. Thrilled to be returning to something familiar; someplace that had—in just a few years, in spite of its many quirks (and dangers) become the setting in which I would feel most at ease. Sara would wait until I contacted her with whatever news I got about my assignment and how that would dictate her living arrangements. I suspected she'd be hoping for me returning to Saigon and her returning to the good life she had known in Bangkok, with her circle of good friends—not to mention, cook and driver (that I had so thoughtlessly uprooted her from).

Chapter Eighteen
SOUTHEAST ASIA AGAIN

Assigned to Another Country

By the time the tickets were in hand it was late November. I was flying first to Taipei, to do some paperwork and receive an update on our current support of the Agency's effort to assist in winning the Vietnam War (as well as a not-minor conflict in a neighboring country). I was surprised (and honored) when I learned that I would not be going back to Saigon, but rather straight to Laos, where according to almost all accounts, the *real* war was going on, and the *real* flying was being done (*by the company's uncontested best and most daring pilots*). I would be stationed in the sleepy, French provincial town of Vientiane. Whereas in Vietnam many of our flights were conducted over non-hostile areas and consisted of semi-safe humane missions such as refugee relocations; Laos was a different story—a very different story.

And Why Was Air America There?

As a result of the Geneva Accords of 1962, the country of Laos was declared "neutral." *No other nation was allowed to have a uniformed militia within its borders.* However the North Vietnamese did not abide by this, and during the Vietnam war were moving thousands of troops and armaments southward *through Laos* on the notorious "Ho Chi Minh" trail. This meandering and mostly obscured route kept them safer from US air attacks. When the soldiers and logistical columns had made it far enough south within Laos, they turned east and crossed into Vietnam as a surprise lethal fighting force with fresh supplies.

But this was not the only issue. Laos was in the throes of political unrest. In addition to their Ho Chi Minh trail presence, thousands of North Vietnamese troops were also engaged in country-wide combat operations to topple the U.S.-friendly Prince Thayavong Savang, and convert the country into a communist state. Since our (uniformed) US military could not legally enter the country, the Department of Defense appointed the CIA to thwart this effort by arming, training, and taking into battle almost every able-bodied male member of the Hmong nation—the mountain tribesmen of Laos. (A similar breed to the Montagnards in Vietnam.) Although far from being a ready or able fighting force, the Hmong were our only line of defense to keep Laos from falling under Soviet dominance. And the US government thought that should this happen, Cambodia, Thailand, and Malaysia (Singapore) would be next! (Remember? "The "Domino Theory.") And we were not only up against the North Vietnamese troops, but their Laotian supporters—the equally hostile "Pathet Lao" (the "Viet Cong" of Laos). For this overwhelming last ditch defensive action, the CIA required air support for troop movements, weapons and ammunition delivery, medical evacuations, and armed close air support. *Enter Air America!*

Welcome to the Tiny City of Vientiane

My final flight into Vientiane was from Bangkok, in a decades-old four-engine propeller-driven, oil-streaked antique—the ill-fated Lockheed Electra. For the last thirty minutes before our scheduled arrival time—through the scratched and yellowing small acrylic windows, I scanned the landscape in all directions, searching the horizons for some—*any* kind of developed town or city; but nothing, just varying shades of tan and brown. As far as the eye could see—to the four compass points, was an unending uninhabited dirt plain with no more than isolated patches of scrub trees. Ten minutes before landing I spied the snaking, mile-wide, muddy (coffee-with-two-creams-colored) Mekong River. On the north side of one east-west stretch I saw what appeared to be a small village, which although it was the only populated area for fifty miles, I doubted it could be Vientiane—the capital of Laos (or any other country). *It was.*

Here at last. Walking on the tarmac at Wattay International Airport I could only think "desolate." There weren't six buildings on the whole airport. The terminal was only two stories and all wood, painted what appeared to be a well-faded pink. Just a few hundred yards from the terminal I could see a couple unmarked hangars and the familiar silver and blue of parked Air America aircraft. I had contacted one of my Saigon pilots—now flying out of Vientiane, asking him to meet me. He did, and with a pleasured excitement that humbled me. A handshake was quickly replaced by a robust two-armed hug. "S.K." exclaimed, "Rog, you son of a gun, you're a sight for sore eyes!" Once we got through laughing at the accidental pun (me returning after my eye problems) S.K. led me to his car—an old English Triumph that we had a tough time getting my stuff into and onto (thanks for bungee cords with hooks). As we passed the Air America facility I noticed that there were no helicopters.

"No Rog. As you know, the Mekong here is the border between Laos and Thailand. Ten minutes south across the River in Thailand is a large Air Force base—Udorn, and on it there's another Air America facility where all our helicopters are based. Each morning, for the 'up-country' (northern Laos) work, the fixed-wing aircraft launch out of here and the helicopters launch out of Udorn."

On the drive to town (still without passing a single building over two stories) he began to give me the lowdown, and it was an interesting lowdown. "Rog, you're gonna love it here in Vientiane. As you're going to see, it's a tiny, peaceful town—quaint, I'd like to say. You'll hear more French than English—as well as a half dozen other languages. Since it's a neutral country, every country has an embassy here. You'll be rubbing elbows with our declared enemies—and in particular, Russians, North Koreans, and Chinese." It only took us ten minutes to get to town. He recommended I stay in the Lane Xang hotel—the best hotel in town, located right on the banks of the fast flowing, muddy Mekong. He drove me past it for a look, then past the second-best hotel in town—the Settha Palace, which was on the other side of town (which meant only 1000 yards from the Lane Xang). On the way to it we went past a low budget hotel that none of us ever stayed in; a dust-coated, peeling, faded yellow, lap strap sided, one-story string of about ten rooms. "See that hotel Rog. That's where the Russian pilots stay." *Russian pilots?* "Their van usually picks them up and takes em out to the airport the same time we're going out. They fly outa the other side of the field. And nice looking guys too. I was at the handball courts a couple days ago and two of them were on the next court. According to standard procedure we both feigned not seeing each other."

The tour of downtown entailed no more than driving two blocks on one east-west street, and three or four blocks on one north-south street (one barely two cars wide). The first street was lined with charming French cafes, bistros, and an ample presence of silver and goldsmith shops; the second—just non-descript commercial buildings on one side and a giant empty square (the Vientiane "morning market") on the other. On this—my first visit to a neutral country, hosting embassies from just about every nation, it was not long before I was feeling the southeast version of the Continental atmosphere I had fallen in love with in Europe. I was sure I was going to prefer this station to Saigon. S.K. next showed me where most the Air America guys with families lived: a recently-built development called Salakoktane, located about three miles east of town. Once there I was surprised to see well-kept and appealing, stateside-appearing three-bedroom two-bath homes with large grassy yards. I was favorably impressed; surprised at the tranquility and sufficiency of this potential living arrangement.

S.K. left me off at the Lane Xang, where I was able to register, unpack, lay on the bed in wonderment, eat dinner and speculate about what the morrow would hold for me. In the course of these deliberations—and something that once again demonstrates my inability to think sufficiently into the future: while still aware of my desperate need to find that one woman who would unlock my manhood; to my own amazement *I phoned Sara and told her that we no longer had to live apart. She and the kids could join me in Vientiane!* What on earth I could have been thinking eludes me to this day! While in a country at war, the city of Vientiane was considered by the world (in spite of a hint of espionage in every conversation) to be "off-limits" for any violence or even mild confrontation; an internationally designated safe enclave of cosmopolites. I told her to forget Bangkok. I'd be sending tickets for them to join me in this neat place.

Assigned an Aircraft and Area Fam

In addition to several large WWII cargo planes, this Laotian operation (even more so than Vietnam), required aircraft able to fly in and out of unprepared, almost unrecognizable muddy and narrow valley strips or high spiny ridgeline excuses for landing areas. For this there were two different types of "Short Take-off and Landing" aircraft: the reciprocating-engined Helio Courier, and Yup—you guessed it, my trusty turbo-prop-powered, Swiss-built Pilatus Porter. I of course was reassigned to it.

A Porter on the job

Before I was allowed to start my flight training, I had to learn the layout of the country (which to actually gain the necessary familiarity would require months, if not years)! Laos is a landlocked country, stretching mostly north to south and nestled like a buffer zone between South Vietnam and Thailand. The upper half—north of Vientiane, consists of an irregularly square-shaped portion, about 250 miles by 250 miles—stretching all the way north to China, with Burma to the west and North Vietnam to the east. The topography of this northern area was awe inspiring, being comprised of rugged mountainous terrain as far as the eye could see; a foreboding, cluttered array of high rocky ridges and tall limestone outcroppings (called karsts). I quickly concluded the chances of walking away from a forced landing would be 'slim to none' (and according to my first day's pilot— if you did get out of the wreckage, your chances of being shot within thirty minutes were excellent). South of Vientiane, Laos was a southerly extending narrow tail—a flat, arid, peninsula-like region that stretches over 400 miles down to Cambodia.

Out-Stations

At the upper northwestern corner of the country is the famous "Golden Triangle," where Laos, Thailand and Burma all meet (and half the world's supply of heroin is produced). In this area—in a small town called Ban Houie Sai (300 air miles northwest of Vientiane), we had an outstation where pilots would go for five-day tours, flying daily for the Customer there. The town had a small strip (sand bar) in the middle of the Mekong.

Laos countryside

Karst outcroppings

During the rainy season there was always the risk you could come back at the end of a hard day, to find your strip under water! Once again, similar to the necessity of maintaining the outstation at Ban Houie Sai to the far north, we also had an outstation at the far southerly tip, just outside a small town called Pakse. Pilots would also be stationed there for five-day tours. The country was large enough that we couldn't do what we had to do, just always launching out of Wattay airport in Vientiane.

A Pilot's Best Friend, His Maps

I was issued a set of about twenty maps covering the whole country, and told that for at least two weeks I would ride all day long, every day, with another Porter pilot. During which time I was supposed to mark the map with every landing strip and every notable landmark or unusual terrain feature I saw (that I might someday need to use to orient myself). Fortunately—here as in Vietnam, all the strips were given a Lima number, and there were over 200 of them! There were no radio beacons in Laos. All our navigating was accomplished by visual pilotage—identifying and utilizing terrain features. Our maps therefore were life-savers. Recognizing the importance of them I spent most of the second week on how to best connect the now well-marked assortment of separate maps. Some pilots had taped together a set for northern Laos and another set for southern Laos. Some pilots had arranged them in north-south strips covering the whole country and some pilots taped them together in east-west strips covering the whole country. (This was good except it produced a map eighteen inches wide by six feet long!) I tried another way, that made a reasonably-sized booklet you could open vertically—like a calendar with a binding along the top edge. Instead of having 12 pages (months), it would have about 20 pages. As you flew north you just flipped through the pages from top to bottom. I made another set to use for east-west travel. In the years to come I would make hundreds of additional marks and notes on these maps, and redo the preferred arrangement of them many times.

Retraining

Once I started flight training, I was surprised (and grateful) that handling the aircraft came back to me quickly. After a day or two it was like I'd only been out of the cockpit a week, although I must admit, here in Laos the strips were harder to find, shorter, rougher, and more steeply uphill.

I GUESS I JUST WASN'T THINKING

Typical STOL strip

Plus Laos being at a higher elevation, the winds were stronger, which could produce sudden (violent) up or down drafts. At many strips, to avoid shearing a wing, collapsing the gear, skidding over the side, or plowing into a rock wall at the end of the landing roll, required unique planning and bold technique (as well as urgent prayers to the gods of aviation). I was to learn that flying twenty-plus short flights a day was the norm, so every day was bound to include at least one heart-in-the-throat white knuckler!

I had experienced line captains as my Checkout Pilots. One—an old hand and well respected was a nice enough guy, but whose train of thought was uncharted by anyone. He was continually blurting out four or five words vaguely associated with something we may have discussed an *hour* ago, or something in his distant future that just happened to cross his mind. While attempting to become part of the team, I could see there was engrained skepticism about a "Saigon" pilot doing the job here in Laos. Moreover, there was a small cadre of old hands (led by KD Novak) who held serious doubts about me. I was sure they were anxiously awaiting the day when I would confirm their appraisals by leaving a tail wheel, or a main gear, or a wing tip (or better yet—parts of my anatomy) draped on one of their STOL strips. (Though I've got to admit, there were a couple of senior pilots—Willie and Lee for instance, who were respectful and ready to give me a chance.)

Important! The CIA Command Post in Laos

About ninety miles north of Vientiane, in a narrow hidden valley between two east-west ridges was the village of Long Chien (sometimes spelled Long Tieng)—*the infamous CIA secret airbase in Laos.* Every day, the fixed wing aircraft from Vientiane and the rotary wing aircraft from Udorn—assigned to fly up-country, would first land at the runway at Long Chien

The CIA secret base

(Lima Site 20Alternate) and receive their missions for the day. LS20A had only recently been occupied as the secret base. The previous "secret" base twenty miles northwest—LS20 (Sam Thong), had come under attack by North Vietnamese troops and heavy artillery, and everything (including the runway) was destroyed. The Company now kept a full complement of Hmong soldiers on top of a ridge just north of 20A! An attempt to not let the same thing happen here at the new base.

Equally as Important: The Plain of Jars

About 30 miles north of Long Chien is the eighth wonder of the world— *La Plaine des Jarres* (French for "The Plain of Jars"). Encircled by steeply rising mountains and karst peaks on all sides, it is a low, table-flat, oblong of high waving green grass. Its size was about 50 miles north-to-south, and 30 miles across. Archeologists generally agree it's where a small asteroid or meteorite tore into the earth tens of thousands of years ago, leveling the mountains and leaving a huge lake of molten material. In the centuries that followed, layers of dust slowly accumulated on the cooled surface. It was too shallow for trees to root, and it thus ended up just miles and miles of grass and weeds—now six-foot-high or higher. Scattered across it are thousands of huge stone jars, six to ten feet tall, each weighing at least

The Plain of Jars

a ton. One theory is that the jars were associated with prehistoric burial practices. Deceased Chinese emperors and their valuable possessions were put into the jars and they were then hauled hundreds of miles to be sanctified here. It's one of the most important prehistoric sites in Southeast Asia. *But that's not why it's important to Air America pilots flying in Laos!* For many years the "PDJ" had been the unrefuted property of the North Vietnamese Army, who not only established well-armed encampments, but brought in modern anti-aircraft weapons, including the small but feared Soviet 12.7 machine gun (effectively used as an anti-aircraft gun against Air America aircraft). *Only under dire circumstances would you hazard a short cut across the PDJ.* Your chance of being shot down were excellent! If your destination was on the other side of it and you were in a hurry or feeling brave, you could nervously skirt just inside the karst peaks ringing its edges.

Being Released as Pilot in Command

My Captain's Check Ride would be administered by Ed Starika—the Senior Instructor Pilot for Porters and a real old hand. He flew here in the early sixties when Air America first started, using the well-revered De Havilland workhorse—the DHC-2 Beaver. During breakfast, Ed told me a story about when he was being checked out in it by an old Army pilot. "I was trying to land at this narrow, ridgeline strip, during a strong crosswind that kept blowing me to the side of the extended centerline of the strip. I was aware of this and kept trying to get the aircraft back on it. In spite of my efforts the Army guy kept yelling 'Get on centerline! Get on centerline!' I said 'I *am* doing it!' He said 'It's taking too long!' I said 'I'm trying to be smooth!' He said *"Get on centerline now, get smooth later!"*

Ed was a good guy and I very much appreciated that although he was the best of the old hands, he never made me feel like a 'new guy' (which of course I was—at least here). We arrived at Long Chien at 7:30 and reported to the CIA dispatcher for our flight assignments (which strip we would go to first and which case officer we would be working for). We were directed to drop off a load of medical supplies at six different strips, whose location, features, and wind patterns (thank God) I remembered from my training. Mercifully I made six good landings and take-offs; never scaring either of us (or at least not much).

Around noon, ready to depart LS32, where because of a high hill on the east end of the strip, you had to take off to the west. Today—unfortunately, there was a gusting tailwind which can *double* your take-off distance, causing you to fail to achieve liftoff airspeed, and result in plowing off the end—still on the ground, wiping out the gear and destroying the airplane. This downwind thing happens a lot (even to major airliners). *Okay, this is going to be my first real test. It could make or break my check ride.* How long am I going to wait for the tailwind to subside? If I don't wait long enough, I could end up running off the end and sinking in the rice paddies at the far end of the strip. But then if I wait too long he may think I don't have the balls to fly in Laos. There was a wind sock at the strip. I watched it, timing the duration of the downwind gust, and then timing the lull that followed; trying to get a pattern. My plan was to pour the coal to it at the end of the gust segment (in hopes the anticipated lull would follow). Ed didn't say anything (I think just waiting to see what I would do). The tailwind gusts appeared to last about fifteen seconds, followed by shorter ten second lulls. I eyed the second hand on my watch through two more cycles to confirm my timing. The times repeated. So the split second the next gust died down I rammed the throttle forward. *It worked!* I accomplished the whole takeoff run during the lull that followed, allowing us to reach lift off speed a good hundred feet before the end of the strip. Airborne, Ed didn't make a comment, but out of the corner of my eye I think I saw him make a slight nod of (I hoped) approval. Upon our arrival back at 20Alternate, Ed surprised me by getting out of the aircraft, coming around to my side, reached up to shake my hand and said, "Well, you're on your own now." *I'd just passed my Captain's check. I'd be solo the rest of the day!* I shut down the engine and not very assuredly walked to the dispatcher's shack to volunteer a brand new guy's services.

My First Captain's Flight

"Hey Jerry, Ed and I finished the med drop offs, Whataya got next?"
"Wait over by your airplane, I'll be sending over some guys for you to take to LS 213."

Hmmmn, Lima Site 213? Never went there before. In fact during my training I never heard anybody mention it. Just for this type quandary (locating a little-used strip) Air America had printed a booklet listing all the strips by their number, giving their geographical coordinates and pertinent data. I found LS 213, and checking the coordinates I could see it was about 40 or 50 miles west, "3,900 feet elevation," "520 feet long," "steeply uphill to the north." While standing there studying the page with LS 213,

Lima Site 213

another (unusually clean-cut) Porter pilot named Gar Bogden approached me. The Lane Xang hotel was his permanent residence and I had seen him there quite a few times, in fact had dinner with him once. To me, he didn't fit the Air America mold; too quiet; too well mannered. A real gentleman and evidently happily married; never left his room in the evenings.

"Where you going Rog?"

"Lima Site 213."

Hearing it triggered a noticeable look of concern on his face, causing me to wait for some amplification—which didn't come. He checked my clipboard to verify I was really going there, handed it back to me, turned and started back to his plane, throwing a "Good luck" over his shoulder. This last remark—coming from Gar, was worth consideration, and went some distance in deflating the surge of confidence I had been feeling just fifteen minutes ago. Behind me I saw four young Hmong soldiers and one stern-faced older guy in fatigues climbing into my aircraft. Satisfied it was the whole load—and getting a thumbs up from the dispatcher, I started the Garrett TPE331 powerhouse, taxied to the runway, poured the coal to it, and was excited to be alone in the cockpit, *airborne in Laos—solo, on my first official captain's flight!*

I found LS213 no problem—really no problem, since it was bright red dirt and perched atop the highest terrain for miles. It was the most uphill strip I'd seen to date—by far! *Geez, this is going to be something, and on my first Captain's flight.* This far west (almost in Thailand) I was pretty sure there wouldn't be any North Vietnamese on the ground and only a few Pathet Lao in the area. So with little chance of taking ground fire I risked a couple low altitude circles to examine the strip, gauge the wind effect and plan my approach. The wind was not only strong, but unfortunately—out of the south. Since I had to land uphill to the north, I'd be doing so downwind (the wind on my tail). Normally, this is not a good idea. Pilots always land *into* the wind to slow their speed over the ground, and thus facilitate stopping the aircraft. But this strip was so markedly uphill, even with a tail wind, there was no chance I'd have trouble stopping. But another problem: When a strong tailwind hits the rising ground just short of the runway, it is deflected sharply upward. This produces a huge updraft just before you cross the end of the runway; at the last minute lofting the aircraft up fifty feet or more. (On a flat runway this can cause you to land long and go off the other end of the runway!)

I levelled the wings on final approach. Everything was looking good, in spite of the tailwind rushing my approach to touchdown. I knew just short of the runway I would encounter the updraft, so pushed the nose over. We were now pointed, (aimed) frightenly low—as if I was going to purposely crash the plane into a spot on the face of the cliff, *thirty feet below the runway.* Held it. My passengers weren't scared. They didn't know any better. Any American on board would have been screaming "Pull up! Pull up!" As I anticipated, just before impaling ourselves into the face of the cliff, the updraft hit, popping us up high enough that my wheels cleared the runway edge by five to ten feet! Crossed the end, set her down (although I can't say gently) and threw it into reverse.

Now a *new* problem: This strip was so uphill, if I left it in reverse too long, I could easily come to a stop *and maybe even start skidding back down the runway.* If this did happen, it could result in going backwards off the cliff at the touchdown end of the runway (and cartwheeling several hundred feet to death or serious bodily injury in the valley below). I added power to try to maintain enough speed to make it to the top, and more importantly, have enough speed to be able to swing the tail around—be able to make the 180 degree turn to be pointed back downhill for take-off. *Shit!* Didn't have enough speed. Hadn't added the power soon enough, only got the plane half way around. Shut it down and set the parking brake. Before my passengers got too far from the aircraft I corralled them and explained that I needed them to help me pick up the tail, and swing it around towards the top of the hill. I must not have been the first guy they'd had this problem with because they turned to like they did it every day, and in a minute the plane was pointed directly downhill. I was all set for take-off. The rest of the day was uneventful. I felt proud and justified during the 6 pm van ride from Wattay airport to the Lane Xang. I may have caused too much of a scene with all my circling, and drawn a crowd of 'unfriendlies', because the next day, one of my pilots trying to land there had his big toe shot off while on final approach.

Chapter Nineteen
STARTING A NEW KIND OF LIFE

A Family Together

After a couple visits to Salakoktane I found a great house for the family. A new three-bedroom, two-bath home, with a large yard alongside, and a nice car port adjacent to the front porch (which I was told was a real necessity during the monsoon season). It also had a small housekeeper/cook's cottage behind the house. I asked the company to ship all the furniture that Sara had stored in Bangkok up here (which was a lot—of *good* stuff). It arrived a week before the family and I placed it as best I could throughout the house. Another good thing: on the same street were two other Air America families whose kids were about the same age as mine. As far as schooling went, the company sponsored a school for all the dependent kids; a great little school about a mile north of town. Most the teachers were wives of Air America guys or guys who worked at the embassy, who had been teachers in the states. Things were coming together.

Upon the family's arrival in Bangkok I was at the airport to meet them and escort them to the gate for the hour and a half flight up to Vientiane (in a Lao Airlines WWII C-47). I was gratified because the whole group—as tired as they were, seemed excited to be returning to their Southeast Asian life style. We weren't airborne more than 15 minutes when Mark came running up to my seat, to ask me about a common practice that he was perplexed at noticing. "Dad, I think there's a big gold bar under my seat, and every seat!"

I told him, yes he was right. "The gold is so heavy, to keep the aircraft center of gravity within limits they had to distribute them in this manner—the length of the cabin; can't just have one big stack in the cargo compartment." I'll have to admit when they disembarked at Wattay airport I think I saw a bit of apprehension. But then that was how I felt as well. It was a primitive airport with no hint of any city nearby—no buildings protruding above the trees in any direction. We cleared customs without any problems. Even at the airport, as my family would find—here in Vientiane no one made problems for anyone. I had bought an old black and white 53 Chevy that we all piled into, and like S.K. did for me, I first took them on a tour of the town. Knowing they were tired, I made it short, but long enough to see they seemed as captivated as I had been.

When we finally pulled into the driveway of our new home their wide-eyed expressions indicated any expectations they might have had, had been exceeded. They were surprised and pleased. We carted all the suitcases inside (from that carport next to the steps to the front porch). That done, the kids occupied themselves running and tumbling on the large grassy lawn alongside the house. And from Donna I could overhear ambitious plans for part of the yard: building a corral *for the horse I would buy her!* Sara was particularly pleased seeing all the familiar Bangkok furniture in the home. In the living room she went from one piece to the other, stroking the rattan finish, plumping cushions, and surveying the various locations. The girls chose their bedroom and the boys theirs. Mom instructed them to begin emptying their suitcases and putting their clothes in the chests of drawers (the same ones they'd used in Bangkok). The third bedroom of course was the main bedroom—for Sara and me. There was a large dining/living room. (No need for a separate family room—no TV in Laos.) After the long trip, rather than cook in, we went out for dinner. Thank God again. The meal (several different specialties) were just great, and a half dozen of my pilot friends and their wives came over and introduced themselves—one, a lady who would end up being Kevin's school teacher.

Of course—fearfully similar to my first night home from the carrier cruise, and the first night Sara joined me in Hobe Sound, we were at some point going to have to call it a night *and crawl into bed together.* I knew that Sara (in view of my history of inabilities) was perhaps already rehearsing her "Oh, don't worry about it" line. Myself—pessimism was winning. Having thought since 'day one' the problem was strictly a lack of chemistry between us, by now realistically and discouragingly I had to conclude it was not just between Sara and I. (Too many women had been added to the list.) This night and under these circumstances, I was quite sure I would not be successful. However, with gritted teeth and pleas to the Almighty, after a longer wait than she was expecting, I felt I had what could possibly pull it off. But as had happened in the past, in the mere seconds it took me to roll over on top and prepare to enter her, *it was gone!* Rather than give up and try to come up with a credible excuse, I disguised the aborted attempt as just another repositioning, and set about a delaying tactic of more foreplay (which if it did not turn the key for me, would be doubly frustrating for Sara). But tonight—good news, I was (mercifully) responding—to the extent I believed I would be able to affect a penetration of sorts. I entered her and was able to maintain a just-barely (and brief) sufficient firmness. Surely not what would have been expected from a normally testosteroned male who had just spent a half year without having sex. But at least mercifully my modicum of success cancelled the necessity to explain it away as a result of any single justifiable situation. *Thank You God.*

The next morning I drove Sara and the kids to the Vientiane American School and it was a big hit. Almost every kid there ran up and introduced themselves, and the teachers seemed genuinely pleased to have a new addition to their enrollment. My kids were thrilled to find out they wouldn't have to walk or take a bus; *they'd be picked up each morning by one of those silver and blue Air America vans.* Vientiane—being the capital had a US Embassy, and attached to it was a commissary for government employees. And this time (unlike Saigon, or Bangkok) Air America personnel were able to shop there, buying staples and stateside specialty foods. A few days later Sara was able to contact her friend Sandy in Bangkok, and between them worked it out that Thalee—the pleasant young Thai girl who had been Sara's cook and housekeeper in Bangkok, was going to be able to come up to Vientiane, and carry on just like in Bangkok. Most entry into Laos from Thailand, was accomplished at night across the Mekong in small, dugout, canoe-like boats. For about 100 Baht to the boat owner, you could lie huddled under tarps and bunches of fruit. This was not a big secret, but for other reasons was ignored by officials of both countries. Thalee entered Vientiane, from the small Thai town of Nong Khai, on the south bank, just a few miles east. I couldn't have asked for a better start!

Chapter Twenty
ONE SOUL LESS

Something New

He'd arrived yesterday with more than the usual fanfare: Ron Wilheim—William Holden's personal cameraman! Remember? William Holden the movie actor in *The Bridges of Toko Ri*. He played Harry Brubaker, the navy carrier pilot. Or maybe your dad told you about him in the WWII movie classic *Stalag 17*. In any case rumor was that he had been hired by the Company to do a 'constructively misleading' documentary on the genesis and current operations of Air America. He was here in Vientiane to do the part on Laos, which would be titled *Flying Men Flying Machines*. Some years later there'd be a second more accurate and exciting documentary titled *The CIA Secret Airline*. (No secret to me and my friends I can tell you.)

I left the house at six, anticipating another normal day of flight ops (if there ever was such a thing). I'd takeoff at seven for Long Chien where I'd fly shuttles in and out of there all day, or be sent off to some remote strip where I'd work for the case officer assigned there. Either place I'd fly about twenty missions moving cargo and troops between the small strips on top of the ridges that looked down on enemy-infested valleys. Some strips were so close to NVA or Pathet Lao positions, they could rush the strip and the aircraft could be destroyed on the ground (not to mention what might happen to you)! When this possibility existed, rather than land we'd *air drop* the rice or water or ammo or whatever. Remaining airborne was safer, but our patterns would usually still take us close to overhead the enemy positions, resulting in us taking a couple hits every time—usually just small arms fire, going through the tail or aft cabin area. Those kind of hits didn't scare us too much. A good scare is when you're high in the sky—maybe just finishing a tuna sandwich, feeling safe and relaxed, when with no warning there's an ear drum-shattering airburst right in front of you, you see the shrapnel go by, and smell the burnt powder as you fly through the black cloud. These "heart-in- the-throat" occurrences we referred to as "Leemers." (A Leemer is a cold shot of urine right through your heart.)

Six-twenty and sitting by a window in our tiny restaurant. It was cool and gray outside—a real low pressure day. The ramp looked gloomy. The aircraft looked old. It was windy and the corrugated metal buildings looked flimsy and vulnerable; made you feel antsy; bad vibes. I was having my favorite: creamed beef on toast. (I was in the middle of a two-week study to determine which stayed with me longest: creamed beef or pancakes. This was important since lunch was never a sure thing. Surprisingly to me I later concluded it was the pancakes.)

"Hey Roger! Jim Ryan wants to see you." (Jim was the uniquely qualified and well respected "Manager of Flight Operations," about whom you will hear much more.)

"Three more bites and I'll be there."

"No, right now!"

Here's what I found out: I was going to bring Mr. Wilheim and one of our Taipei big-wigs to a remote village, just over the ridge that comprised the north side of the *Plaine des Jarres.* They were going to go to Lima Site 218 for some filming activities. I'd drop them off, do whatever other work I was assigned, and then pick them back up around noon.

"LS218? Geez Jim, why are they going to LS218? I'm not aware of any operations up there, and don't even think there's a case officer assigned there. I've never landed there or even heard any other pilot mention it. It's no-man's land. Who chose that strip? We got all kinds of activity going on down at 20Alternate and Lima Site 272 every day. They could get all kinds of footage back where we have a handle on things."

No doubt Jim knew what he wanted, that's where we were going, and whatever the reason I was not going to be made party to it. I added: "Of course they'll have to bring a hand-held radio with them, and while they're there, if they see or feel something brewing, they'll have to give me a call right away."

As every pilot did every morning, I had my "FIC" briefing. The Flight Information Center was our intelligence section. It had the latest positions of gun emplacements and known or suspected locations of North Vietnamese troops or the hostile Pathet Lao. No real changes since my last flight a couple days ago. It was just going to be we three for the trip up. All the passenger seats were removed from the Porter (as they almost always were). We were in the semi-cargo configuration; just a two-person canvas fold-down against the rear bulkhead of the cabin, and another five-person canvas fold-down seat that ran the length of the port side of the aircraft (from right behind my pilot's seat to the rear of the cabin). The Porter was thus configured for seven passengers, although often—by necessity, those seven seats would be filled, plus six more passengers crammed on the floor, and one more in the co-pilot seat. (This totaled fourteen passengers in a seven-passenger aircraft.) My guys piled in with their expensive molded aluminum cases and I directed them to sit on the rear fold-down.

Ron Wilheim looked like a cameraman—at least, if not a Hollywood director. He had distinctive features; was handsomely balding and spoke with a European accent. He was wearing a faded denim shirt (probably bought on the Champs Elysees) and a suede vest with lots of pockets. And something I noticed right off: he was wearing a neat-looking leather and bone African necklace. Mr. Christiansen—our Company rep from Taipei was a nice fellow, but not sure he needed a white button-down shirt (with a gold Cross pen in the pocket) for this trip.

The Standard Morning Flight to Long Chien

The two were noticeably impressed by my powerful Porter, which I allowed to leap in the air, and then (I admit—for effect) hauled the nose up to its steepest approved angle. I'm sure Jim told them they were going to be flown by the past master of the program: *the one-eyed guy with the silver bracelet.* We left any semblance of civilization behind us, flying northbound over the sparsely vegetated and uninhabited flat land that stretched thirty miles until reaching a sharply rising escarpment. We buzzed steadily northward, albeit slow and noisily. The large-engined but thick-winged Porter gnawed the air like a gargantuan bumble bee. Lots of power but unable to get out of its own way; not designed for speed it had other advantages—being one of the best Short Take Off and Landing ("STOL") aircraft ever built. It was designed and fabricated in Switzerland for rescue work in the Alps.

Now over the escarpment which was higher by several hundred feet, but likewise flat; a similarly stretching plateau bearing the same scrub brush. A few wispy columns of smoke marked the locations of tiny one-hundred-person villages. This higher ground was soon more rugged, and then became a series of sharp ridges and limestone peaks. The next fifty miles to Long Chien were over this foreboding terrain. It would be almost impossible to make a successful forced landing during this part of the trip (or ever be found if you did). It's a daily-traveled route and to our knowledge the bad guys weren't in this area (this far west and not too distant from the capital). However a couple months ago a covertly flown Air Force Cessna O-1 "Bird Dog" coming up in the morning, just like we were today—went down. Who knows why, it just disappeared. We were never able to locate the wreckage; some mother's son never to be seen again. Another MIA that is not in a POW camp, just peat moss somewhere. (The Air Force guys in civilian clothes who illegally flew these light observation planes in Laos, were called *Ravens*—of which the best-known and good friend of mine was the now deceased Fred Platte.)

With no radio facilities we always navigated by "Dead Reckoning" which on this leg was the embarrassingly simplistic task of just overflying the river gorge that ran south from Long Chien. It would lead us right to it—nestled down in its bowl. Two miles out I started jockeying for position; making a few "S" turns to create spacing, and get into the queue for landing. In addition to me, another dozen aircraft were also maneuvering for landing sequence. I could see a look of concern on the faces of my passengers as they saw the numerous globs of silver and blue aluminum above, below, and all sides of us. Checking left and right to make sure there were no threatening aircraft, I dove towards the end of the runway while shouting into the mike, "Five-Eight Foxtrot short final, number two behind the one-twenty-three!" With no tower each pilot used a common frequency to announce his position and landing priority (as he saw it.) We were all on the same team, vulcanized through many months of harrowing scrapes and escapes, so there were few discussions about who should have been first, and who had been "cut out of the pattern."

After parking at LS20Alternate the normal routine was to get refueled and receive our assignments. We used to do this while having a cup of coffee in a small cafeteria that bordered the parking ramp; that is up until about three weeks ago when a DK82 rocket scored a direct hit on it. Now we just wandered around the debris on the tarmac. We didn't stand in one place too long, in fact spent most of the time crouched on the south side of a tall limestone karst that protected us from incoming rounds.

The NVA troops had somehow (incredibly) been able to haul the several-hundred-pound parts of their howitzers up almost vertical cliffs to the top of the high ridge that bordered the north side of the LS20A bowl. And frequently—within ten minutes of our morning arrival, they would fire an artillery barrage right down on the ramp where the aircraft were parked and some of the pilots were still standing!

My Work for the Day

First I'd fly north to LS218 and drop off Wilheim and Christiansen for their filming project (whatever the hell that was). Then I'd go to LS32 (about thirty miles *east* of LS218), pick up cargo there and shuttle it to LS310 (about thirty miles *west* of LS218). *This would mean I'd be passing overhead LS218 every thirty minutes and could look down and check on my guys.* LS310 was never safe; no CIA-trained Hmong there. "No Man's" land. Just three weeks ago, Herb Clarke, near it—making rice drops out of an old Curtiss C-46, took several incendiary rounds through his right wing—which immediately caught fire. (People who say there's nothing worse than a fire at sea, have never been in an airplane on fire.) He turned immediately towards an open area, hoping for a successful forced landing. According to another pilot who was flying behind Herb, it was only ten seconds before the wing just folded right back over the fuselage. Before the aircraft inverted and spiraled in, one "kicker" bailed out; the rest went down with the aircraft. (Kickers—usually Laotian or Thai, but often ex-Special Forces guys or ex-smoke jumpers, were the stalwart crewmen who on the air drops, shoved the loaded pallets out of the aircraft.) The location was so bad it never was safe enough to get a recovery team into Herb's crash site. The NVA would have been there in fifteen minutes, set up a ring of automatic weapons, planted mines in the area of the wreckage (even booby-trapped the crewmember's bodies)! They're still there somewhere; more Air America guys rotting in Laotian soil.

With both my guys back on board I was airborne and up and over the rim of the Long Chien bowl. Away and completely on my own again (something I think we all cherished about this job). I climbed rapidly to an altitude that would give me maximum glide distance in the event of an engine failure, and more safety margin in the event of small arms fire. Most the terrain (the Long Chien strip included) was about 3,000 ft above sea level. The valleys averaged 2,000 ft., the ridges at 4,000 ft., and the karst peaks at 5,000 ft. From here I could get to LS218 in twenty-five

Kicker shoving out rice

minutes *if I went across the Plaine des Jarres.* However as said before, that route was a definite "no-no." Numerous anti-aircraft weapons were hiding in that high waving green grass—just waiting for us to take a short cut overhead. No friendlies for miles. *Forget about being rescued if you went down.* So I made a left turn towards the southwest edge of the PDJ. With no radio beacons in country, like always—I was navigating solely by visual reference to the terrain features beneath me. Since the flat lead-colored overcast was at 8,000 feet, I stayed just below it. If I went any higher I'd be in the clouds and lose all reference to my necessary landmarks. It was still gray and gusty, but good visibility under the cloud layer. I was going northward, skirting the western boundaries of the PDJ. Not bad but sort or eerie.

I motioned my passengers forward to the side-mounted fold down seat right behind me, so we could converse during our trek northward. Exciting 1950's Indochinese history was made in this area. The PDJ was just off our right wing; a perfectly flat, bright green plateau completely surrounded by sharply rising rugged charcoal-gray mountains; few trees, just that high green grass. It didn't surprise me that Ron knew the area's history. We were too high to clearly see the large stone jars on it, which were pretty much empty now, after centuries of grave robbers had ransacked them for gold and gems. Thirty-five minutes later we were at the northwest corner of the forbidden PDJ, where it was safe to start my right turn eastward towards LS218. It would be another twenty miles across completely uninhabited, gray-black ridges. I had seen it many times before, but never landed there. It was as if the CIA had decided they didn't want to mess with it. As far as I knew we didn't have any troops in the village there. It was a hundred miles from the nearest English-speaking person or village with running water. *This morning would likely find these two gentlemen as far removed from civilization as they had ever been.*

I overheaded the strip higher than usual, not wanting the villagers to hear us and be aware a plane was going to land. An early announcement of your intended landing could lead to two kinds of big trouble mentioned earlier. I surveyed the village—in the bowl at the bottom of the north side of the ridgeline (and runway). It was a mundane mottled assortment of browns: dirt huts, faded materials, dried mud, bleached and dust covered boards, piles of straw—an absence of any color. There were a bunch of kids wandering about—all exposed, people walking at a normal speed, dogs playing, old women seated around some joint activity. As best I could tell, all indications were of an unconcerned village, not one that had been overrun the previous night, or in impending danger of an attack.

At some time in the past the villagers had hacked out a fifteen-foot wide, five-hundred foot long, almost straight, almost flat, rutted path that we called a runway. Like so many others, it was hewn from the backbone of a ridgeline that rose steadily higher to the east—*ending with a vertical rock wall.* It was an "up-hill-er" like LS213. (Remember? My first Captain's flight.) I'd be landing to the east—up the incline. (You always land uphill, never downhill. Hard to stop when you're also fighting gravity!) I would touch down at the low end and plan on the upward angle of the strip to slow the aircraft to a stop before I ran into the rock wall. I gave Ron and Mr. Christiansen a briefing on how to use the hand-held radio, and that they should call me immediately if they suspected things were not right. (Watch the dogs!) I reiterated the end of my landing roll would be at the top east end of the strip, *and if trouble did break out they were to get back to that drop-off point immediately.* There was a long winding path from the village up to the runway. If the village came under attack and they were slow getting up the path, the airplane might already be packed to overflowing when they got to it. *They had to be there first if they wanted to get a seat.* An ugly scene could develop otherwise. In the past I had evacuated villages where I had to momentarily get out of the aircraft, and then as I got back in, *noticed a passenger had already occupied my pilot's seat!*

In a pickup at a strip that was presently under attack or imminent attack, I wouldn't shut down the engine (for fear I wouldn't get it started in time, or as had happened—get it started at all). So I cautioned them about the engine being running: "For God's sake be careful of the spinning prop!" We'd already killed dozens of Hmong who ran right into it without ever seeing it, leaving the pilot to look through hair and pieces of flesh stuck on the wind screen. (One of my pilots to whom this happened found a fingertip in his trouser cuff when he got home.) They grimaced then nodded they understood. I spiraled down onto a short final approach, pulled off the power and "*Kalunk-thud!*" Banged it on. Careened up the incline. Spun it around. Hit the brakes, leaned back in my seat, grabbed the door and slung it full open. They were out and waving (but certainly not looking all that confident). In less than a minute I was back in the sky. We'd surprised the villagers. Only a handful of them had time to make it up onto the runway (and fortunately stayed on the edges).

The trips back and forth between LS32 and LS310 were uneventful. The weather held the same—gray and gusty. Okay, but certainly not uplifting. It was as if I was in my own private layer of the world, between the ridges and the cloud bases; feeling a strange, false comfort, in my own quiet compartment in an uncared-for corner of the world. No other planes. Not a sound on the radio. The cold air made the visibility great. I could see forever under the overcast. To the north I was looking fifty miles into mainland China. It was a solid greenish-black canopy and appeared completely uninhabited. While a China border is marked on the map, there are absolutely no indications of it—no signs, posted on the ground. *The people there have no idea (nor do they care) what country they're in!* I was an apt spy in the sky, peering down each time I flew by LS218, checking for any indication that there had been a change in its security.

Uh-Oh, Something's Cooking

About ten-thirty, while staring at the runway where I'd left off my two guys, *Bingo!* a flash of fire and cloud of smoke on the south side of the ridgeline. Didn't know if it was a grenade or a rocket, but could mean an attack was coming. The hamlet was on the other side of the ridge, and low, so neither the villagers nor my guys would have seen it, though they may have heard it. Uh-Oh, another impact that threw a bunch of dirt. No two ways about it, after feeling it in my bones since breakfast, here it was— *something bad starting.* For me up here of course, no danger. I was far removed from the action. High and above it. I was observing it from a safe distance, although I knew I was soon going to have to put myself right in the middle of whatever was occurring! Visually I could see the gray fire flashes, but from this altitude there was no sound track. Grabbed the hand-held radio. "Ron, Ron! You hear me? Do you guys hear me?" They did. Surprisingly they responded loud and clear. I was afraid by now the radio would be lost in the bottom of a case.

"You guys gotta start up to the strip right now! I'll turn onto final when you're almost to the top of the path. And when you get to the strip, run to the high end where I left you off!" I could see the activity in the village becoming chaotic. People were running in every direction—like a stream of RAID had been sprayed into a bunch of ants. Lots of movement. Two more impacts, almost right in the village! After a couple minutes I spied my guys, scrambling up the path, in the lead and not far from the edge of the strip. Some villagers behind them, but they were first. I bent the Porter around, pulled off the power, wound down half flaps, and dove towards the touchdown end of the strip.

Wilheim and Christiansen were now on the strip—running, aluminum cases banging off their knees, on their way towards the spot I had let them off. I wound down the rest of the flaps. Oops, too high and fast. Had to force her on, banging the struts hard and wrestling with a left swerve. The Porter lurched and bounded crazily up the inclining strip. Bunches of people were now appearing at the top of the path, clutching pots and bags, chattering and pointing. I threw it into reverse and blew a swirling cloud of sand in front of me, obscuring the spot where my two guys were waiting. *Whoaa!* A deafening explosion! Somewhere *real* close behind the aircraft. But no pain, no sounds of ripping metal. Spun her around. Ron and Christiansen were right there. Slung the door open. The crowd of villagers was still a hundred feet away, but coming fast.

A Brave Woman

My guys were in, *but what's this?* Where did *she* come from? Out of nowhere, one hand grasping the door frame, the other covering a badly bleeding neck wound, was a Hmong woman—maybe thirty years of age, stumbling on the step, trying to board the aircraft. My two guys were dumbstruck, their eyes locked on this barefooted woman, her foot slipping on her own blood, dark eyes bolted on me, still trying to pull herself in. It looked like a piece of shrapnel had gone through her throat. More people closing on us fast.

"Yank her in! Grab her! Up here! Push the door shut, just shove it! Yeah! Good! Got it!" Full power and we lurched ahead. Thank God no people still in the center of the runway. Some loud clunks. The rough runway was pounding the hell out of the struts. *Hang in there gear!* More acceleration. Off the ground. In the air. Outa there! I climbed due west— my first best heading to avoid the PDJ, and the attack had come from the east. The plan was to skirt the north edge of the PDJ before turning south. Got to 7,000 ft. The overcast was lower now. We were about 3000 ft over the level of the PDJ, 1000 feet above the ridges, and 500 feet above the karst peaks. Safe—or as safe as we could be. Initially in an attempt to help, my guys maneuvered the woman to a lying position. In a minute I could hear the gurgling as her lungs were filling. Got them to get her back upright where she could hawk up the blood in her throat.

I twisted around and checked my passengers. Ron and Christiansen were seated on the rear fold-down seat, their equipment sprawled at their feet. The woman was sitting on the side fold-down seat, right behind me. Her left hand was clutching the back of my seat (her fingers touching my left shoulder), her right hand still to her neck. Her gaze was fixed straight ahead—out the other side of the aircraft. This woman who perhaps had never seen a car, only witnessed electricity for a few hours each evening off the USAID generator, probably never in her life been more than ten miles from this village, had now just boarded this screaming, strange piece of silver machinery, filled with strangers, opting to leave her only known existence.

Looking over my shoulder I could see her color fading and knew time was of the essence, and made the decision to risk it—turning due south before I got all the way to the west rim of the PDJ, *which would have me cutting across it.* A dangerous route but one that would save at least ten minutes. We'd only be about five miles inside the PDJ, so if I took a critical hit I would be able to turn west and glide out of harm's way. (Out of harm's way from the enemy, but into hellacious aircraft-rending terrain; meaning an almost certain fatal crash.)

With course set, power set, aircraft trimmed, we plowed with a constant, monotonous drone southward; no one speaking—overcome by the situation. The feeling of being alone was paramount. Miles from civilization or help, in our own private pearly layer of space between the enemy in the rippling green of the PDJ below and the wet gray clouds just above. The sound of the passing air and the steady drone of the engine were so constant, it seemed to have reduced itself into an atmosphere, rather than a sound. Ten—fifteen minutes now. Every other minute I would twist around and check my brave passenger. She was the same each time: left hand on the back of my seat, right hand to her throat, eyes fixed straight ahead across the cabin.

Midway across, the somewhat safe terrain beyond the south rim of the PDJ was now visible. Still in dangerous isolation but soon to be out. No words. No movement. The constant hum never varying—not wavering, as if the aircraft itself felt the urgency and realized its mission. I twisted around several more times to check my courageous passenger, who was hanging in there; not knowing when or even where she would arrive. Only that she had seen the wounded leave in these loud crazy machines before.

Holy shit! The engine quit! My heart was in my throat! In terror I scanned the engine instruments. *They were okay! The engine was still running!* But absolutely no question about it, I had definitely heard a sudden change in the sound of the engine, or change in the vibration level—*a change in something!* An input had quit. Part of the hum had just suddenly gone quiet! Like when you're in the kitchen and the refrigerator compressor shuts off. You hadn't been aware that it was running, but suddenly you hear the new quietness when it stops. *Something had ceased to emit in this airplane!* I heard it. I whipped around. Her hand was off her throat. Her arms were at her side. Her head was back. She was dead. We were one soul less at that moment, *and I had heard it leave.*

Chapter Twenty-One
A BIG PROBLEM AT BAN HOUIE SAI

Covering the Whole Country

It would have been great if we could have just slept in our own beds every night and flew out of Vientiane every morning, but we couldn't. As mentioned earlier, the country was so big the Company had to establish two "out-stations"—one about 300 miles north, and one about 300 miles south. Pilots would be positioned there for five-day "RON's." (Remain Overnights.) There we'd fly local (150 mile radius) missions for the Customer at that location. It was my turn to fly for the Customer at Ban Houie Sai—the northern outstation, located in "The Golden Triangle" where Laos, Thailand, and Burma meet. (This area was known by the DEA to be populated by hundreds of small, bamboo and sheet metal heroin factories). We'd fly out of a sand bar strip alongside (in) one of the many twists in the wide brown Mekong. We ate the evening meal and slept at a small company-provided shack. It was located outside the tiny village—at the far end of a deserted, pitch black street. (Of course without electricity, at night the whole village was pitch black.) I say "street," actually it was a winding rutted, 10-ft wide dirt path, and the only thoroughfare in the whole village. The house was okay, but no vacation cottage, having its share of mosquitos, small frogs, and luminescent blue geckos. Two to three guys to a room.

The case officer at Ban Houie Sai was far and away the Agency's most notorious character—Tony Poe. He had been with 101st airborne in WWII and a platoon leader in the Korean conflict, and was a callous, battle-hardened military man. Here he was like a battalion commander, supervising about a thousand Hmong troops in their almost daily firefights with the encroaching North Vietnamese soldiers. And listen to this: He wouldn't just accept the word of his soldiers as to how many NVA they had killed; *he made them bring back the right ear of each one they had killed!* One time in his cabin, I noticed a row of Zip-Loc bags pinned high on the walls, circling the entire room, with what looked like dried apricots in them; *only to find out they were the ears!* Another actuality regarding Tony (not a story): one time one of his Hmong soldiers (perhaps with PTSD or just crazy) began firing his rifle at the Air America helicopter that had just dropped him off. The guy was accosted, put in a large burlap bag, thrown in the Mekong, *and then beat to death by his comrades, using big rocks.* One time when Tony went on Home Leave for a month, they sent a young agent up to Houie Sai to take his place. Well Tony had a huge (maybe a five-hundred pound) black pig, that he loved. Not knowing any better this agent fed the pig white bread and it died! The Agency was so afraid of what Tony might do to the guy, they transferred the young guy to somewhere in Africa before Tony got back. (I don't know how he got the information, but Francis Ford Coppola—in his classic Vietnam War movie *Apocalypse Now*, attempted to portray Tony, as the unbalanced colonel living in a cave—played by Marlon Brando.)

Out of Houie Sai, we did a lot of rice drops. So all day long the first two days, that's what I did—twenty times a day. This led to a serious issue. Each time the old rice bags—made of brittle and decaying jute, scraped their way out the bomb bay opening, it would result in the cockpit filling itself with swirling jute fibers. Try as I might—holding my breath (and even using handmade foam masks) I could not avoid inhaling those minuscule filaments. By the third night I was experiencing brutal asthma attacks, usually hitting about nine each night. (And I suspect the ten-year-old blankets and huge dust woolies under the bed didn't help.)

This was before the advent of those neat inhalers, so I had no choice but to take an oral asthma medicine—a prescription pill that I was able to get at a pharmacy in Vientiane. The good news was: even continuing to make the jute bag rice drops at Houie Sai, the pills worked! It let me breathe. No attacks. But the bad news was *it didn't let me sleep.* Couldn't get to sleep until four a.m., which made for a hell of a "rise and shine" at five-thirty! I told the pharmacist who had given me the pills, that while they gave me relief from the asthma attacks, I was awake the rest of the night. He nodded that he well understood, since they were heavy duty amphetamine. *I was taking pure "speed," and flying!* But no worry, he gave me another bottle of pills to counter the insomnia effects. Though I didn't know it at the time, they were a generic 150 mg Seconal (perhaps the most potent sleeping pill ever concocted.) For a period of about six months, each time I pulled "RON" duty at Ban Houie Sai and had to do the associated rice drops in those jute bags, *I was unknowingly taking "uppers" and "downers" at the same time, and flying!* The panic of a bad asthma attack remained sufficiently memorable that it would be ten years before I could linger in a room that had jute padding under the carpeting.

A Short Family Vacation

Even though I didn't have to travel to Bangkok to visit my family, they being here with me now, I still got my 7 days 'Scheduled Time Off' each four to five weeks. Enough time for us to avail ourselves of the discounted travel and take a short vacation. I asked Sara to pick a place that we could get to non-stop from Bangkok. One of her friends had recently been to Malaysia, and spent most their time in a laid-back small city called Kuala Lumpur, and had nothing but good things to say about it. (And it was only a two hour flight from Bangkok.) I don't know how excited the kids were about a trip, but thankfully I was happy to see Sara looking forward to it (a nice break from the not improved ignominious state of being married to me). The kids were fascinated by the hustle bustle of the airports and eager to again be aboard an airliner. Arriving at the airport in Kuala Lumpur (called "KL" by everyone) I was surprised at how small the terminal was; only one room and not big, and the good thing—just about no confusion.

Sara was proud to have done so much work beforehand, having the name of the hotel her friends used, as well as a list of sights, and one special place they visited. Although now KL is a giant, modern, sky-scraper city (with over 60 major hotels), at this time it was completely undiscovered; narrow streets and early 1900 buildings, and only a handful of hotels. We took a taxi to the Majestic Hotel, a white, colonial style edifice, actually built in the late 1800's. Check in went smoothly. In fact we were treated almost like visiting dignitaries. The kids noticed the attention and respect the staff was showing, and I think were impressed at the apparent status of their parents. We were shown to our rooms, one for Sara and I, and one with a large bed and sleep sofa for the kids. We had a great Malaysian-food meal that was quite tasty, minus it being a little too hot for Stacy.

The next day—well, we made a big day of it. First we went to the Kum Lum bird park and saw about every shaped and color form of avian in the world. Donna and Mark may not have been that thrilled with the bird park, but were really into our next stop which was the Batu Caves. They were hard to get to (a steep climb, surprisingly). But it was worth it. Inside were huge limestone stalactites and stalagmites (always forget which is which) that were artfully illuminated by colored lights. Guess what happened for lunch? The kids spied a food cart. Mark started it, "Dad, look! Just like in Bangkok. I'll bet they have the same stuff—that pork on a stick and pineapple, and the other great stuff. Let's just eat lunch here."

Donna who was no coward, having stretched the envelope in Bangkok, and was doing the same thing in Vientiane, was quick to endorse Mike's suggestion. "Yeah mom, and look, there's some benches right behind him. It'll be like a picnic."

Myself, I wasn't sure. I was hungry and I could smell some enticing aromas coming from it. "What do you think Sara, shall we"? She would die before ever disappointing the kids and agreed, *we'd give it a try.* It turned out to be a great idea, not only did we get a smorgasbord of delightful Malaysian specialties, but there was an empty bench only fifty feet away. While the food cart guy didn't sell anything to drink, close by was a guy doing just that. Mark was the first to bring up he wanted something to drink, so I gave him what I thought would be enough "ringgits" including several coins of an unknown value that I had received as change at the bird park. I jokingly told him to get what everyone wanted; and that for me—get a beer. A few minutes later he comes back, looking *real* proud of himself!

"Dad! Look dad, I bought a *beer*—a real beer!" He couldn't believe it; was smiling and shaking his head, and what's more—surprisingly, the beer was a Carlsberg, a very good Danish beer. Now I was smiling. In the afternoon we toured the Sri Maha Mariamman Hindu temple. On it was a high tower, supposedly the tallest thing in town; a "must see" if you visit KL. We spent almost two hours there, and it was something to see. By four-thirty the kids had had enough sight-seeing.

The real vacation started the next morning. We hired a car to take us an hour south to Port Dickinson Beach, which when I say it was a yet undeveloped area, I'm not kidding. (In fact Sara was afraid the driver might be taking us to some remote location for nefarious reasons.) Once out of the city, no one spoke; just sat there watching the passing complete uninhabited landscape (with increasing uneasiness). For the last ten minutes we were on a dirt road that paralleled the beach, but did not pass a single house or commercial building. Not even a clapboard soda stand! When the driver stopped and indicated we had arrived, and were to get out, Sara and the kids were all looking at me with some concern. The driver, seeing our hesitancy, trotted about fifty feet ahead of the car, spread some foliage and pointed at an arrow-shaped sign in the ground, alongside a footpath, indicating the lodgings were in that direction.

The arrival included some initial apprehension, but it was about the best five days any of us had spent. We were lodged in a big thatch-roofed, circular dwelling, on the beach, only about fifty yards from the water line. The temperature was just right, with a soft breeze, and no mosquitos! We spent a lot of time on a blanket on the beach, or in some neat rope hammocks that were strung between the trees just behind our hut. I had a chance to have more frequent and longer conversations with the kids (since I wasn't still reeling from my day's flights. or filled with concern about the ones coming the next day). It ended up being a chance for me to do some bonding with the kids. Unfortunately or fortunately, I had no serious conversation with Sara, about us or our future. One thing I do remember about this vacation: I had just decided to try reading for entertainment, and had picked the book *In Cold Blood* by Truman Capote. At the time, it was the most gripping book I had ever read, and I hated to turn that last page.

When our time was up, as great of a vacation as it had been, we were ready for the quiet and simple life in Vientiane. The trip back was uneventful (which many past trips had not been). It didn't take the kids long to pick up their activities and be right back in the swing of things. Sara and I were right back in the same swing of things.

Saddle, Bareback, Rain or Shine

Well, I'd delayed it two months—almost three, when one of my pilots (living just three doors down from us) up and did it: *He bought his daughter a horse!* You might imagine, enhanced by the level of her enthusiasm, I heard every last detail from Donna, especially how with no trouble at all we could convert the back half of our side yard into a corral. Sara and the other kids wholesomely agreed: a horse would be a fine addition. The outcome was not in doubt. There was no way I could dodge it any longer, we were in the equestrian market. And luck was with us: one of Donna's friend's was tearfully putting her horse up for sale. Her dad's tour at the US Embassy was finished, and the family was rotating back to the states.

Personally, I didn't know squat about how to check the general health (or anything) of such an animal, and we more or less closed the deal on hope. However the transfer wouldn't occur for two weeks, when the family would be leaving Laos. And guess what that gave me the chance to do: build the world's neatest corral and stable west of the China Sea. I bought a bunch of materials from the flea market vendors (no Home Depot or Lowes around), and set about the task with purpose, optimism, and a lot of suggestions from Donna. Holes were dug, concrete was poured, poles were set and railings were artfully installed (inserted like in one of those country split-rail fences). The key project was the stable, which was constructed adjoining the side wall of the garage (allowing the horse's feeding trough to be filled through a chute made in the garage wall.) All was primed and ready when Princess was delivered. I guess it was a proper gift and addition. Every day, as soon as she got home from school Donna was off on Princess, and was gone till dark, and evidently having the time of her life; each night at supper there were all the details of new trails they'd found, and even one small Buddhist temple with monks that they had discovered way back in the woods.

Couple of not-so-good things: One day Donna couldn't get the bridle on Princess. The horse would repeatedly shake its head and dodge. Donna called for my help. I straddled the top rail, entwined my legs about the hefty pole supporting it, wrapped both arms around the horse's neck, grabbed my wrists, and vowed to constrain the animal's head no matter what. Perhaps I shouldn't have said "no matter what" because what occurred was not anything I was anticipating. I once again had one of those 'something's wrong with the world' feelings. True, I had the horse's head pretty much stabilized, but unknown to me this resulted in her nose being pressed against the left side of my waist, and her set of choppers nestled into my "love handles," of which she chose to take a wholesome mouthful!

And if you ever build a stable; alongside a garage is fine, but do not use galvanized metal sheets for the roof. The first torrential rain we had produced such a fierce drumming the horse went berserk and my well-made stable became a pile of wood awaiting reassembly.

Chapter Twenty-Two
MY REPUTATION GETS A CHANCE BOOST

I'd Rather be Lucky Than Good

There was a passable strip located at a Hmong training camp on the south banks of the Mekong, halfway to China. The case officer in charge was a tall, strong, outspoken, bald-headed WWII hero—Burr Smith, who we all referred to as "Mr. Clean" (from the TV commercial). Today I was sent to his site to assist him in whatever he needed; and he did need something. *Boy did he need something!* Just twenty miles from the strip his Hmong troops were trying to hold a position atop a high knoll, which was presently under an aggressive mortar and small arms attack. His troops were running out of ammunition and my mission was to make a quick parachute drop of ammo—not just near it, but *dead center* in this position! And why? His soldiers were crouched in a trench that completely encircled their position. If my drop went outside this trench by even fifty feet, they would not be able to scramble down the side of the knoll to retrieve it without being shot for sure. They could only expose themselves for short dashes *inside* the perimeter. It was imperative I not miss, *and the whole position was only 75 feet across!*

First problem: To facilitate being able to deliver cargo to small targets like this, we would usually skim over at 50 feet of altitude and make an un-parachuted drop. However, Mr. Clean told me there was no way I would be able to do that today. I'd be shot down for sure! He told me to be safe from small arms fire *I would have to do it from at least 3,000 feet above the terrain.*

Second problem: A parachute slowly descending 3,000 feet would not only drift a couple hundred yards, it could drift a mile! To eliminate the lengthy descent, exposure to the wind, and resulting large drift, we used "proximity chutes." These chutes did not open immediately after leaving the aircraft. They free-fell all the way down to about 100 feet above the ground when an explosive charge dangling beneath the chute would hit the ground and cause the chute to open at the last minute. This drastically reduced the descent time and drift error. *But today they were all out of proximity chutes.* I was going to have to use *regular* parachutes; do my best to determine the wind direction and velocity, and with the long descent time, whether it would drift a quarter mile or a half mile! I sadly realized that the position only being 75 feet across at the widest, was going to make this precisely centered airdrop *all but impossible!*

Third problem: On our airdrops we would always have a Hmong kicker on board, who on our command would push the load out. *Today, Mr. Clean himself was going to be my kicker!*

The aircraft was loaded with a pallet of ammo, Mr. Clean arrived and jumped onto the rear fold-down seat, and we were off. The sky was clear blue. The air was clean—even sweet. The ground passing below was a peaceful, unsuspecting verdant mantle. From up here, all was right with the world, though I knew below and ahead of me was raging gunfire, screams and moans. The position was easy to spot; a sandy dirt oval atop a dark green rising knoll. I could see the foxhole surrounding it and the troops in it. Although it was not likely we'd get hit at 3,000 feet above the ground, there was the occasional sound of a round snapping by. (They were trying.) I circled the position searching for any nearby ripples on water or

Hilltop troop position

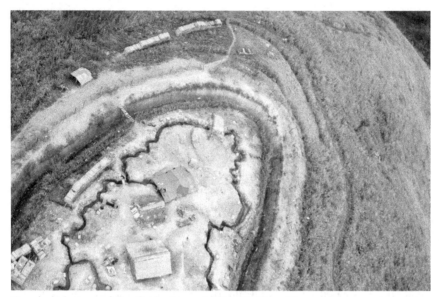

Overhead view of the foxhole encircling the position

drifting smoke to give me an idea of the wind direction and velocity. I spied some smoke; a little far away but enough for an initial calculation. I estimated the wind was from the northeast about ten to fifteen knots.

On my northerly inbound run I was side-stepped so far to the right (for the wind drift) that Mr. Clean began shouting at me that I was way off target. By the time I convinced him of why I was where I was, it was too late to make the drop. I circled and set up another run-in (right where I was the first time). I could hear Mr. Clean mumbling unconvincingly under his breath. Furthermore, because the wind was also somewhat from my *front,* besides being "side-stepped to the right," I would have to fly at least a quarter mile *past* the position before making the drop. I hadn't explained this the first time so had to abort this second attempt while I calmed down Mr. Clean. Another circle. Another run-in, a half mile *right* of the target. Still waiting. Now a quarter mile *past* the target, "Now! Now" I hollered. Surprisingly and thankfully, without objecting, Mr. Clean kicked out the load.

Due to our continuing movement forward and the resulting visual parallax the now opened chute (*with 3,000 feet yet to fall*) appeared to be going to hit way far to the south. Mr. Clean was screaming this to me. Continuing my pattern I did a 180 degree left turn to the south, to set up for my next run-in to the north. As we moved southerly, the changing visual parallax caused the chute to now appear too far to the north. Mr. Clean began screaming this to me. I hollered back to him that while I might miss, I wouldn't miss twice in two different directions! Thank the Lord for small favors. Somehow, in spite of Mr. Clean's running diatribe on how far and which way I was going to miss, the damned load of ammo hit *dead center* in the position!

Mr. Clean was ecstatic as he watched his guys scramble out of the foxhole, retrieve the ammo and get safely back into their protected positions. I have to admit, I was more ecstatic than he was; barely believing the load had miraculously landed dead center. Well at least I *was* feeling ecstatic, but that was before Mr. Clean told me to hurry back to the strip, *we had two more pallets to drop! What!* Somehow and I solely credit good fortune for this, Mr. Clean observed me do the same thing two more times! Probably the luckiest day I ever had in Laos.

Something That Almost Never Happens

While it seems every "screw-up" gets back to the Manager of Flying, rarely do any "well dones" get back to him. A week later I was talking to an Air America operations officer who had recently had lunch with Mr. Clean and our esteemed Manager of Flying, Jim Ryan. He told me Mr. Clean was excitedly describing the accuracy of my airdrops to Jim; raving about the pilot with the wrap-around sun glasses and the silver bracelet. He told Jim if he ever needed to select a pilot for a critical mission, be sure to put that guy at the top of the list! (Thank God again.)

A Near-Death Case of Self Medication

My ability to be intimate with my wife did not improve. The thoughts of my failures to erect and consummate the act, to offer her what I suspected every other wife was experiencing, lived with me—plagued me. Sara and I went on a short vacation in Tokyo. One evening while she was out shopping, I decided to make a quick trip to a Japanese pharmacy; knowing their penchant for weird brews: rhino horn powder, shark fins, and other herbal compounds, I thought they might have something for my situation. I found what appeared to be a well-stocked pharmacy, went in—and half through broken English, pointing at my crotch, and a downward-bent index finger, made my problem known. He supplied me with a small tin of brown pills, nodded affirmatively and smiled knowingly while giving me a "thumbs up".

I GUESS I JUST WASN'T THINKING

Back in Vientiane I was excited about the prospect of possibly—at long last, being able to satisfy Sara—to do it! The first morning before leaving for the airport, I did what the pharmacist had said, popped one or two of the pills, earnestly praying they would bring about a noticeably more successful outcome that evening. The morning's flying went uneventful, minus a leaden overcast, windy conditions and bumpy rides. About noon I was returning to LS20A from a northern location, bouncing along at 7,000 feet of altitude while overflying the 5,000-feet-high rugged mountainous terrain below. About twenty miles from Long Chien, I began to feel odd, not nauseous, but strangely light-headed. A few minutes later I felt a marked weakness beginning to seep through my body; into my arms and *into my hand holding the stick!* I realized I was experiencing sensations that I had never felt before. I terrifyingly suspected this is how one feels *just before passing out!*

Then it happened—my vision! Instead of the normal complete peripheral image, a solid gray began to edge in from the top and sides, exactly as if I was looking through a slowly closing circular opening. It was if I was looking through a smaller and smaller aperture, and frightenly I could feel my grip loosening *and my hand sliding down the stick!* There was no question about it, I was passing out! All alone in this plane, *I was losing consciousness!* The opening not only got smaller, but closed completely! *Eyes wide open but nothing but solid gray*! I could hear the airstream noise increasing and knew I must be picking up speed in a dive, but could see nothing! Surprisingly, in spite of the other indications, I could still think normally, and was aware enough to try some things: take giant inhalations and pull my calves back against the seat edge, as hard as I could. But I could see nothing and knew in another minute (or half minute) I would crash into the terrain rising up to meet me. Mercifully, seconds before that occurred the camera shutter began to open! I foolishly turned my head sideways to aim my one eye through the perfectly round, half inch wide aperture, as if it were something *in front of me*, rather than an interior ocular condition. I was so low *I could see the bark peeling on the branches and the edges of the leaves browning!* I hauled back on the stick! A matter of only one more second and I would not have been here today, writing this. I landed okay, found a place to hide and a reason not be looked for, for about a half hour. I finally came to the conclusion the effects were over and I would not suffer a reoccurrence, so was able to complete the afternoon's work. Needless to say the first thing I did when I got home that evening, was find the small tin, and throw it as far as I could over the back fence. (And in spite of everything, I did try it with Sara that night, but experienced not an iota of improvement.)

The Next Day at Our Out-Station in Southern Laos. Not Too Good

The area surrounding Pakse was considered safe, so no worry when the local case officer asked me to fly him to a nearby strip. (He was just back from a short Home Leave—having taken two weeks off to get married and go on a short honeymoon.) At the strip we boarded an armored personnel carrier that took us to an area closer to where his troops were engaged. (Why I went along is not clear.) We weren't there ten minutes when we heard artillery retorts—from nearby! Seconds later the rounds started impacting; some distance short of us, but working their way toward us. Needless to say we began an all-out dash for the APC. A Lao soldier was first, Denis (the case officer) was second, and I was behind him bringing up the rear. A DK82 rocket (going the same way we were running) passed just overhead me and hit behind Denis. A piece of shrapnel ricocheting straight ahead, struck him in the lower back (with such force he was thrown, tumbling ahead). The Lao soldier and I were able to scoop up his body and cram him into the APC. As the vehicle lurched forward I looked at the wound and saw a gaping hole, in which *a three-inch section of his spinal column* was missing!

Sometime before he went on Home Leave Denis had told me an interesting story: Not sure why he was there, but he said he was at Chappaquiddick the night of Teddy Kennedy's tragic incident: the one in which after his car went off the bridge, he had supposedly dived repeatedly into the dark waters, but was unable to rescue his passenger, Mary Jo Kopechne. Denis said that story was conjured up in the morning when they first realized that Mary Jo was nowhere to be found. When asked, one of the young ladies at the party said that about 10:30, Mary Jo (having had enough of the cigar-smoking, bourbon-swigging men in attendance) exited the house, found the parked Oldsmobile, wrapped herself in a coat and fell asleep on the back seat. Kennedy was actually leaving the party with *another* girl, with whom he easily got out of the car, *never knowing Mary Jo was in the back seat!*

Chapter Twenty-Three
A NOT-SO-TYPICAL DAY

Waking Up. Musing About my Job

5:30 a.m. Getting my uniform on and reflecting on how I'd been sampling what should have been the usual, unusual day—almost every day for just about a year. Wondered how long I could keep flying over those marshy green valleys and rocky gray ridges, all the while knowing them to be infested with North Vietnamese soldiers and Pathet Lao guerrillas. How long would I consider it normal to be taking two to three hits from small arms every week (including one up through the back of my seat cushion)! At almost any time during those days, an engine failure would have put me right in the bushes with the people trying to kill me. (And trying to kill me with perfectly good reason I might add—since all I did everyday was transport arms and ammunition to the people trying to kill them.) True, if I got in contact with one of our helicopter guys on the radio on the way down, he might be able to arrive in time to whisk me out of there before my scalp was nailed to a tree. The statistics probably would show that we only got one out of three crews back alive. And several times when one of our helicopter guys was able to locate a downed US Military pilot the day after he'd bailed out, we found him sitting at the base of a tree, shot in the middle of his forehead.

And Something Becoming an All Too Frequent Event

There was one pilot (like Gar Bogden) that I could never understand how in the hell he got with Air America and out here in Laos: Earl Baxter from Banner Elk, North Carolina; as straight and dedicated a family man as you would ever want to meet. He was an ordained Baptist minister and had no physical or personality traits you would associate with a pilot (especially one like us). His only shortcoming being the lame homespun jokes he would drag out too long, to our respectful laughter. He was here in Vientiane with his wife and two kids, involved in charity work—mostly helping refugees with food, clothing, and how to assimilate into their new city life. I didn't know a single person who could think of a bad thing to say about Earl.

Got to the airport at 6:00 a.m. as usual, but it wasn't at all usual this morning. I wasn't sure what was going on in our little cafeteria, but could tell before I entered, whatever it was it wasn't good. Some pilot's wife was in there—in hysterics, screaming unintelligibly. Jim Ryan and several pilots were doing their best to comfort her. Not long before I understood: She was Earl's wife. He had been piloting one of our large C-130's yesterday, in real bad weather—rain, fog, and low-lying clouds, *and did not return as scheduled.* There was a smaller (also CIA-sponsored) aviation organization alongside us on the ramp: Continental Southeast Services. One of their pilots had radioed in late last night, that he had flown over the wreck of a large cargo plane, not far from Luan Prabang—the royal capital of the country, *and Earl's destination.* With low hanging clouds, there was a narrow cut in a ridgeline that we descended into and squeezed through to get to LP. It was in that cut that the Continental pilot had spied the wreckage. Most likely Earl had been trying to do just that when one of his wingtips failed to clear an outcropping, causing a fatal crash. Mrs. Baxter was given a sedative and escorted out of the cafeteria, but not before a noticeable pall settled on the rest of the pilot group; me included.

Maybe the Worst Morning I Ever Had

Things were really buzzing at Long Chien. It was even more chaotic than usual, and no one was smiling. Evidently the enemy contacts were closer and worse than ever before, and the Hmong soldiers were definitely on the receiving end. Jerry dispatched me to a strip about 30 miles northeast— right on the southeast corner of the PDJ; less than one "click" (1000 yards) south of where a critical confrontation with the NVA had been raging for two days. He told me the case officer there would brief me on my duties; which I was afraid would be evacuating the wounded; shuttling them to the field hospital at LS272, dropping them off, and then rushing back for another load. I'd done that before, and it was a disheartening job. (After these days—back in Vientiane, I wasn't ready for supper, and at the airport they spent half the night cleaning the airplane.)

Luckily I would be coming in from the south and the fire-fight was going on just to the north of the strip, in which case I not only didn't take a hit, I didn't even hear a single round snap by the aircraft. Landed okay—unscathed and not yet shaken. The case officer there was a guy named DuBois, and I saw him running towards me at the end of my roll out, He was inside and up in the cockpit as soon as I had the aircraft turned around. He was dirty and soaked with sweat, was carrying an M-14 (steaming and smelling of hot oil), *and missing all his grenades*. It was a cinch he wasn't more than two minutes from having been right in the middle of it. Moreover he was (for once— almost politely) asking me if I could help him out by making three or four 'special' trips for him. What it was, was something I had not yet done, or at least not done to this scale. It would be hugely different from my usual logistical cargo work.

His troops were retreating and the NVA would soon occupy the terrain where many of the Hmong were lying dead. DuBois and his still able-bodied troops (all those not stuck in critical firing positions) were in the process of gathering the bodies of the dead Hmong, just ahead of the advancing NVA. For morale purposes it was essential that not only did the villagers need to know the body of their deceased brother or father or son was not gathered up and disfigured by the NVA, but that furthermore, the bodies of these dead soldiers *be immediately returned to the villages from which they were recruited* (to be interred with the proper ceremony).

This morning I wouldn't be evacuating the wounded to a field hospital, *I would be filling my aircraft with corpses and delivering them back to their villages!* I was able to do it in three trips, personally—one by one carrying the dead soldiers to my aircraft and stacking them on the cabin floor. To get in as many as possible (and be able to do it in three trips*), on each trip I had to put one soldier in the copilot's seat—right next to me!* While understandably this was macabre and disconcerting to say the very least; presenting the dead soldiers to their waiting family at each village was worse; a scene of wailing and disbelief, with no words exchanged. No one could have been more relieved than I was when the job was done and DuBois released me to return back to 20 Alternate,

The Rest of the Day Didn't Go So Great Either

After landing at Long Chien I was sent to LS 69A, to work for a case officer I had gotten to know and like: Tom Matthews. Today I'd be making air drops, *but without chutes*; just fly by real low (50-100 feet above the ground), pull the drop door handle just before you crossed over the target—usually a slight ridge, and hope the bags would hit right on it. With the aircraft going 120 knots, it's an art: First you had to hit a spot not much bigger than a ping pong table, and second, make the impact angle of the flying bags be such that they hit flat and didn't split open. My first delivery was to a platoon of Hmong soldiers holed up in a cave, halfway down a sheer cliff that continued down another few hundred feet to a heavily wooded gorge. What made this drop next to impossible was that my target—alongside the cave, was a twenty-foot-long ledge *that only stuck out about six feet from the face of the cliff!* I arrived over the spot and saw the soldiers in the opening to the cave, pointing to the adjacent ledge. Unfortunately, after pulling the bomb-bay door handle and watching the string of 8 bags plummet earthward, I was hugely embarrassed to see them miss the ledge by just a couple yards, *and continue their plunge into the tree tops below, spraying rice in every direction.* Even from my altitude I could make out the disheartened expressions on the soldiers' faces. (Had they been Americans I'm sure I would have seen them 'giving me the finger').

Back at the loading dock I was able to fabricate a reason for an extra load, to try again after my first miss. I did, *and missed again.* (This time there was no doubt about the mood of the soldiers.) But I had a plan: I would hold back one bag from each drop the rest of the day, hide it, and after my scheduled drops were finished, gather them all up and drop them where I had missed twice. But I got sabotaged. After dragging away one bag from my first drop, they sent a Laotian kicker with me, to shove the rice bags out with his feet. With him there I couldn't hold back a bag on any of the next seven trips. When the day was over, instead of heading directly back to Vientiane, I gathered up the single bag I had saved and diverted northward to the cliff-side drop zone. I got there, dropped it and scored a direct hit on the ledge! But I can tell you, the soldiers did *not* seem pleased and I could imagine them saying: *one bag!?* I made a "U" turn southward and continued back to Vientiane; my day thusly not a rousing success, in spite of my good intentions.

Would This Save the Day?

Arriving back at Vientiane, I shut down the aircraft, turned in my paper work and started for my car. Another pilot hollered at me that Jim Ryan wanted to see me. *Uh-Oh, what have I done now, or what did I not do?* As mentioned before, Jim was the more than well-respected Manager of Flight Operations, and emphatically, not someone to be fooled with. His word was law! But more importantly, he was a testimony to aviation. Most of us were checked out in one type aircraft (me—the Porter). Some guys were checked out in two types (if they were very similar aircraft). Jim Ryan was checked out in all six types of aircraft parked on our ramp. He could fly them all, and well! Not only that, in his house he had built a small bi-wing aerobatic airplane called the "Pitts," and flew it in airshows at the US Air Force bases in Thailand. And if that wasn't enough to convince you, besides those two accomplishments he was the President of the Vientiane Remote Control Club—flying those small motorized model planes at a big soccer field every Sunday afternoon. Like I said, he was an honor to the profession of aviation. I was hoping whatever it was he wanted to discuss with me, was not going to be confrontational.

"Afternoon Jim."

"Good, Roger. Take a seat."

I did, and waited—a bit nervous to see what kind of conversation would ensue. With Jim, you couldn't read his face; never knew what he was about to say. They were almost the same words as George Calhoun in Saigon: "Are you ready for some more responsibility?"

I didn't answer; having no idea what was coming.

"Ed Starika just handed in his notice. He's going back to Texas."

Ed Starika was the guy who had given me my Captain's Check Ride. Like I had been the Porter Chief Pilot in Saigon, he held that position here. And evidently was quitting (finally, he'd been here forever). "So Jim, if I get you right, you're offering me the position of 'SIP' for the Porters?" (They'd changed the title from "Chief Pilot" to "Senior Instructor Pilot.") You had all the same duties: training, releasing new pilots on their "Captain's Flight Checks," and giving the six-month "Line Checks" to the already-captains. This was a serious flight check and not stress-free for me or the pilot, because if I failed him, he and his family were going back to the states. And this doesn't count the other responsibilities such as breaking up fights and bailing your guys out of jail!

"Geez Jim, I've only been here a little over a year, and skipping over the old hands like K. D. Novak and Smoky Marshall is gonna piss those guys off. But, yeah, I think I can do it."

"Well do you *know* you can do it?"

"I know it."

Jim was never a man of many words. Upon hearing that, he rose, extended his hand, and let me know the meeting was over.

Home, and Things Take Turn for the Worse

Was only thirty minutes late getting home. Thalee had made us a great supper (which all along I had thought was a meat sauce in a casserole dish). She referred to it as "Aubergine," and it would be a year before I found out it was eggplant—not ground meat—strictly "veggie." Of course, tonight, I had her put my portion in the fridge. I might get hungry in the middle of the night, or I could always eat it tomorrow evening. With no TV (or reliable radio) most evenings the family either did projects together, or the kids played in their bedrooms. An hour or so after supper I heard a ruckus and shouting emanating from the boys' room. Rushing in I saw my older son Mark, on top of his younger brother Kevin, and *punching him.* My brother and I had been very close; we never had a cross word, let alone an actual fight. I was thusly greatly disheartened to see this activity among brothers—my own two sons!

Talk about feeling bad: In an effort to interrupt it as soon as possible, I took a big swipe at Mark on top, attempting to knock him off Kevin. Mark must have raised up and looked my way at exactly the wrong time, *because my palm hit him squarely in the mouth!* What's worse, I was wearing a heavy silver ring (made from and old pair of metal pilot's wings), and the bottom of it had struck him on a front tooth. There was no blood, but a small piece of the corner of the tooth was missing. Mark spit it out, put his hand to his mouth, and looked at me with an expression of disbelief, which to this day pains me dearly. Needless to say I barely slept a wink all night—ashamed and belittled by my action (even though it had been a coincidental accident).

The following morning I was scheduled for a test hop in an aircraft that was returning to service after a major overhaul. (It's the most dangerous type of test hop since lots of things can go wrong when they completely re-assemble an aircraft.) However I was glad, since it would only take an hour and a half at best, and I would be able to drive to the American School, *find Mike and extend my heartfelt apologies.* The test flight went as planned and I was in my car bound for the school by 10:30. I parked and started up the expansive grass lawn in front of the school. Far ahead of me—just in front of the school building, I could see a large group of students encircling a raised platform. They were waving their arms, yelling and cheering. As I got closer, I saw one young boy on the platform, apparently shadow boxing to the delight of his schoolmates. As I got closer, I realized, *it was Mark!* And he was saying, "And then my father threw a right, but I blocked it. Then he threw a left and I blocked it. And then….." This was enough for me, Mark was having his fifteen minutes of fame, and we'd talk it over that night.

Chapter Twenty-Four
LLOYD, AND A PERSONAL CONFESSION

Administering a Captain's Line Check

Only had my job a short while before I was scheduled to administer my first Captain's Line Check (the one not designed to release a "new" captain, but to ascertain an "already checked-out" captain was doing the job the way it had to be done). It was going to be with Lloyd Randell, who I had known reasonably well and who I had occasionally spent some off-duty time with. Lloyd was well-liked, but somewhat of a loner; one of the few guys who did not get a house or apartment, choosing rather to live permanently in the Lang Xang Hotel (like Gar Bogden). It was well known that Lloyd had some personality quirks, as perhaps does anyone with Master's degrees in math and physics. While he was reasonably easy going, it was hard to tell him anything; almost whatever it was—he was already well familiar with all its details. Like many other Air America pilots, he was single, but had a shapely live-in companion from the local population. Many of these guys later married oriental women (and interestingly, almost all of them—to this day, are still happily married)! Lloyd's girl was a nice looking young woman and the two stayed pretty much to themselves. Several of their closest friends hinted that a wedding date had been set.

Serious as he was, he could be mischievous as well. Sometime ago he made an engine-out landing and broken his right tibia. The doctor at the embassy clinic set the bone and made the cast (in those days, by wrapping the whole leg in about 15 feet of that white gauze cloth soaked in plaster of Paris). The company was instructed to leave him off the flight schedule for at least six weeks while the bone set. But Lloyd had another problem:

before the broken leg, he and a couple of his college buddies had made plans to meet in Aspen for a week-long ski vacation. And although that week was just three weeks after the broken leg incident, Lloyd was not going to cancel the trip. He went into the shower, drenched the hardened cloth windings (the floor of the shower now apparently covered in milk) and unwrapped the whole 15 feet of gauze! After a week of skiing, he returned to Vientiane, mixed up a batch of plaster of Paris, and re-wrapped his leg! The doctor never suspected anything.

I met Lloyd at the aircraft at quarter to seven. He knew he was up for his Line Check, and was expecting to see me there, knowing I would be riding with him for at least half a day—to make sure he did everything in the most aggressive, efficient, and safe manner. No briefing was necessary, he would go wherever he was directed and do whatever he was instructed, while I just sat there, mouth shut (hopefully) and observed. It didn't start as well as it might have. In those days the instrumentation was primitive—mechanical and analog, rather than the circuit boards and digital "video screens" used in today's cockpits. Air-driven gyros were used to provide the stabilization to the compass in the center of the instrument panel—which gave you your aircraft heading; one of the most referred to instruments in the cockpit. Frequently the airflow would be interrupted or restricted—the result being the gyros stopped spinning fast enough to hold the compass on the correct heading. It would surreptitiously slowly drift from the correct heading.

In this regard, just a week ago I put out a directive saying that when pilots were taxiing out for takeoff on the parallel taxiway (precisely the opposite heading as the runway they would use for takeoff) that they manually set this air-driven compass; and then when they made their 180 turn to position for take-off, check their compass again—*to make sure it had in fact rotated the exact 180 degrees.* If not, they would at least now be aware of the extent of the error, and be on top of it the rest of the day. (Five degrees could be the difference between slipping through a narrow cut in a ridge line or catching a wing like Earl Baxter had done.) Taxiing out, Lloyd not only didn't do this new procedure, he never set the compass to any of the headings we were on. He told me his reasoning: the gyro-driven compass was so unreliable, he not only didn't do this check for precession (error) he never bothered setting it at all! *He just ignored it all day and referred to the "wet" compass.* (The wet compass is your old Boy Scout magnetic disc floating in kerosene in a glass-fronted, non-ferrous case.) In our Porter, like almost every other aircraft, it's mounted on the center metal brace of the windscreen. While this primitive instrument was never *exactly* right, at least it didn't need air or electricity to power it, and had no gears to stick. They are still mounted in today's 767's!

I told Lloyd that if he wanted to pass this check ride, he was going to have to start over again; go back and do the procedure in my directive. Begrudgingly he did, but saying under his breath that as bad as our gyros were, it was a mostly useless drill. Once into our routine at 20 Alternate the rest of the morning went well. Lloyd had no problem with loading the aircraft, man-handling the passengers and cargo, and making a series of challenging landings and take-offs. Unfortunately at one point he mumbled something about *not using the gyro driven compass when he would be flying alone.* Hearing that I told him, "Lloyd, don't be saying shit like that if you want to pass this check ride." And added *anytime a pilot chooses—for whatever reason, not to use one of his flight instruments, the procedure is to cover the face of that instrument, even if with just a round piece of paper.* (If not—in an emergency loss of orientation, a distressed pilot desperately scanning his instruments will not be able to avoid seeing the [uncovered] erroneous indication, and instinctively take action based on that info, which could produce disastrous results!)

The clear day began clouding over about 10, and by 11 there was a low hanging cloud layer, obliterating many of our landmarks, and calling for some timed legs while enveloped in the white, wet clouds (praying to break out before we went into the side of a mountain). Sorta glad it happened, gave me a chance to see Lloyd calculating the times and distances with no reference to the ground. About noon I had convinced myself that in spite of me having to reaffirm to him the correct usage of a key flight instrument, Lloyd was doing a perfectly good job. On one stop for fuel at LS272 I jumped out, gave him a thumbs-up and waved good-bye. Didn't know how long it would take me to get a flight back to Vientiane; hoped not too long. I saw a bunch of pilots clustered around a vending stand operated by an entrepreneurial Hmong villager (who undoubtedly had some physical limitation excluding him from being conscripted). Got myself something steamed and something grilled, that I was able to swallow. Once finished with that I passed the time (in a persistent drizzle) shooting the bull with some of my pilots who were regularly landing and taking off, but unfortunately—not heading back to Vientiane.

The Rest of the Afternoon

About an hour and a half later, after parking his aircraft one of my pilots spied me and knowing I was flying with Lloyd, trots over (more quickly than normal).

"Lima is really pissed at you!" (Lima was the call-sign of our radio operator at Vientiane, to whom every pilot had to call-in a position report every thirty minutes.)

"Pissed at me? Why?"

"You and Lloyd haven't checked in for over an hour."

"Not me. I'm not with Lloyd now. I finished his line check about noon. He's on his own."

It wasn't ten minutes later I noticed a lot of commotion down where the helicopters were parked. One of the pilots comes running up to the Agency dispatcher standing within earshot. I heard him saying he'd just spied a crash site about thirty miles northeast of here, on the south side of a narrow east-west valley, some crumpled white metal at the bottom of a clump of hundred-foot-tall trees. "Could've been a Porter, but looking down through the full canopies I couldn't be sure." *Oh my God, could be Lloyd!* It was he that Lima had said had not checked in for over an hour. At this point I began numbing over with the "what if" premonition.

A search and rescue mission of two Hueys (that's what we called the Bell 204 helicopters) was immediately launched. I was on the first one, 12F, being flown by the guy who had discovered the crash site. With the worsening weather I wasn't sure we'd be able to get to it. It was raining harder and the clouds were now even lower—almost in the tree tops. As a result of some flying that impressed me, we got there, and sadly I could determine that not only was it a Porter, I could make out part of the fuselage markings: 92R, *the one I was flying in with Lloyd.* We lowered the sling, letting down our flight mechanic—the "do-it-all" single crewmember in the back of every helicopter. (And it did take a hundred feet of cable.) He radioed back he needed 6 body bags, everyone was dead: Lloyd and five Hmong soldiers. We radioed for the body bags; got them after about a twenty minute wait, and lowered them to Cliff. He set about putting the bodies in the bags. My chopper pilot radioed him that he had to be back up in ten minutes max, no matter how many he had bagged. The weather was closing in and we might not be able to get out of this valley in another fifteen minutes. We could pick up the bodies in the morning. Ten minutes later Cliff called for us to lower the sling. He was coming up.

The Next Morning

At first light we sent two more helicopters to the crash site to recover the bodies. (One evidently not quite dead was squirming around inside his zipped bag!) They brought Lloyd back to 20Alternate—unbagged. We carried him to my waiting aircraft. I'd fly his body back to our base at Udorn. There we had a clinic, the facilities, and authorities for what would be necessary. I don't know why Lloyd wasn't in a body bag. He was of course—still in his uniform, *without any noticeable injuries*. I laid him on the cabin floor behind the pilot's seat, closed the door, got in the cockpit, started up the engine and taxied out for take-off.

On the way to Udorn I couldn't help but often glance back at Lloyd laying there as if he was just taking a nap. No contorted limbs, no blood; surprisingly his skin was still normally colored. He was wearing his 18 Karat gold "President" Rolex. I considered taking it off him now—for safe-keeping, and holding on to it until it was determined to whom it should go, then discounted the idea. If word got out I'd taken his Rolex it could be misinterpreted. On one of my later glances rearward I noticed that in the center of his forehead there was a deep triangular depression. That "Boy Scout" wet compass mounted on the windscreen brace—that Lloyd said was all he needed to navigate, may well have been what left that dent in his forehead and caused his death. Although it wasn't discovered until later, Lloyd's fiancée was pregnant. And oh, *the Rolex never did show up in his belongings delivered to Vientiane.*

My State of Mind and Marriage

I am not proud of the deteriorating relationship with Sara (in fact feel almost ill when I reflect upon it). It seemed that ever more frequently, things she would say or do were to me not well thought-out, or worse—unnecessary or pointless, and cruelly I didn't hide that impression from her. I shudder now (embarrassed and regretful) when I remember my inappropriate verbal comments. This may have been a sub-conscious effort on my part to widen the gap between us, to make it easier for me to consider a separation (still couldn't say "divorce"). Although she never complained, my inability to perform like I continually and jealously imagined was expected and being done by every other man, I still attributed—at least in the most part, to us having the wrong chemistry; that in spite of not finding the right chemistry in half of Europe, I clung to the hope there *was—still* was, would be, one woman out there—somewhere, who would unlock my manhood, complete me; allow me to shake this dragon and validate my life.

On top of this more than sufficiently damning deficiency I had *another* critical relationship problem. Many associations—and particularly a marriage must be considered permanent (for me, another word for "final")! I have spoken before about first realizing this huge shortcoming of mine: It seems I absolutely cannot do anything—make any commitment which would stamp my life a "closed book." *God knows who or what I thought was waiting for me, or how and why it would be any better than the way of life I would be committing to.* I don't know. I just couldn't! It was a fear so strong I could not overcome it with rationale, or even the shame at having this selfish and possibly psychotic ailment.

Chapter Twenty-Five
OF ALL THE SELFISH, SHAMEFUL THINGS
I'VE EVER DONE

As Best I Can Remember

I'm going to try—really try, to explain this unjustified, abominable act of mine. Our life, living in that nice home in Salakoktane, our domestic situation; our day-to-day activities and amply satisfying Vientiane undertakings left very little to be desired, and I suspect, as a family unit we not only appeared just perfect from a distance, but frankly speaking, were! So what was it, that even as the head of this wonderful family, caused me to be plagued by an ever-present feeling of discontent? I'll tell you what: that damned, marrow-of-the-bones wanderlust; my inability to refrain from almost constant speculation about who or what might be out there for me (without having the slightest idea of what that might be). In fact I think I avoided trying to nail down exactly what it was (besides you know what) that was lacking, or could hope to find to fill the void. In any case, it was sufficient for me to somehow, someway, relay to Sara that I thought a legal separation (avoiding the word divorce) would be an appropriate step.

I can't imagine what she thought upon hearing this. However, she took it in stride—surprisingly to me, without any arguments to the contrary. Perhaps she had long since grown accustomed to my lack of devotion and affection towards her, as most embarrassingly demonstrated by my past infidelities (or attempts to do so, as narrated in Part Two). I spent a large part of one evening explaining to the kids what was transpiring. I thought I was laying it out in a thoughtful and digestible manner, but soon realized *it was a pitiful attempt to justify something that was in fact unjustifiable.* It was an issue beyond understanding by the children. I may as well have been speaking in Chinese; and even more damning—I think my discourse was less intended to make the *kids* feel better, than to make *me* feel better.

The Move and Some Details

The decisions and logistics of the next two months are not accurately recountable. The first decision: where would the family locate was fortunately quickly decided upon. Though they had only been in Hobe Sound a couple months, Sara and the kids had taken to it, living near the beach, and Florida life in general. So that was that. I made a trip there to reconnoiter the area, while Sara stayed in Vientiane, packing and taking care of closing out our affairs. After several days with a realtor I found a highly desirable three bedroom, two bath home on a deep water canal. I knew as soon as I laid eyes on it that Sara and the kids would love it. Got it for only $2,000 down! Our household goods made it from Vientiane to Bangkok, to Miami, to Hobe Sound in six weeks—probably a record. I had the house completely appointed (with all our Southeast Asia furniture) several days before the family flew into West Palm Beach. When Sara walked in she may have well thought she was back in Bangkok or Vientiane. I could do no less. I also bought a new Buick hardtop convertible for her. I remained in town about a week, getting the kids enrolled in school, setting up bank accounts, lining up doctors, and updating the family's new address with a number of institutions and correspondents. Everything had undeservedly gone smoothly. The kids were excited about their new school and new friends and new stateside conveniences (a brand new thing called McDonalds), as well as now living only a five minute walk to the ocean.

While there we contacted an attorney and got the documents establishing us as legally separated. Sara seemed to have no complaints. One reason: Immediately and justifiably beset with guilt, I offered a generous monthly alimony and child support, and not only that; but promised to pay the monthly mortgage payments, the home insurance premiums, the real estate taxes, and any household maintenance necessary. With one caveat: I would do all this for as long as she would need the home—in fact, even if she lived there the rest of her life! Or if it were to occur: until she remarried and chose to leave the home. At that time—whichever caused her to no longer need the home, it would return to me. This would require no new documents since the home had been purchased by me, in my name alone. Her future security guaranteed, she agreed.

My Departure

It was not an easy goodbye. I don't know how to describe the mélange of feelings that overwhelmed me at our parting. The whole family came to the airport. I was a zombie boarding my flight, though I remember looking back at them—*waving to me*. I should have known then that while Sara surely understood, nothing I had said to the kids had registered. I hurried up the steps and into the safety of my aluminum cocoon, unable to bear the site of my handiwork a second longer—much too ashamed. The flights back were uneventful, solely marked by mind-eroding considerations and reproaches; what I had just done; and what the future held for any of us.

Back in Vientiane

I suppose I'd accomplished it; for all practical purposes, I was—at long last, a bachelor! The stage in life I'd missed; the thing I'd longed for repeatedly during my escapades across Europe while based aboard the Forrestal. (Part Two.) In the coming weeks and months we'd see just what I'd make of my new status. Although it was too large for just me, I moved back into the Salakoktane house—now a misfit in a residential area of married couples. A small apartment downtown would be more fitting (plus I was sleeping on the floor).

In all honesty, during the last year and a half—when the family was here in Vientiane with me, while there had been the occasional card or phone call to my wonderful and ever-hopeful June, in spite of a handful of attractive single French ladies living in Vientiane, there had been no attempts, or even thoughts of, any local romantic endeavors. Of course I had enough problems with the physical act in bed with my own wife, I could not think at all optimistically about my success during some covert rendezvous with a stranger.

Though I have to admit in the weeks after my return, I did take notice of one of these young French women, who it seemed each time I saw her, was dressed in the most provocative long-sleeved but skin-tight, see-through blouses (to where you could make out the lace designs on her crimson bra)! She had a cute, short—what I perhaps erroneously referred to as a "shag" haircut, on which she had evidently used an appealing dark red rinse. She was the leading femme fatale in town, and the only source of female association that I could envision possibly occurring. Our cook and housekeeper Thalee was still with me, but understood little of what had transpired—knowing nothing of a "legal separation," or that Sara and the kids weren't coming back.

191

Chapter Twenty-Six
BACK TO THE OLD GRIND

One of the Big Parts of My Job

The morning road trip to the Houie Sai airstrip was a real hassle; seven of us crammed on the ribbed metal floor of an open Land Rover (with no apparent springs). Before we tackled our day, we'd have to endure this dust-smothering, spine-cracking trip. Had to do it with one hand wedged under your butt-bone, and the other holding a handkerchief over your nose and mouth. Today I suspected would just be another day; fifteen to twenty legs, dropping rice and delivering Hmong soldiers to combat areas. *Just let me get through the day, make sure I hit the drop zones, don't have to pick up wounded, and don't bend the plane.*

But I wasn't going to do that today. The customer wanted me (as the Laos Senior Instructor Pilot) to confirm the safety of a new strip that he had not yet been into. Like so many other marginal strips, one guy would find it, land on it (on a clear windless day), and be so proud of surviving it, he'd say *"Yeah, no sweat, piece of cake, open it."* The next guy would fly over it, take one look; recognize its unusual and multiple challenges, and not even attempt a landing. Just fly back to Vientiane and recommend its closure—which is better than trying a landing, blow both tires, knock off the tail wheel, skid over the embankment, scare yourself half to death, maybe get fired (or hurt).

After a thirty minute bumping flight I had it in sight and it didn't look good. As usual it had been hacked out by the local tribesmen using primitive hand tools; and as far as this one was concerned—apparently without much supervision. Once finished, they'd just wait and hope that the barely distinguishable oxcart path they had created would be sufficient to someday coax in a flying machine. Flying machines they had heard were often loaded with rice, cloth, and strange civilized items. Descending to six thousand feet, I exercised the controls, rolling hard from left to right to test the cables and pulleys, stretch the rigging, and get a feel of the sudden control that might be necessary in another few minutes. I adjusted myself in the seat, pressed the rudders with both feet and shrugged my shoulders as high as I could; then caught myself doing something that I was becoming more aware of: In a tense situation I'd close my lips tight, blow full cheeks of air, then suddenly pop my lips apart letting the air escape.

You couldn't take landing at any of these strips for granted; had to examine each one for its particulars. This one was the usual mostly flattened surface on the backbone of an upward sloping ridge. But the ridgeline wasn't straight, so the runway fashioned atop of it, wasn't straight either. *Halfway up it there was a visible bend to the left!* I was becoming less sure by the minute of even trying a landing, but, it did fall into the category of a possibly acceptable STOL strip, and I was the guy to say officially, yea or nay. It was not yet in our site book, so no printed details available. I could see it was a northeast/southwest strip, markedly uphill to the northeast—thus dictating a landing in that direction.

With a strong crosswind from the right, it would shove me to the left during the final approach; what's more, during rollout it would be pushing my tail to the left, resulting in the nose swerving to the right, *exactly opposite to where it should go if I wanted to make that damned bend in the middle.* Lots of our strips had "dog-legs," but this one was ridiculous, it was shaped like a boomerang. And another complexity: that "uphill-ness" I spied at first, wasn't the whole way. The damn thing "humped" in the middle; uphill for the first half, but then levelled. And this hump occurred right where the strip bent, which would make a left turn there, very difficult if not impossible. After hundreds of landings at strips with "dog-legs" you got a feel for just how much bend you could negotiate at the spot where it occurred, and at the speed you'd be doing there. You couldn't just use brakes, you'd also have to use the flight controls; slam rudder and ailerons to try to half 'fly' it around the corner.

Though I had made all the normal checks I still felt as if—for some other reason, this strip was really going to put me to the test. It was there seemingly boasting, *"C'mon in, try me."* I certainly didn't have a feeling of confidence (more worried about my reputation than my life). And, it was one of those gray, low leaden skies, bad-vibes days! The strip was so remote, it was like it was not meant to be messed with; that bringing a new, shiny, modern piece of machinery to rest on it was a violation of its sanctity, and that it would not take to it lightly. I hoped that I wasn't about to do something foolish. (I already knew that undeserved good luck had saved me more times than it should have.)

With just the faults I could see from the air, I could easily have decided the strip was not sufficiently safe to use, and should be closed, *without attempting a landing*. In fact Operations may have already decided not even to put it in the site book. As usual, my first step was to make a low pass right up the runway—get an idea of how much the wind would affect me on final approach, and how much uphill the strip was. Also get a better idea of how radical that bend in the middle was. Plus as always, get a feel for the length. The wind was a battle! The aircraft was buffeting and wanted to roll left as I straightened her out on a final approach. Sixty knots, I'll try that for a fly-by. Half-flaps in case I get sucked down. As I flew over the runway, checking for rocks, tree stumps, and other airplane-snatching traps, I felt that pride that one feels when he or she considers themselves to be uniquely qualified for a very specialized and extremely difficult task; the rush of adrenal when you know you're going to be taxed to the hilt. *And as a STOL pilot in Laos, I was about to be!*

Here—without any help, any input or guidance from anyone, I was going to reap the rewards (or otherwise) of my own decisions and skill. I was completely in charge—at least for the moment, before inertia and centrifugal force would take over. Passing the far end of the runway about thirty feet above it, I eased the nose up and rolled into a not too sharp left bank, putting me out over the "nothingness" (deep valley) that was now under me. The turn to the north had me turning *out* of the 15 to 20 knot wind from the southeast, and could be dangerous. I knew I would lose that much airspeed and start a sink, so came on with power early to avoid it (but still felt the aircraft wanting to fall out beneath me). There's only so long, and for so many reasons you can delay just doing it; matching your skill and letting it all hang out.

Okay, now for real. I turned onto a downwind leg on the north side, at 4,600 ft mean sea level; three hundred feet above the elevation of the strip. I'd be making a left base, into the wind. That'd give me more time, but I'd have to avoid angling. Everything was okay so far; about on a one mile final, flaps two-thirds, speed's right, but a hellacious crab (instead of being pointed down the runway, the nose was cocked at least twenty degrees to the right of the centerline of the strip—something I would have to kick straight before touchdown. If not, a cartwheel would result! I levelled at 4,400 feet—about one-hundred feet above the strip (but five-hundred feet above the base of the valley beneath me). The bend to the left halfway down was getting to look worse. As I got lower the hump in the middle obscured the second half of the strip. The high ground in the middle, now falsely appeared as if it were the end of the strip, hiding the amount of actual rollout distance available beyond it.

Now about a hundred yards out, five seconds from touchdown, fifty feet above the strip. Wow, just like a carrier landing. There was no overrun at the end of the strip, just the precipice of a steep slope. If you went off the end you would be in for a long, tumbling descent. And no leeway as far as the width; not near as wide as the aircraft wingspan. And not only was it narrow, the edges were real hard to discern; crumbling, fading, and blending into the adjacent ground. A guy could easily run off the side and be a candidate for a long, somersaulting tumble; not coming to rest until he was several hundred feet below the strip, wedged upside down between a dead tree and a pile of rocks! I'd seen more than one of my guys like that.

I'd done this before, Lord knows, every kind of strip: the shortest, uphill, downhill, bent to the right, bent to the left, narrow, rutted, completely overgrown, and otherwise unfriendly strips, but for some reason I sensed or feared some hidden pitfall. I pulled off a tad of power, popped the nose down a degree or two, giving away five or ten feet of altitude. Did it again; was sure I was now at touchdown zone elevation; a nice flat approach (which is necessary for an uphill landing). The wind was strong from my right, pushing me to left as I suspected. Speed's good; just right—fifty-two knots. Soon as I got it made I'll drop the rest of the flaps, chop the power and go for it. *Goddam, what a gust!* The aircraft popped to the left like I'd been hit in the side with a giant rubber mallet. The right wing wanted to come up. I threw it back down; crossed the end; chopped the power; held full down right wing and almost full left rudder. *Please God. Please. Down, c'mon down!* I was still floating—about five feet over the brown dirt (and fighting that right crosswind). Gotta get this thing on the ground! Still airborne I eased the power lever about a quarter inch into reverse (a giant "no-no" while still in the air), touched down immediately, and then yanked her into full reverse. The Garrett engine screamed and shuddered. I felt it try to 'swap ends'. Keep the rudder in! Keep it straight! Brakes!

More left! Uh-Oh, here comes the turn. Shit! Gotta get left, full left rudder! Can't use much left wing down because the right crosswind was already trying to lift my right wing and flip me over! Got to keep it down! I hit the brake! Shit, I don't think I'm going to get around it. *I'm not gonna make the bend.* I could feel the left main tire trying to roll under, and the strut was creaking under the strain. *Please God!* Aileron control gone. No longer enough airflow over them. The visibility in front went to hell; reversing the engine had thrown clouds of dust and sand right ahead of me.

I felt it going! I felt the right main wheel skidding, trying to hang onto the crumbling runway edge, then go over it with a hard jolt, throwing me sideways in the cockpit. *Oh God, I'm going to go down the side of the ridge.* In the same split second, the airplane bounded back up, and when my eyeballs locked on, lo and behold, I was back up on the strip—looking right down the second half of it! *Don't know what happened!* Through a windshield streaked with dirt I could make out the rest of the runway, dead in front of me! I got back on the brakes (which I guess I was never off) popped it out of reverse, and brought her to a stop. My legs were shaking, my hands were aching, and my shirt was soaked. But we were motionless, upright, level, and safe. It was over, and I was right-side-up on the runway, at the far northeast end, sitting there with the engine running, like nothing had happened. What the fuck *did* happen? Spun her around and pointed her back down the runway for takeoff, shut her down and sat there a minute to stop shaking. Soon as I could I'd get out, check the aircraft, and walk the strip to inspect its snares firsthand.

Silence. Not a sound. I knew one thing, *I was lucky! Lucky as hell.* I didn't know what had saved me. I knew I'd touched down late, thus having too much speed at the place where the runway bent. (And that it didn't just bend a little, this one bent ten or fifteen degrees!) The problem making the dogleg (left turn) was the right crosswind. The wind against the right side of the large area of the vertical stabilizer (tail) was pushing it left, which forces the nose to the right; *the opposite direction from which I was trying to swing it. Geez!* But what got me back up and on the runway? Gotta take a look. When I thought I'd be able to stand up, I unstrapped and climbed out of the cockpit. Outside the aircraft, much to my surprise (and deep gratitude), I found that neither tire was blown or off the rim. Why, I don't know. They were scarred and scraped, but they were up. Pure luck. I stepped forward to examine the strut, the brace and the housing on the side of the fuselage. No evidence of any cracks. The paint wasn't flaking. No seepage from the bushings. And finally, at the rear of the aircraft, would you believe—the tailwheel was intact. (It's the flimsiest part of the aircraft and usually the first thing to leave the plane on a hard landing.) I don't know how. I know I shouldn't have, but *I had escaped.*

Halfway down the strip I paced off its width; nine steps—about 25 feet wide. Even landing dead center and staying there, I'd only have about seven feet on each side of the wheels before they'd go over the edge. I walked further down the runway—to the threshold, to see where I had touched down. Yeah I'd touched down in the center, but too far down the strip—a good 50 feet from the end. Normally not too bad, but it didn't work here. (For you Frequent Flyers, an airliner usually touches down 1,000 feet from the end. When they touch down too late, it's 2,000 feet down the runway, not 50 feet like here today.) The strip was much higher than the surrounding terrain. Just twenty or so feet short of the landing area, it went almost straight down for two-hundred feet before slightly shallowing out. It was scary just looking down (while standing in loose rock at the edge).

I followed the tire marks from my rollout. I could see where I hit the brakes. I could tell by the increased left tire track width where I had first thrown in left aileron to bring it around the bend. What I also noticed on this walk, that I hadn't noticed before, was that the strip, in addition to being uphill and having a bend in the middle, was also tilted—sloping down to the right side—*away* from the way it curved! No frigging wonder I had trouble making the turn. (I was leaning to the left just to stay upright while walking.) When they'd built this strip, they'd missed the backbone; they'd built it a bit over on the right-side slope. The strip was like one of those theme park "Mystery Houses" (the illusionary attractions where balls appear to roll uphill). This strip was crazy! When I got to where I had slid off the right edge, I saw the spot where the right main gear had scraped about three feet down the incline. And *Bingo!* There, imbedded in the ground was a huge log. It looked like it had been wedged in the ground forever, *angling upward towards the strip.* I could see the black rubberized smear on the gray wood where my tire had hit on the inside edge of it, *and been guided right back up onto the strip like it was on a train track.* If I would've gone off three feet sooner, or three feet later, my tire would've missed the log, and I'd have been on my way down to who knows what fate.

I now felt attached to the strip, and was melancholy about leaving, knowing I'd never be on the ground here again (or anyone else either)!

Poured the power to her, lurched forward and bounded down the packed dirt like I'd done a thousand times. No sweat, no strain. I was away, free, saved. Racing along again, high above the unknown and uncharted browns and grays beneath me. The planet was the same on the way back. It had not been altered or impressed by my experience, but I didn't blame it. One little person, and one little airplane can't make much of a dent anyhow— in all this time and space. And I felt good as new, but also knew I'd been lucky as hell. I had to shake my head, and smile (now). It was the tilt, the damned sideways slope I hadn't picked up on my fly-by. That's what had given me that unsure, incomplete feeling about this site. *I knew that son of a gun had a secret!* You might imagine on my return, I officially declared it never to be opened!

Checking With the Family

At this time and in a country like Laos, international calls were not a piece of cake; you had to go to the cavernous and shadowy, ITT (International Telegraph and Telephone) office. There, you'd stand in line, finally get up to the counter, give the clerk the desired phone number (with country code), and go sit on a hard wooden bench until they called your name, and pointed with some urgency at one of a line of phone booths on the other wall. You'd run over, yank the door open, pull the phone off the cradle, and hope you'd hear it ringing. In spite of this hassle, I'd been back in Laos three weeks and had not yet received a letter (not that I deserved one). I wanted to speak to Sara, find out how things were going, and make sure there were no crises. I was surprised that there were no problems, not even any bumps in the road. She loved the house, the kids loved the house, and especially spending time on the dock behind the house, observing the huge manatees rolling and floating in the canal. School was going great. They had made lots of friends, but Sara said they soon learned not to talk too much about their Southeast Asia adventures, since the other students had never experienced anything like it, and were beginning to think my kids were lying. When I hung up, in spite of the unjustifiable separation in the first place, at least this portion of it was going smoothly. In fact, after he visited her, Sara's younger brother from upstate New York, sold his house, moved down, *and bought a house on the same street as Sara.*

Chapter Twenty-Seven
DANIELLE

A First Date

Been here now—living alone, for a couple months, and didn't know how long this self-arranged, presently boring bachelor life would last. I was anxious to put my search back on a front burner, while at the same time being justifiably worried about my contribution if I would be lucky enough to get a female in the rack. I was only interested in a Caucasian woman. If I wanted her to be American, she would just about have to be a government employee with our embassy. If she weren't going to be American, I have to admit I had continued to keep an eye out for that one French woman I spoke of earlier (the sexy one with the dark red hair and see-through blouses). When I described her to some of my French expatriate friends, they told me her name was Danielle Ricard, and listen to this: adding to her mystique—the whispered rumor was she had supposedly been the wife of the famous French mime, Marcel Marceau! Due to the particulars of French law, in the divorce she lost custody of their son. Shortly after that she was hospitalized with a nervous breakdown (or suicide attempt), and when released chose to flee the country. (Sounds like the kind of woman you would imagine me picking.)

Upon further inquiry I learned she worked for a big French insurance company whose offices were on Samsenthai Road—the narrow, hundred-yard-long quaint main street in town. Knowing where she worked, I began acting like just another window-shopper, but with an ulterior motive: at lunch time I'd position myself near the entrance of her office. One day it worked. She passed right by me as she was exiting. I was proud of myself for finding the nerve to nod a hello and flash the best a smile I could. Almost stopping me in my tracks, *she* flashed back a ready smile and replied something that sounded real sweet (in French); to my way of thinking—more than would have been necessary. Just *maybe* a connection had been made!

One day—not on the flight schedule and with no reason not to (although the decision was only reached after an hour of debating it) I decided to risk approaching her directly; a face-to-face meeting. I groomed myself as best I could and put on the most Continental-looking clothes I owned. I paused for a minute under the sign that read *Compagnie Francaise d'Assurance pour le Commerce Exterier.* A moment more, a deep breath, and—hardly believing I was doing it, I strode in. Scanning the large office I spied her at a desk in the far rear, and she had evidently seen me walk in, because she was looking straight at me! Thank God for small favors; her countenance at first quizzical, quickly changed to a welcoming and to me—a seemingly pleased expression, almost inviting me to continue towards her, which I did.

I introduced myself, and discovered that while the majority of the French men I knew spoke almost perfect English, Danielle was in the throes of just learning it. Our conversation therefore was difficult to say the least. Plus I was at a disadvantage being dismantled taking in her sensuality! It exuded from her—everywhere, especially from her giant green eyes (which I could only look away from when distracted by the expanse of smooth white skin exposed above her deeply cut neckline). The feelings I was experiencing gave me reason to hope, that the aura of this lithesome, foreign creature, might—just might be, what I had been waiting and praying for, for years; *the woman who would unlock my manhood.* Thinking about that (as I was right now, combined with the fear of yet another failure) produced an awkward silence in the midst of my already disjointed comments. However, I *was* able to arrange a dinner date the following night; my first date as a bachelor, and with an alluring French woman. Exalted, I was singing at the top of my lungs as I drove home. What would lie ahead of me?

The next day couldn't have passed quickly enough. (And thankfully I had an easy day of flight ops). I once again groomed myself as best I could and outfitted myself with my next best European-looking clothes (having already worn my best stuff to set up the date). She gave me instructions where to pick her up. Part of her employment benefits was her company affording her a place to live. They owned the building she worked in and gave her a tiny (miniscule) one-room apartment on the third floor of that building. It contained only the bare essentials. She was a little embarrassed about it but I commented on all the positive things (without mentioning the pea-green walls). Soon enough we were on our way to the Settha Palace hotel. It was the second-best hotel in town, after the Lang Xang, and one of only four hotels in town. The other two not having any facilities that would merit them being selected for a first date (or even staying overnight)! The Settha Palace had a small dining room and a lounge which was occasionally graced with music by some travelling Filipino band. Of course the conversation was stilted—barely adequate. Since she was on a project to learn English, it was not an opportunity for me to begin learning French. She wanted to speak English. To hold up my side of the bargain, I bought a book titled "Learn French in Thirty Days." So my nightly before-turning-out-the-light, foreign language sessions now expanded from just Spanish, to include French!

One thing I did learn from her: me being only 5' 8" was a surprise to her French friends who could thusly not refer to me as a "One-Eighty-five," which they did for Americans. (1.85 meters being the height of a six-foot tall person.) The meal was just fine, and afterwards we paid a visit to the lounge where we had a *digestif* (French for an after-dinner liqueur) and listened to some music. Not wanting to press my luck, things so far having gone as well as I could have hoped, I thought it wise to quit while I was ahead; make it a short evening and return her to her apartment. After a few awkward moments on the sidewalk, she somehow conveyed to me that I could escort her up to her room (which of course had me shaking in my boots). *Was she going to invite me to spend the night?!* At the moment, I certainly didn't feel ready. I was actually relieved when we parted at the doorway. But our parting was not without a goodnight embrace that included a longer than necessary kiss. And (thank God) I think it *did* cause me to be aware of some not great, but slightly arousing sensations—just a bit of heaviness beginning to occur where I would perhaps one day soon need it. Real or not, this caused me to hope that this 'chemistry thing' may hold water, and this could be the beginning of something with a potential to justify my male existence.

Hope at Last

A second, and a third date rapidly followed; the third consisting of me inviting her to a homemade dinner at my house in Salakoktane. Danielle's presence (in *Sara's* house) was enough of a shock to my housekeeper Thalee, that she was gone for good the next morning. In any case I prepared the meal and bought the wine, and learned something else from Danielle: true French people do not like sweet wine; the dryer—the less sugar, the better. I thought I was going to have a real treat for her by buying an American favorite—Mateuse Rosé, *which unfortunately was just about the sweetest wine you can get!*

The evening was a gamble. It would play out just twenty feet from a bedroom, with a recently purchased queen-size bed. *This could well be the night.* This could well be a "Eureka" moment… or another devastating disappointment (and in this case—with the international overtone and her undoubted anticipation, a huge embarrassment)! *I think a valium would have helped.* And true enough, about ten, after girding myself (and loosening Danielle up) with a couple glasses of Sandeman Porto, I found myself escorting her into the bedroom. There, she went into the bathroom to disrobe and freshen up, while I did the same in the bedroom (as well as while praying to the gods of love-making, exhorting them to gift me with—if only this once, an erection capable of penetration). When she came out naked, I couldn't help notice the thick expanse of hair on her mons pubis. She saw me looking and volunteered, "Yes, I have much hairs." (Not realizing the word "hair" is both singular and plural.)

As she approached me—but was still three or four feet away, I again began to feel something different, not what I'd hoped for, but encouraging! (Just as I imagined what I would have felt could I have stood close to that young, succulent, red-headed new bride I saw on the dock in the Bahamas, or that skinny, big-eyed, rock band singer with waist length hair I saw in the Wichita airport.) Now I was becoming even more convinced there could be something to this 'chemistry' thing. It was not too awkward getting into the bed, and I started by kissing her in as devoted a way as I could—honorably, her lips and eyelids; and then began more daring manipulative foreplay (in my case, more necessary to excite *myself* than the woman—though it rarely worked). And Holy Christ, it may have been happening. I think I may be getting firm. She wasn't doing anything special, not moving in any seductive way, or touching me in any manner to arouse me. It was a result of her persona—her close physical presence—that aura! *I was going to be able to do it.* And I did, no matter how lackluster; it constituted a breakthrough for me. Though I'll admit it well could have been no more than the legal claim: *"Penetration, however slight, constitutes the act."* Still, it happened with a minimum of my usual pleas to the Gods of love-making. For the first time in my life I believed there might be a chance. I couldn't help thinking that "chemistry" thing was responsible, and hoping against hope that it would not be a one-time fluke; that I would be able to have a repeat performance.

As a result of my weak erection (and resultant inhibited motion) I'm not sure if she climaxed, although afterwards she did mumble some French words, that although perhaps wishful thinking on my part, sounded as if she was commenting on a pleasant experience. (If so, she would be only the third out of fifty females to have sampled me and felt so.)

It was not long before I moved out of the house in Salakoktane, found and rented a large second-story (modern) apartment in town, and… as you might have guessed, before long invited Danielle to move in. We did everything together, although rarely were the outings without misunderstandings or disagreements (completely different mindsets). I'm sure, the sole factor that kept me with Danielle, was my long sought-after feeling of being able to "be a man" when it counted. *I was doing it!* At least I was doing it. Even achieving only 3 hits out of 5 'at bats' (and no line drives), I was doing it. As long as I was sexual partners with Danielle, *I could at last deny complete impotence!* I could see it was going to be very difficult to give this up. How could I leave this woman, return to the search, and perhaps again find myself with *zero* capability!" I was marooned in this relationship.

Our landlord was the Fiat dealer in town, and I ended up buying a baby blue Fiat sports car—which although here in the states we know it is definitely not the top of the line, in Vientiane cruising Samsenthai Road with the top down still hinted that Danielle and I belonged to the privileged few.

I would like to say our life was easy and comfortable, but it wasn't. While I was grateful as hell my performance in the rack held up at least passably (me continually thanking the gods of love-making and promising them all sorts of recompense), there were a couple problems living together. Probably the most serious: I wasn't as financially generous as I could have been with Danielle. In fact I was a real cheapskate. I don't think I ever gave her "knock around" money in excess of twenty, or maybe once in a while— fifty dollars-worth of Lao kip. I didn't realize it then, but all the French and Lao and Thai and Chinese women who had landed American men; when they weren't playing MahJong must have spent the bulk of their time bragging about the devotion of their man—the uncontestable proof of which was his financial generosity. This was the key determinant of how desirable they were and how much he loved them. On this score, Danielle—with a not-bulging wallet was unable to demonstrate any such devotion from me. She had one perk (in addition to the modern apartment and the baby blue convertible) that she could wave in front of her lady friends: We were to go on several fine vacations; a couple times to Paris. This helped.

Regarding my modest but present capabilities in the rack, I now think—after years of experimenting, there was another aspect that aided me: knowing in just a few moments I would get to see and feel Danielle's apparent intense enjoyment of and unrestrained exclamations during the act. I think her spirited responses were not so much because of my actions, but because of heightened sensibilities provoked by a fragile and volatile mentality. I had not only seen this volatility on other occasions, but found out from a friend of hers that the hospital stay after the custody battle with her husband, Marcel, in France was because she *did* attempt to commit suicide. From what I've seen and heard, it may be possible that a woman with a background of trauma, or one with a bipolar condition , may have a unique need for sex—be more demonstrative, and reach unusually heightened orgasms. Of course this cannot help but raise the level of the gentleman's arousal (in this case perhaps having been half of what made mine possible).

One thing that caused me (deserved) discomfort, she would often ask me what my (our) long term plans were. I personally (as usual) had not brought myself to think that far ahead; in fact had no idea what employment I might secure, or where, after the end of this Southeast Asia adventure (which someday—perhaps soon, would be ending). I *should* have been thinking about that very thing. I often heard my pilot friends saying how much money they had put away, and I was stymied at the sizes of the amounts being bandied about. I had almost nothing put away, but of course half my salary was going to Sara and the kids (and I was spending all the rest). The Vietnam War wasn't going to last forever. Being so unsure I don't think I ever considered the possibility of Danielle and me settling down—in the states or France, or anywhere. I could think of no type of work I would be able to do that would provide the same kind of lifestyle we were now enjoying. Being in my thirties and with a one-eyed pilot's license—unfortunately the airlines were out. One day in our apartment, discussing this very subject she got up, grabbed a piece of paper, and told me she didn't care when it would be, but just write down a date when we would get married! Couldn't do it—at least at first, then (not knowing what I might have been thinking) wrote down her birthday (about ten months away). Not sure this was convincing. Not sure why she stayed with me. I think as far as she was concerned, it was a lot more security, and perhaps status, in that she had landed an American. Much more on Danielle later.

Chapter Twenty-Eight
REALLY LOST BUT LUCKY AS HELL, AND RON AGAIN

The Smoky Season

I was on my way up to work for Mr. Clean, at nine thousand feet and couldn't see anything in any direction; just banging and thumping along in hot brown clouds. From time to time I'd get a good scare when a piece of charred debris as big as a telephone book rocketed by the aircraft. I don't remember it being this bad last year. *You ask: What am I talking about?* I'll tell you what—the "Smoky Season"! Each spring half the population of Southeast Asia burned off any of their previous year's crops, and in fact any bordering foliage they could get to; each year the same thing at the same time. We're talking ten times worse than your nastiest LA haze. The smoke obscured everything in sight, enveloping the earth. Even on the ground—day and night, the strong acrid smell of smoke filled your nostrils. You couldn't see the sun except maybe at high noon, staring right at where it should be you might make out a faint outline. And it could be this way for six weeks! The smoky season was much worse than the monsoon (rainy season) which while it had towering cumulonimbus clouds, torrential rains, thunder and lightning; you could always circumnavigate them. If one happened to be over your destination when you arrived, it would be just a matter of minutes till it blew past. The unique challenge of the smoky season accentuated the excitement we had just being out here. We had willfully abandoned civilization, traveled here to a largely unknown and primitive land, to live an unregulated life, engaged in a largely unpublished secret war.

The smoke rose to well over fifteen-thousand feet. Its base was ceiling-like at about five hundred feet above the ground. Almost immediately after takeoff your forward visibility dropped to almost zero. You were surrounded by and immersed in a thick brown, smelly world; couldn't see fifty feet in front of the airplane. There would be absolutely no visual clues, so all aircraft maneuvering had to be done using your flight instruments. And here's the worst part, not only do you have no forward visibility you have no visual reference down. With no terrain features to navigate by, getting from point A to pointy B is a big problem (and sometimes impossible). In Laos there were no radio beacons or electronic aids to assist you in navigating (and this of course was a long time before GPS). During February and March we spent half of every day lost, trying like hell to find out where we were, and if lost, *could we find our way back to where we took off!*

All navigation was done by flying 'headings plus times'. That meant first figuring out the true heading of your intended route on each leg, factoring in your best guess of the direction and velocity of the wind, and how much it would drift you off course, decide on a crab angle, and finally—calculate the headings you would fly. But that's only the half of it. You had to know the exact distance of each leg, divide it by your anticipated ground speed (the miles per minute you'd actually cover), and come up with a precise number of minutes (and seconds) for each leg. Soon as you were on the heading you'd click your stop watch (mine hung around my neck). When the time on the last leg was up you'd dive down out of the smoke, into that thin layer of clear air near the ground, praying to see the valley floor a safe distance below you (rather than dirt and rocks rushing up to meet you and end your life).

My Day With Mr.Clean

No parachute drops this time. Probably good, since I'd never be able to repeat that hugely lucky performance I had with him a few months ago. I was going to bring ammo and water and the usual stuff to a small strip about 70 miles southeast of here. The smoke was as thick as I'd ever seen it. I'd be immersed in it with no chance to catch even a glimpse of the ground. I'd have to use that 'headings plus times' method to get to the intended point of landing; fly an exact heading for each of the legs, at an exact speed, for a precise time. As I suspected, visual contact with the ground disappeared ten seconds after lift-off. The last thing I saw was the hedgerow at the end of the strip. I was immediately inside a tan cotton womb. The best way to get to my destination was to fly in two valleys; the first ran east until it intersected with a valley that ran south; at the end of that second valley was my strip. And if everything was exactly as I had calculated, when the time for the last leg was up I'd be overhead my destination. Even if I *was* over it, I wouldn't be able to look down and see it. I'd just be *hoping* it was directly below me. I'd say a short prayer and start my spiral down through the smoke. I would make this descent knowing that when I broke into clear air, I'd either find myself rewarded by a patch of terrain still a few hundred feet below me, or become a statistic impaled in the Laotian countryside. The latter ending could be as a result of calculating a heading that was off by only a couple degrees, or making a fifteen second error in computing the flight time. Northern Laos is decorated with compacted silver and blue aluminum—like ornaments on a Christmas tree. Instead of breaking out at a safe altitude, their pilots had a stunning black curtain slammed across their existence.

The Actual Trip

I flew the first 31 mile eastbound leg for 15 minutes and 30 seconds, which should put me over the intersecting southerly valley. *How did I come up with 15 minutes and 30 seconds?* Well at 120 knots (two miles a minute) it would take me exactly that long to cover 31 miles. When the time for that leg was up (still seeing nothing outside the airplane) I started the second leg by turning right to 180 degrees (due south). This second valley was 40 miles long. I calculated my time to be 21 minutes and fifteen seconds, since the wind was almost right on my nose, slowing my speed over the ground. I was still on "solid instruments" in soupy dense smoke—zero visibility. Now here's the part that petrifies most pilots and air traffic controllers: the route I had chosen and the altitude I was flying, gave me plenty of clearance over the valleys, *if I was really over them.* But unseen and only a couple miles to both sides of this route was higher terrain—ridgelines 500 to a 1000 feet *above* my flight level. This type of flying is unheard of anywhere (except maybe by Alaskan bush pilots). A slight miscalculation of heading or airspeed could have me flying full speed into what we call a "granite" cloud.

My second timed leg was up, so I should be over my destination. *Please God.* Hopefully, with teeth clenched, I started a spiraling let down, praying to the gods of aviation that I was over a valley, and better yet— when I broke out, be in sight of my destination strip. The good news was *I broke out at about 500 feet above the ground.* The bad news was *I didn't recognize anything!* I was in a valley—maybe even the right valley, but if so—short of or past my strip. Nothing looked familiar. *Shit!* No runway of any size or shape in sight. My speed calculations or wind drift must have been wrong (but thank God not wrong enough to cause me to crash into the higher ground on each side of my route). I had no choice. I had to go back to the strip I had launched from, and try the same thing all over again (just use different headings and speed). Then it hit me: *"Roger you dumb shit, if you aren't where you think you are now, how in the hell are you going to backtrack your way to where you took off from!"* Wow, I was in a pickle! *Really* lost. What in the hell am I going to do?

Reorienting Myself

I had an idea: I knew Mr. Clean's strip was alongside the east/west running Mekong; just a hundred feet from its south bank. Okay; based on the headings I flew to get here (wherever the hell I was) one thing was for sure: I *had* to have positioned myself quite a distance *south* of the Mekong River—no way not to be south of it. So I'll fly north, just high enough to clear the ridges, but not so far up into the smoke that I won't be able to make out the wide Mekong when I came to it. When I was overhead the river I'd just turn left and fly west—centered over it, until in ten or fifteen minutes I would see Mr. Clean's strip on its south bank.

I commenced the first leg—the northerly one bound for the Mekong. But after twenty minutes, *no Mekong was showing up.* I did it longer, and according to my calculations—too damned long. The Mekong couldn't be *this* far north. I should have been to it by now! Then a terrifying thought hit me: *Holy Shit, I may have already crossed it without seeing it pass under me, and now I'm in China!* And not only in China, but over where they were building a highway that was continually protected by trucks mounted with anti-aircraft guns. Panicked and just as I was about to reverse course to the south (and granted: still be lost, but at least be lost over safer terrain) *there it was! Thank God.* The Mekong was under me. If I hadn't have been staring straight down right then, I would have missed it.

Navigating by One Bank of the Mekong

I made a hard left turn westward over the middle of the river and descended to about fifty feet above the fast-flowing muddy water. In this area the river ran in a deep gorge, bordered by 100-foot-high, cliffs on both sides (substantially above my flight level). My plan was this: During certain stretches the river would make unique bends. By checking these bends against my map, I should be able to identify exactly where I was on the map, and thus be able to begin looking for Mr. Clean's strip on the south bank—which I figured to be about twenty-five miles ahead of me on the left. One problem: the sky was brown, the cliff walls on each side of the river were brown, and the water itself was brown. The only way I could keep visual track of the bends in the river, was by keeping my eyes on a contrasting five-foot-high bleached white band on the left-side cliff wall, just above the present water level. (The dry season had caused the water level to drop, leaving this white band.) This was the only thing of a dissimilar color I could use, and even it was not that easy to keep in sight. And since I was below the heights of the cliff walls, it was imperative that I stayed over the middle of the river. My wingspan was 49 feet and the gorge opening couldn't have been more than 150 feet across. If I didn't stay dead center over the river I could easily catch a wing on one of the cliffs, resulting in a metal-rending fatal crash.

As I said, tracking the white band was *not* easy! My forehead was pressed against the acrylic windscreen and I was squinting hard with my good eye to keep it in sight. But trouble! My map showed the river making *a sharp jog to the left*, but as best I could see—the white band *was still going straight*. That didn't make sense. *Then I discovered why!* Somehow in the last minute or so, the barely visible white band had been overlaid by a reflection in the windscreen—*of the bottom half inch of my white t-shirt sleeve!* I was navigating by my t-shirt! Having lost my reference point I now had no idea where I was, *but not likely in the middle of the river*. Full power! Climb! Pray to God that (through no skill on my part) I'm still some yards from the cliff walls on either side! I must have been. Escaped! Got out of there. Continued westbound and ten minutes later, saw the strip! Landed—soaked with sweat and calves shaking. Whew. Talk about lucky. My wingtips may have missed the sides of the cliff by ten feet, *or two inches!*

Ron's Back!

You must remember him: On my first try to return to Air America after the cornea transplant, I had to spend the night in Los Angeles, and got the (bad) idea to visit my friend and furloughed Air America pilot, Ron Wogman. As the master salesman he was, he talked me into joining him in that nausea-producing "pyramid sales" scheme. Well lo and behold, who do

I see walking down the street in Vientiane but Ron Wogman! *The company had called him back.* In spite of his flight duties, it wasn't long before Ron's entrepreneurial spirit was re-ignited on an "STO" he took to Spain.

Most travelers are familiar with the southern coast of Spain, and especially the glittering holiday destinations of Malaga and Torremolinos (on the famous Costa-del-Sol). But somehow Ron found himself touring the rarely visited, undiscovered southeast corner of Spain; a more native and private area of Spain. He was booked in a small (the only) hotel in the town of Salobreña; a white-washed village with an old Moorish castle, perched atop a high hill, only about a mile from the shoreline. At the foot of this high ground and all the way to the pebbled beach had been a couple hundred acres of sugar plantations. Ron had a chance meeting with the owner of those plantations, who told him the family had recently plowed the cane under and were in the throes of *building the most unique seaside condominium development in Spain!* And guess what: he needed an English-speaking sales-oriented person to head up a global marketing program. I don't need to tell you Ron quickly convinced him that he was their guy!

The gentleman said that they had dismantled almost a whole village halfway between Granada and Seville, trucking all the original building materials: wrought iron railings, heavy oak doors, floor tiles, shutters, etched glass windows—everything, down to Salobreña, to use in building the condos. The finished product would be called *Playa Granada* and appear to be an old Andalusian village! The architecture was such that while it was only going to be three stories, there were actually ten small, but varying floor-levels, and every unit had a different floor plan. It did sound like a great location and a unique project. As Ron had done before, he talked me into agreeing to join him in a plan to market the condos to American, British, and other European individuals living here in the Far East. Ron told me he had already proposed this idea to the owners, and worked out a great commission rate, and that I had to travel there and see it for myself—as soon as possible.

Interesting News From the Home Front

Gratifyingly to me, while of course I always sent the kids birthday cards or cards on the holidays, as well as occasional gifts, I probably did not write enough serious letters to them. In spite of this—gratifyingly to me, they wrote to me as often or more often that I could expect. In one of Donna's letters, she mentioned that mom had met a really nice guy, an Air Force Major, and they had even gone out to a couple movies together. Of course I had no reason to be jealous, and of course wasn't, in fact, felt somewhat relieved at this. (Perhaps even welcoming it.)

Chapter Twenty-Nine
THE EERIEST FLIGHT I EVER MADE,
AND A TRIP TO SPAIN

My Briefing

It was my turn in the barrel again; a five night RON up at Ban Houie Sai. And this time it would include something new and different—*really* different. I had my asthma medicine and my sleeping pills with me, but I wasn't going to need them. There'd be no rice dropping this time, so I wouldn't be inhaling lungfuls of jute fibers. Tony had something else for me and it would be a trip like no other I had while flying in Laos. He told me he had some special cargo for me to take to a strip up north. (I couldn't imagine how far north, because we already were about as far north in Laos as you can get before entering Burma or China.) He had a couple—I guess agency personnel that I had never seen before, load (gingerly) six specially made, unmarked crates onto my Porter. They didn't even say "How ya doing;" just went about their business.

Tony called me inside his hooch where he gave me the coordinates of my destination: 23.50 north and 101.30 east; *well over a hundred miles into China!* These coordinates were so far north, they were only an inch below the top edge of my map. (If the strip would have been ten miles further north, I wouldn't have had map coverage of it.) I had never heard another pilot mention having gone up there, or that the Customer even had any operations there. None of we pilots would ever question Tony, but I think after I saw the coordinates, my glance up to him did not hide my wonderment. He couldn't have missed it but made no comment. Fortunately I was just smart enough not to ask any questions. I used my red "Sharpie" pen to circle the coordinates on my map. He gave me one main VHF frequency and another backup frequency to use to establish contact when I got there, as well as a call sign to use and an affirmation code. Obviously this strip was not going to be in our Laos site book, so I'd have no advance details about the strip (length, elevation, etc.). I'd have to get there and find it by comparing the actual terrain—valleys, streams, peaks and ridges, to the features shown on the map. On a map, concentric circular lines—called "contour lines," indicate rising elevation. The more and closer together the lines were, the higher and steeper the hills or peaks were, and according to the contour lines around the coordinates he gave me, this friggin strip was the top of the world! Tony got up and left the cabin, letting me know I had received all the info I was going to get, and should make like the Nike slogan and *Just Do it!*

And What Kind of Day Was It?

To make matters worse, it was *not* a pleasant day! No blue sky anywhere; a leaden gray overcast from horizon to horizon. Sort of a "You and Me Against the World" day; a weird, blustering, low atmospheric pressure, not user-friendly day. Made you feel "antsy." I later heard that in Europe, these kinds of days are called "foehns" (or something like that). In Switzerland, they discovered that when this weather condition was present, the citizenry was more depressed and the suicide rate jumped way up. (In fact, doctors there began opting out of performing any critical surgery when this type of weather condition existed.)

Embarking

I drew a long line from Houie Sai to the strip location, then custom-folded the map so as to display a two-mile expanse on each side of the intended route. Once in the cockpit I used a small alligator clamp to attach the map to the trouser leg on top of my right thigh. This way—navigating northward I could continually glance down at it to confirm that *the terrain features I was passing over aligned with those on the route line I'd drawn on the map.* Surprisingly the guys who loaded the cargo didn't tie it down. On takeoff the boxes slid at least a foot rearward, which as heavy as they appeared to have been, could have put me out of "center of gravity" limits. When aircraft are manufactured and flight tested they only do it within the CG envelope. (Safe control and flight characteristics are *not* guaranteed if you are out of the CG limits.) As soon as I was airborne I felt that familiar and welcome jolt of newness and waiting adventure. I'd "slipped the surly bonds." And thankfully, in spite of the new cargo positioning, the handling characteristics were normal.

Enroute

Upon levelling off I pried open the side windscreen porthole, wedged my hand into the buffeting air flow, and deflected a cold blast into my face. Keep on trucking. Do whatever the Customer wants (just "don't bend the metal"). I was racing along now at eight thousand feet, just a couple hundred feet below the ragged gray stratus clouds—safe in my own aluminum capsule, in my own private, pewter-colored world, untracked by the rest of humanity. While I felt invigorated and special, I was also more apprehensive than usual; *never did this before*. Forty-five minutes north I was able to scan a thousand miles of uncharted topography, virtually untouched since time began. As far as the eye could see, there were no cities, no towns, no buildings, no roads, no power lines, no bridges, not the slightest indication of civilization—nothing; just a million acres of dense canopy. Today, because of the overcast the landscape had lost its green and given way to a washed-out grayish brown; below me the shell of the oyster, above me the gray-white of the pearl. Here I was in my modern flying machine, whirring overhead a zillion never-seen nooks and crannies; of daily use and value I guess to some creatures, but perhaps never visited by Homo sapiens. I was out of radio contact with Houie Sai, but no big deal; in fact it added to the mystique—to the exciting feeling of abandonment. Even with full squelch (reception) on my receiver I could only occasionally hear bits of transmissions from airliners—somewhere. I just kept droning northward.

An hour; more than halfway. I was on my own, almost in another age. If there were other people on the planet, other places, cities and such, there was no way to tell that, or ever suspect it from here. I felt as if I was in a time warp at this remote spot. (If a pterodactyl had flown by I wouldn't have been surprised.) No government regulated this area— national or local. Probably no one was even here to care. No one living here knew of any international borders or boundaries. While we see them printed on maps, on the ground none were marked anywhere in any way. From the air it continued to be a non-stop endless expanse of tree tops. Sure, I worked for Air America, but the company wasn't involved now. No one was controlling me, no one watching or even having the slightest idea where I was, or if I was dead or alive. I was my own boss for sure, and unfortunately, before long I would have every chance to see just how much in control I was. An hour and forty now—deep into Red China. Getting close. *Whew*. And let me tell you one thing that was on my mind: Not being a uniformed member of any branch of our country's military services, if I went down, the rules in the Geneva Convention about the treatment of military prisoners would not apply to me! I'd be declared a mercenary and that's a war crime *punishable by death*.

Arriving

According to the map, I was at a spot that should have been about 25 miles south of my destination; close enough to try to begin making radio calls and identifying distinctive terrain features that would lead me to the strip. And that shouldn't be all that hard because based on where I had marked it on the map, the contour lines indicated it would be the highest terrain within fifty miles. And it was! I now had it in sight. It was uniquely located—on the very top of what I would describe as a pinnacle that stretched upward at least 1,000 feet above the surrounding terrain on all sides. No one could possibly miss *this* strip. The peak it was on was so narrow, rose so steeply, and jutted up so high above any terrain in sight, it was as if it was the earth "giving me the finger." I made quite a few calls on the primary frequency, but had not yet been answered. *Not good*. I over-headed the strip (still at a high altitude) and tried to make contact using the alternate frequency. Still no answer. It wasn't like so many other strips, hidden by brush, surrounded by trees, overgrown with grass or tucked in the fork of two streams. This guy was standing tall—above the rest of the world, with his chest stuck out, damned proud of himself and his perhaps never landed-on strip. It was as if I was being dared to attempt a landing. He was there for any inclined pilot to view with awe.

These kinds of strips in Laos, always service a small village located alongside it, often many hundreds of feet below it—at the base of one of the steep side slopes. Not only was there no village at the base of this mountain, there wasn't the tiniest hamlet anywhere in sight. In fact, not even a road or trail or any cultivated ground in sight. Hard to imagine there were any humans at all in this remote and desolate area of the world. Nothing was moving on or around the strip. I scanned the length and breadth of it, but didn't see a single person. It looked abandoned, in fact that's the best word I can come up with for the whole area: *abandoned!* It was as if it had been years since a plane was on this strip (and maybe no plane had *ever* been on it). These wary observations and complete lack of activity would normally be all the signs I would need to get the hell out of there. However today, even without having made radio contact, based on my briefing and what I sensed to be a critical—perhaps Top Secret mission, I was reluctant to throw in the towel and just bring my cargo back. After orbiting for ten minutes and continuing with the radio calls, still no answer. I had to make a decision, and soon. I didn't want to just keep circling around up here in China for any longer than necessary, though I doubt there was any radar coverage of this area—at least 200 miles from a major Chinese city.

I made the decision to land. It's possible that the guys here to receive the cargo had heard my calls but their transmitter didn't work. Or they may have seen me overhead and were on their way (from somewhere) to the strip. *Gotta do it.* Minus the mood of the place—almost a defiant sanctity, it was not a difficult approach and landing, except for the strong gusty winds always encountered at these high elevation strips. Landed to the north which was slightly uphill, rolled out to the top end, spun the aircraft around (pointing it downhill for takeoff), and shut it down. I sat there motionless—minus the buffeting of the plane in the gusty winds. Besides the sound of the wind, all was silent—dead silent. This was the most removed from activity and humankind I had ever been. For 360 degrees the horizon was a dark enigma, holding its own secrets; sharing nothing.

As overwhelmed as I was by my environs—the surrounding extended desolation, broken only by the marked protrusion of this peak and the strip, I couldn't wait any longer. I jumped out, latched the doors open and began unloading the crates. Hopefully a couple Americans would soon appear. The boxes were heavy; tried to lower them to the ground gently, but once clear of the floor of the cabin, the best I could do was slow their fall to the ground. I finished without anyone arriving, and while I was in a hurry to get out of there and be headed back to the relative safety of a neutral country, I took a couple minutes to walk the strip, *which comprised almost half the total area of the top of the mountain top!* That's how small this summit contracted to. The terrain dropped precipitously from it just a few yards from each end, and about 50 feet from both sides! And I mean dropped steeply. One would not be able to start down the sides without losing their footing and stumbling. I climbed back in, took off, turned to the south, and had an uneventful (but still holding my breath) trip back. I found Tony and explained what had happened. He mumbled something and I think—nodded an okay. (We Air America pilots are kept pretty much in the dark—not necessary that we understand what's going on.)

Playa Granada

I bought a pair of round-trip tickets to Spain—taking Danielle with me (after being unable to come up with sufficient reasons not to), to see firsthand this project that Ron was so hopped up on; that he was sure was going to end up as the most sought-after condo development in Spain (if not the entire Mediterranean coast). We stayed at the family-run, non-pretentious, Salobreña hotel. It was just fine, but the area appeared sparsely populated—in fact, desolate. Definitely not yet a tourist destination. It was obvious Ron's project was in its infancy. There were no representatives or sales office or even workers on the premises. However, after spending several days traipsing the property I had to agree with Ron, it really could be something special; the construction was first class—materials and workmanship. And the few exterior facets that were finished were unique and strikingly attractive; glistening white stucco with windows bordered by heavy dark oak and brightly colored shutters. To help in the future sales pitches Ron and I would make, I took about a hundred photos of every aspect of the project—many showing detailed shots of the exceptional construction methods. I even rented an airplane (that wasn't easy) and took one panoramic shot that showed the village of Salobreña, the coastline, and the development in between—only 100 yards from the Mediterranean. It was so special, the units were so attractive (and so inexpensive) I considered buying one myself. I loved Spain—particularly Barcelona (as you might remember from the Clinica Barraquer) and it was not out of the question, that I might someday retire there.

Chapter Thirty

A EUROPEAN VACATION WITH THE KIDS, AND PLAYA GRANADA

I Had an Overdue Great Idea

It had been about a year since I ditched the family (and in truth—as callous as that sounds, that's the term I should be made to hear and face up to). Although I wrote, called, sent gifts to the kids, and even made some one-week trips to the USA to bond with them and do maintenance on the house, we hadn't really done anything special together; that was about to change. I was going to take all four kids on a fast-paced, hop-scotching jaunt through several Mediterranean countries, featuring *two, five-day-long, sun-drenched stays at "Club Med" super vacation resorts*. At this time, Club Med was the "in" thing for carefree and well-heeled Europeans; pristine mountain or seaside locations that offered every known activity. (It was a package deal: you paid for everything in advance, and when you arrived at the resort, you didn't need any cash; they just gave you beads for spending money.)

The plan was I'd meet the kids in Paris. Pan Am had a program whereby if you paid for one extra round-trip ticket, they would assign one of their employees to escort your minor children across the Atlantic (and take a short European vacation for him or herself). I requested this, and a lovely but slightly overweight Armenian office-worker named Alice Arslanian, would bring my four to Paris. *But I had an adjunct to the program;* not a big one (at least I didn't think so). The kids wouldn't discover it until they arrived in Paris. When they did, not only would they see their smiling dad with open arms, but next to him, *Danielle and her son Eric.* I didn't think this would make any difference to the fun my kids would have. And

218

God knows back in Vientiane I did everything in my power to convince Danielle why I couldn't take her along. It didn't go good. She tearfully kept bringing up the fact she hadn't seen her son for almost two years. I gave in and included her. Plus it could actually improve my time and attention to the kids. Her presence would minimize my frequent mental (or actual) absences when my wandering eyes would spy a passing female that could be that one.

Seeing the Continent

We spent a day in Paris, doing everything that tourists do, and it wasn't long before my appreciation for mothers went way up! Trying to keep up with four kids; even trying to just keep them in sight, and the strain of attempting to ascertain that at the same time, in various locations, they were safe, or not about to get in trouble. *Geez, don't tell me this is what mothers do every day!* We left Paris by train for the Club Med in Zinal, Switzerland, located at the foot of the world's most impressive mountain: the Matterhorn! (In the train station at Paris, prior to boarding, I bought five brightly colored plaid hats for my kids and Eric—thinking this would aid me in keeping them in sight.) At Zinal, among other things I quickly noticed if you wanted to be part of the crowd—be cool and blend in, an Adidas warmup suit was a "must." I never saw so many three-striped leggings. At Zinal we did everything including climbing the first few hundred yards of the Matterhorn (slipping and sliding on rough ice) which soon had the kids complaining about their chafed and scraped hands from reaching down to arrest their backward slides. However, the kids really enjoyed themselves and seemed to recognize they were in a special place doing something special. Obviously I was gratified at this. (And I have to admit Danielle was a better sport than I'd anticipated.) One of the activities at Zinal was a .22 caliber rifle target range. I took Mark there and he got the high score of the day! (This provoked an announcement of that fact at the resort dinner that night, as well as a certificate personally handed to Mark.) Of course he was proud. Things were going well.

The next spot on our jaunt was the island of Djerba off the Tunisian coast; the Club Med resort there was gleaming white and right on the beach. It had every possible recreational activity, from bow and arrow training to a premiere sound studio inside an unlikely structure; a white Grecian-style adobe hut where people so inclined could lay back in recliners (in the dark) and listen to classical works from the great composers. (Obviously none of my kids availed themselves of this diversion.) The one thing they did do every day, was take the club's faux sixteenth century wooden galleon (sails and all) to a spot about a mile out from the shore, into the clearest, deepest-blue water I'd ever seen. Anchored there the kids would leap from a variety of higher and more dangerous perches on the ship, into the sparkling water below! In the evenings, back on the beach (only a hundred feet from the water's edge) was a large concrete slab designed primarily for dancing. Donna and Stacy did all the latest moves from the states, gaining the attention of the European observers.

The only hiccup at Djerba occurred a couple hours after checking in: Danielle told me someone must have snuck into our hut, because the hundred dollars I had given her a few days ago, was not in her purse. Of course I went to the person at the desk in the Check-In office and raised hell. Embarrassed now because when I reflected on her other similar claims, I realized no one came into our hut; it was just a devious way for her to get more cash (which was probably my fault because I was not near as generous with her as I should have been).

After Djerba we flew to Corsica, rented a car, and made the beautifully spectacular (but harrowing) drive around the outer perimeter of the island—on roads that would scare you to death. They were hollowed out of the sides of vertical cliffs, the wheels just ten feet from a sheer thousand-foot drop! (There was a two-foot high aluminum guard rail, but a car would go through it like tissue paper.) At this time "Peter, Paul and Mary" were the big hit group, so during this drive (led by Donna) we were all singing "Leaving on a Jet Plane," "If I Had a Hammer," and "Puff the Magic dragon," at the top of our lungs, and surprisingly not doing bad. You might imagine I was grateful almost to the point of tears, at how well the vacation was going. Although I must say I was slowly failing under the strain of trying to keep my eye on all four kids, all the time. *Wow*, do mothers deserve a lot of credit!

The End of the Trip

After a great three days on Corsica we flew back to Paris. There, for a reasonable price I got two adjoining rooms in the FDR hotel—only a half block off the Champs-Elysees. After a day of sight-seeing (including a second trip up the Eiffel Tower) I was dog-tired. Had a good supper and gratefully hit the rack in our double-room suite. I slept in, and when I awoke and checked the rooms, all four of my kids had already gotten up and left! *Geez, where could they be?* I knew they liked to play in that wrought iron, squeaking little elevator, and sometimes took it to the roof to survey the city. I got in it and went first to roof. No kids. Back in it. Down to the lobby. No kids there either! Asked the concierge. She hadn't seen hide nor hair of them. Then I remembered the sweet-smelling *boulangerie* (bakery) just down the street, where we had our share of croissants; the kids loved the flaky pastries and might be there. I tore out of the hotel and ran down the street, hoping like hell I'd find them there. (Although it was on the other side of the street and I had told them not to go there, because I didn't want them crossing the street.) No dice! They weren't there either! Now I'm really worried (and mad), desperately racking my brain for where in the hell they could be. Slumped, stumped, and seriously out of breath, it hit me! *Last night I had handed them back to the Pan Am lady to escort them on their flight back to the states!* I returned to Vientiane several days later; a man much more respectful of motherhood than the one who began the trip.

Selling Units at Playa Granada

Back in Vientiane, armed with all kinds of glossy literature, photos and contracts, Ron and I put the Playa Granada marketing plan to work. To appeal to affluent expatriate Americans and Europeans, we targeted four cities: Bangkok, Tokyo, Singapore, and Hong Kong. We employed the same program in each city: A month in advance, we'd reserve a large conference room in one of their more prestigious hotels; then for the week before the scheduled presentation we'd run an ad in the largest English language paper in that city—advertising the location, date and time of the coming spectacular "Opportunity Meeting," *where they would hear about what would soon be the most sought after condominium development on the Mediterranean.* So as frequently as we could, Ron and I scheduled our STO together and flew to the appointed city. The ads worked; we averaged about twenty-five attendees per meeting, in each city, and gratifyingly made a reasonable number of sales.

The most common excuse ('objection') that reluctant buyers would throw at us was *the project sounded great, but they never bought property without seeing it first.* Our response was, "For sure. Absolutely. That makes sense. You want to see it first, right"? When they responded that was indeed the problem, we'd reach under the table and pull out our fifty-page scrapbook of hundreds of enlarged color photos of everything anyone could possibly want to see! They were not expecting this and it proved to be an effective "objection crusher." However, there was one slight 'in house' administrative problem: six weeks after sending the Spanish family the contracts and purchase checks, we still hadn't received our first commission remittance.

In addition to our international marketing plan, Ron and I sold several condo units to our pilot friends in Vientiane. One night Danielle and I were out to dinner with my good friend Al Case and his wife Lucette. (Remember Al? The guy whose job I saved in Saigon, by having him kneel in the high grass). Well lo and behold after hearing me rave about the Playa Granada location, the construction, the esthetics and the low prices, he up and bought one. Of course he was anxious to see it, so we made arrangements to meet there the last weekend in July, when he knew he was going to be in France. (A schedule meeting that would include much more than I was anticipating.)

Chapter Thirty-One
ALMOST IN THE ABSOLUTE WORST TROUBLE

Necessary Preamble

I worked for other managers before hiring on with Air America, and in the years afterwards—many more. But I have to say, *none* were as respected or feared as Jim Ryan—the Laos "Manager of Flying." A few months ago one of my pilots was shot down just inside China. After several days of unsuccessful 'Search and Rescues', Jim took a plane to the area and dropped thousands of leaflets declaring a big reward for the return of my pilot. Unfortunately while doing so Jim's airplane took several hits, one of them going through his knee, shattering the bone and blowing the kneecap off. The kicker—Bobby Harold, who had been throwing the leaflets out, used his belt as a tourniquet to keep Jim from bleeding to death. Jim spent quite a bit of time at the Stanford hospital in California, and returned with a prosthetic lower left leg. (And listen to this: He not only managed to keep his pilot's license, but still flew each type of aircraft we operated, and still better than most of us!) There was not a pilot at Vientiane whose worst fear, was to somehow get on the wrong side of Jim Ryan. Boy, did I come close.

M.C.O.'s

One greatly appreciated perk we Air America pilots got, was—after we were surprisingly approved as an "International Air Transport Association" carrier, the company issued us a generous amount of "Miscellaneous Charge Orders." They were a sheaf of documents *that could be used to get free or discounted travel on all the major airlines!* (I think my issuance equaled a couple thousand dollars.) Some pilots actually stayed with the company just for these MCO's; an example of how much we all had gotten bitten by the travel bug. And the Boeing 747 which had recently come out was making trips to Europe and the states—half empty; you could almost always find four or five empty seats in one row, flip the armrests up, lay across the seats, and sleep all the way from Bangkok to L.A. or Paris— your choice!

A Slip Up with Airline Tickets

For my recent European vacation with the kids (and Danielle) I had purchased the tickets at the Vientiane Air France office. I bought most of the tickets using my company-issued MCO's. Now, there was a guy working in our embassy here in Vientiane, who I was never keen on. He had his eye on Sara, and I was in the way; for that and perhaps some other unknown reason, I was not high on his list. He had been an active duty sergeant in the Army, but was now retired and a civil service employee assigned to CID—the US Army Criminal Investigation Command. (Not sure what the "D" stood for.) In any case it turns out (and I'm not sure I knew this: *we pilots were only supposed to use MCO's for ourselves or blood relatives.)* In any case, somehow—no idea how, this guy in CID finds out I used some of my MCO's for Danielle's tickets, *and he reports this violation to Jim Ryan!* Of course Jim calls me in and questions me. Well this series you're reading is called "I Guess I Just Wasn't Thinking," and it's called that for a good reason: When Jim asked me point blank how I paid for Danielle's tickets, without thinking of the problem I was creating—instead of saying "cash," I answered "With a check." (*A lie of course, and not a smart one.*)

Jim says "Good. When the cancelled check comes back, bring it in." I somehow responded, perhaps credibly, "Sure." But I can tell you, at that moment a sick feeling—that would last for some time, was overtaking me. Talk about a quandary. Now I'd really done it!

What Has to Happen?

Okay, so I had said "With a check." That means, somehow, someway, I have to come up with a cancelled check (and in the next couple weeks). *But how in the hell am I going to come up with a check that doesn't exist.* I have no choice but to *fabricate* one; make the precise (imaginary) one come into my possession, something which at present, I had no idea how to make happen. I would just have to come up with some plan to do this.

(Anything to avoid going down in front of Jim Ryan.) And terrifyingly, if the falsity of the plan I was conjuring up would be discovered, there would be much worse consequences than just having used the MCO's; one of them for sure, and not even the worst—would be losing my job.

The Challenges of Replicating an Already Cleared Check

I asked for a couple days off the flight schedule to come up with a plan; to just sit at my desk and think. First thing I did was examine some cancelled checks that had already been through the clearing houses and come back to me. I wasn't too worried about the front side; could do that no sweat. But the back side of the check was another thing—and a damned worrisome thing! On the backside of each cancelled check there were two or three stamped logos of the institutions that had cleared the checks. Each one was a different size, shape, and color. I knew replicating them was going to take some doing!

The Easy Side First

The front side of the check shouldn't be a problem (or so I thought). I knew who it would be written out to—Air France, and I knew the date and the amount. I'd fill that in, sign it, and the front side would be done. I got a blank check and did just that. It looked fine. Half done. Now just have to worry about the back side. But wait, *Uh-oh—that's bad.* I saw something on the front side of the cancelled check that I had never noticed before, and it was going to be a real problem. At some time during the clearing process, a series of about ten new numbers (*not* present on a blank check) were added to the front bottom of the cancelled check; and they were those geometric, abstract-looking IBM numbers. I found some more cancelled checks and lo and behold—sadly, in the same location there was a series of new numbers on each one. This was going to really complicate (if not sink the whole project). How in the hell am I ever going to *hand print* those series of digitally printed numbers? I could try, but they will be hard to replicate; they're perfectly squared. I can't imagine reproducing them with the accuracy that would be necessary to escape the scrutiny of Jim (plus who knows how many people in CID). Still, I made a trip downtown, bought a fine-point calligraphy pen, some black ink, came home and went to work.

Many Failures, Two Successes

I was ready to enter the series of numbers in the proper location. But what numbers? *Was there a meaning or connection or sequence to the numbers?* If so, I could not figure it out, and my hope was that Jim Ryan would also not be familiar with that aspect of the numbers. I had a whole pack of blank checks, and with a spot light clamped to the table, a clear plastic straight edge and my new pen, I began trying to precisely draw each squared numeral. I wasted a bunch of checks, discarding them because the numbers I drew were too rounded, or crooked, or not perfectly even, or I smeared the ink. To me those entries jumped out as manually done and would surely be noticed. Finally—on about my twentieth try I had a set of numbers that I was especially proud of, and was pretty sure would be the best I could ever do.

And then—*disaster!* Glancing at the series of numbers on the cancelled check, I realized that the last four numbers of the series were not just any numbers—they were the numbers of *that particular check.* (The ones that appear in the upper right hand corner of every check). On the finally-okay one I had just finished, I had copied the last four numbers from *the old cancelled check I was using as a model,* which of course did not match the numbers on the blank check I was using and going to submit; a critical mistake and dead giveaway. That which I was so proud of two minutes ago, I now realized was unusable. Utilizing this new information I made another fifteen or so try's before I once again had what would be my best effort; one that included the actual check number and stood a chance of passing examination.

The Back Side

There was only one way to possibly reproduce those stamped logos on the back. But at the very least it was going to cost me a round trip ticket to Taiwan and back. I remembered when I was in Taipei, along the sidewalks there were an assortment of individual entrepreneurs: old women darning socks, kids selling cigarettes, and some old guys on canvas stools, behind crude work benches, who for a small charge, would make you a rubber stamp (usually return address stamps or "handle with care" stamps).

Taipei

I took a couple days leave and flew to Taipei. Luck was with me! The old guys making stamps were still there. The first one I approached spoke no

English, which wasn't a problem. I just whipped out the already cancelled check I'd brought along, and pointed at the three stamped logos on the back side. If you can believe this—the guy pulled his head back and looked at me as if he knew that I was up to no good, and this work on his part would complete some nefarious plot. *He wouldn't do it!* Fortunately on the next block I found a willing accomplice. Not sure whether he knew or not, but he wasn't going to let that get in the way of some revenue. He studied the impressions, figured out a price, and told me to come back about five the following evening. He'd have them then, or no later than noon the next day (which was good since I only booked a three-day stay). No one was more joyous than I was when I picked up the stamps. He had a piece of paper with the imprint of each one, and they were perfect! God knows what kind of hand tools he used to carve out such a perfect image. He also was selling small ink pad tins, of which I bought three different colors.

The Day of Reckoning

Back in Vientiane I was actually shaking—breathless, as I got ready to stamp the back of the check (knowing that if I screwed it up, I'd be two days redoing all the preceding forging. I did and it looked perfect! I had not yet filled out the front side, with the payee and amount, and before doing so, sat down, calmed down, and realized I must not foul up on this last effort. Filled it all in without an error, *and was finished with my "get out of jail" card.* Several days later I told Jim I had gotten the cancelled check back. He of course said well, he'd be in the office tomorrow, bring it in. I don't know if I was ever more nervous than I was that morning when I went into Jim's office carrying the check, which I had also creased twice, bent a corner, and made a couple stapler holes through it to make it look even more well-traveled. He held it up and looked up at it *without giving it more than a few seconds scrutiny;* looked back at me and said. "Great."

What I'm going to tell you now, I have thought about for the last 40 years. As I was walking out, half—but only half-jokingly, Jim said, "And don't do it again." With his sarcastic wit, I'm not sure if he was joking, *or if he knew from the beginning I would have to forge a check.*

On Carrying Live Cargo

Fresh food for remotely located Hmong soldiers was delivered in a strange way. With no refrigeration at our upcountry bases and none in the Porter we would carry a *live* pig or goat, fly overhead the troops, and just open the bomb bay doors. The animal would not only be freshly killed, but also—as a result of the ground impact, be half butchered. I was now also a captain in the larger two-engined DHC-6 Twin Otter and flying one today. It had a much bigger cabin than the Porter and could take much bigger animals. In lieu of a pig or goat, I was scheduled to pick up a water buffalo at LS272. When I got there I saw the huge animal—apparently sedated, tied down on a wooden pallet. (How they ever got that done is beyond me.) I taxied up alongside the pallet, anticipating a fork lift to appear from somewhere and hoist the huge animal up into my empty aircraft cabin.

While parked there and looking down at the pallet, it was like a magic wand was waved over the water buffalo. It suddenly came to its senses, scrambled its legs under itself, and bolted upright on all fours—snapping the ropes like string and sending splinters of wood in all directions! It stood there, swinging its head from side to side, glaring at the onlookers, daring anyone to approach it (and I might add no one appeared to be considering such). It was then I spied what was going to be a real bad idea. At the top of a crest a couple hundred feet from the irate water buffalo, were two guys in a jeep. They were revving the engine and obviously preparing to speed down the hill and ram the animal! It was my conclusion that the animal being no more than 15 feet from my aircraft, the jeep would be unable to stop, and would also ram the airplane's left main gear—causing that wing to collapse, *resulting in the spinning left propeller hitting the ground, causing the engine (five feet from me) to explode!* I jammed the throttles forward and scooted 50 feet forward, allowing the speeding jeep (which missed the water buffalo) to pass behind me. I think they shot it, since I heard a retort and when I next looked back, the buffalo was crumpled on the ground. The fork lift arrived and with Dan's help (my onboard American kicker and close friend) got the animal into the empty cabin.

Halfway to our drop zone, while sitting relaxed in the cockpit, the control yoke suddenly moves back into my lap and the nose of the aircraft pops up! Immediately and instinctively I countered this by shoving the yoke forward (which took inordinate force) and was successful in levelling the aircraft. No sooner had I done that than the yoke was yanked forward and the nose plummeted down. Now a hard pull back to raise the nose. There was no doubt what was occurring: a couple thousand pound water buffalo had come back to life and was running back and forth the length of the cabin, radically changing the aircraft's center of gravity! I hollered into my mic, "Dan, Dan, what the hell's going on?!" No answer. Twisting around in my seat and looking back I could see why Dan didn't answer. He was hanging from the ceiling of the cabin, over the rushing animal, his headset had come off and was hanging down to the floor. Fortunately being almost overhead Long Chien, I somehow made a safe landing, and with Dan still hanging from the overhead, a case officer came onboard and did put the animal out of its misery.

Chapter Thirty-Two
YOU LANDED WHERE?!

Something New in the War in Laos

In January 1972 the frequency and intensity of hostile activity (for a good reason) seemed to be on the increase. In the mornings at Long Chien—almost every morning, right after we had arrived and parked our planes, a ten minute siege of incoming artillery from the first ridgeline to the north, began raining down—*right on the ramp where our airplanes were parked.* Fortunately 100 feet away was a tall karst that we ran to and squeezed between the boulders at its south-facing base. It was high enough that if the rounds made it over the karst, they would clear us by at least a hundred yards. It seemed like the war might be getting worse. We all wondered, what the hell is happening? Well it wasn't until months later we found out what was occurring. (Had I known beforehand I probably would have chosen that time to take home leave.)

The notorious military strategist for the North Vietnamese Army, General Vo Nguyen Giap had dispatched 27,000 regular troops into Laos, with a specific goal *to overrun and capture the CIA base at Long Chien!* (Confirmation of this military objective can be heard on a recorded conversation between President Nixon and Henry Kissinger.) Of course that information was not shared with us pilots. All we knew was that we suddenly were taking much more ground fire (which unknown to us was because there were so many more NVA troops now on the ground in this part of Laos). We also were finding that we couldn't land at many of the strips we were sent to; the strip having been taken by NVA troops the night before, *or an hour before.* This meant we had to make longer, more discriminating airborne observations before committing to a landing. This offensive would persist until March of 72, when for reasons unknown (or the valiant fighting efforts of the Hmong soldiers), North Vietnam gave up on this objective.

A Special Request from Hog

During this period, midway through one day at Long Chien I was approached by a CIA case officer, who was the right hand man of General Van Pao (the head of the Hmong army), and respected by everyone. His call sign was "Hog." His real name was Jerry Daniels, previously a smoke-jumper from Missoula, Montana, but now a combat-hardened expert in infantry tactics, and in charge of almost the whole northern Laos defensive action. His troops—numbering several thousand were comprised almost wholly of Hmong soldiers plus a few Thai mercenaries. (He was sufficiently well regarded in Southeast Asia, to have been the subject of a book called *Hog's Exit.*) In any case,

Gayle L. Morrison

Jerry Daniels, the Hmong, and the CIA

HOG'S EXIT

CANCELLED

I could see an urgency in his eyes as he began to speak.

"Rog, I got something for you, if you want to do it. Won't be easy."

"Sure Jerry" I said (naively) without having any idea what the mission was going to be.

"We're going to have to go to a bad area—about 50 miles north of here and just east of the PDJ. It's in "no man's" land, where as you know we never fly. There's an old strip there that we've never landed at. In fact you might not be able to make it out from the air; it's all overgrown with high weeds. One of my companies just finished a three-day firefight there, after intercepting a column of NVA marching south. Due to overwhelming numbers of NVA and heavier weapons, my troops had to retreat. They all got back except three: a captain, a lieutenant, and a staff sergeant. They were cut off and are still pinned down there, and at least one of them is wounded. The last I had radio contact with them they were flat on their bellies in the high weeds right next to the top west end of the strip.

"All the troops back here know their officers are still stuck there, and if I don't get em out I'm gonna lose the trust of the whole company. Now, gotta tell you, the location of the fire-fight was only about three miles from the strip. What's more, and could be big trouble—about three-hundred yards north of the strip, high up in a karst peak—in the mouth of a cave, the NVA have quad fifties (four 50 caliber machine guns) set up, and the strip happens to be right in their sights. So we're gonna have to be in and out in less than a minute." Jerry gave me the coordinates and said, "Here, use these. You won't find it in the site book since we've never had it declared a useable strip; probably hasn't been used since the French landed on it in the early fifties."

Geez, this might be the most dangerous assignment put to me since I was in Air America. I answered (surprising myself when I heard the words come out). "Sure Jerry. Let's do it!" I guess I really had no choice, so may as well make it sound like I'm Gung-Ho.

The Flight and Landing

Jerry was off for something, but returned in a couple minutes with two other guys and a couple of radios. As soon as everybody was on board I cranked it, taxied out, and was airborne. After twenty-five minutes and about ten miles from the strip Jerry told me he had established radio contact with his guys there, and confirmed they were still in the weeds at the west end of the strip. This was good, because it was uphill to the west, and they were hiding only about fifty feet from where my landing rollout would end; right where I'd spin it around for take-off. I told Jerry to tell them I'd only be able to wait five seconds—knowing I wouldn't have any more time than that before the quad fifties in that high karst would open up—in which case we'd all be dead. Several hundred rounds a minute would be going through the airplane (and our bodies)!

The strip went east and west, and like many of the strips in Laos it was actually a sharp ridgeline with the top flattened for a runway. There was a deep valley on each side. I knew I would not be able to check out the strip before landing. If I circled overhead once or twice it would tip off any NVA in the area that a plane was about to land; knowing that they'd advance towards the strip during my approach, and likely be to it as I touched down. Arriving from the south I turned right, now flying easterly up a deep valley just south of the ridgeline. My plan was to make the landing a complete surprise to any enemy that might be in the area, so

I stayed at tree top level, being maybe five hundred feet below the strip, and thus (hopefully) not visible to the soldiers manning those guns north of the strip. The strip had been so long abandoned, that a real concern was that after touchdown I might run into a log, or a big rock, or a rusted 55 gallon drum, or some other thing that would wipe out my landing gear, and have the whole plane collapse onto its belly, where we would either soon be captured or killed outright. *Please God, make the surface obstacle-free.*

When I was the right distance past the east end of the strip, I made a 180 degree left turn, reversing my course to westerly, to position myself inbound on a final landing approach. To avoid detection I remained below the elevation of the strip. Just a few seconds before reaching the east end (the landing end of the strip) I popped up a hundred feet to the strip elevation, cleared the end, chopped the power and touched down. *Kheerist!* The grass must've been over six feet high. The prop hit it like blender blades and my whole windshield was covered with a green mash. I couldn't see whether there was an obstacle in front of me or not; in fact I could just barely see enough peripherally to keep the aircraft on the center of the runway. It was rough as hell and we just bumped and bounded the length of the runway. Don't know how the plane held together (but it was receiving my eternal thanks). Got to the high west end, hit the left brake and spun her around—pointing back the other way, ready for take-off.

Jerry yanked open the door, and I was counting off the seconds (to myself or out loud; can't remember which). I felt the aircraft shake as one body must have slammed into the cabin. And then my heart almost came out my mouth! Twenty feet in front of the airplane, several fully uniformed North Vietnam soldiers climbed up on the runway from the high grass on the south (right) side of the strip. They were carrying Russian AK-47 automatic weapons—levelled at the plane, and I think more accurately— at me! *This was it, we were all going to be captured, or shot on the spot!* Just when things couldn't get worse, the four fifty caliber machine guns up on the peak to the north, opened up on us. But for the moment—were missing us! They were using tracer ammunition, and fifteen feet in front of the aircraft, the air turned a bright fluorescent pink! The good news was, *the stream of gunfire took down one of the NVA soldiers, and caused the others to jump back over the side of the strip!*

I knew in a second the machine gunners would realize their sighting error, yank the guns back to the right, and the stream of bullets would go through the airplane—front to back, killing us all (me first)! And the gunners *did* yank the muzzle to the right, but in doing so must have accidentally jerked it up, because (*thank you Lord*) the stream of bullets went *over* the plane—*above* it! I felt the plane shake as evidently a second body had landed in the cabin. My teeth were clenched, ready for pain, knowing the gunners would yank the muzzle back to the left, and we'd all be hit, but this time from the rear of the plane forward. They did, but this time the muzzle must have been jerked down, because all the rounds passed *under* the plane, coming out under the front side, *miraculously without hitting the landing gear or a tire!* I felt the third body hit in the plane, and with the door still open, rammed the throttle full forward and we were accelerating down the strip. Don't know where the 50 caliber fire was, but it must have been behind me, and the soldiers were still hiding below the south edge, afraid to raise their heads.

Upon Our Return, a Well Done

After landing back at Long Chien, the head CIA guy for Laos—Dick Johnson, who spent several days a week at Long Chien, called me up to his office alongside the ramp. Evidently on the way back, Jerry had radioed him with exactly what had happened. Mr. Johnson told me somewhat sternly that we were paid to take "calculated" risks, but wasn't sure what we had just done, was that. *But I had his confidential thanks.*

An Overdue Action on My Part

I was off the next day, and still sobered by the previous day's scare, availed myself of that dark old IT&T building where one could place international calls. Timed it so as to be most likely to get Sara and the kids at home, and did. We talked a long time—not at all as the situation was—not as if I was the no-account selfish scoundrel I was, but rather like a very concerned and loving husband and father (which perhaps I was as well—at least on this phone call). I was pleased to hear that things couldn't have been going better, in every way; especially for the kids—lots of new friends and a school they thoroughly enjoyed. The boys were already into surfing and on the school's varsity sports teams. Donna and Stacy were both popular and into all the school's activities. Once again I was the recipient of much more than I deserved.

Only one problem—with Sara: According to her she was very disappointed that I didn't send her the $200 to fly to New Jersey to attend her younger brother's wedding. I have no—absolutely no recollection of ever getting a letter requesting that $200. I would like to say I didn't get it. If I did get it, I can't imagine I wouldn't have sent the money! Now, many years later, I wonder if that letter could have arrived when I was taking those 'uppers' and downers' for my asthma and insomnia, but was judgmentally not at the top of my game. But not only had I sent her $1,150 the first of the month, she'd be getting another $1,150 in two weeks (and for God's sake, her younger brother could have sent her tickets.) The good news was she had a great relationship with her older brother and his family—the one that followed her down to Florida and bought a house just down the street. This was reassuring to me, to know she had close family only a couple hundred yards away.

Chapter Thirty-Three
A MAJOR "FAUX PAS" AND ANOTHER TRIP TO SPAIN

A Little Background

A well-known US aircraft manufacturer, responding to requests from the US Navy, designed a special-mission, heavily-armed aircraft for low-level monitoring of the narrow, winding rivers in South Vietnam. It was large-engined turbo-prop aircraft with a huge machine gun installed in the wholly open port side of the fuselage. And, unfortunately, it was a tailwheel aircraft, just like my Porter. Instead of a tail wheel, almost all modern aircraft have a nose wheel. (Nose wheel aircraft sit level and allow for much better visibility and handling on the ground.) But a big political problem arose: It turns out the Navy did not put it out for bid, which is a federally mandated "must." The whole project was scrapped and the planes were sent to a zero humidity, almost boundless area in the Arizona desert, called the "Aviation Boneyard" (where thousands of WWII aircraft are still "moth-balled"). Congress heard about this situation and considered litigation. The Navy or the manufacturer realizing big trouble was coming, had to get the planes out of the country as soon as possible. *They decided to donate them to the Cambodian Air Force, just beginning their fight against the Khmer Rouge.*

Never Knew I Was Specially Qualified for Anything

The Cambodian pilots who would fly these planes were going to need training. The Department of Defense went to the Air Force and asked them if they had any pilots who: (1) had experience in tailwheel aircraft, (2) had been rocket and bomb instructors, and (3) spoke French. Can you believe in the whole US Air Force there wasn't a single pilot who met all three of these requirements. The Department of Defense then turned to the CIA, and guess what—they came up with a guy with all three: *Roger Yanke!* (My still nightly sessions studying those French language books emboldened me to list it as a "language spoken.") When asked I said I would gladly accept the assignment, which would be administered from a secret airbase on the Thai/Cambodian border. They wanted two guys, and I chose the one and only L. J. Broussard, who had spoken a bastardized French from birth. (Remember? He was that "Little Cajun Shit" from Louisiana with two wives.) The US Air Force was responsible for the project, so they assigned two of their pilots to the program; neither spoke French so I was assigned as the "Project Manager."

LJ and I made the trip to Phnom Penh, met our new Air Force friends and awaited the arrival of the aircraft. They had been shipped to Bangkok and were going to be ferried from there to Phnom Penh by a test pilot from the factory that built them. Well, I'd like to say we witnessed an uneventful arrival of those planes, but we did not! The (expert) factory pilot "ground looped" four of the twelve! (A ground loop occurs when certain tail wheel airplanes touch down with the nose canted left or right; a tire digs in, a wing is yanked down, hits the runway, and the aircraft does a cartwheel!) And bad news for us, evidently the Helio Stallion was one of

Stallion with gun

those aircraft! To avoid a ground loop the pilot has to use his legs to shove in full rudder as soon as he feels the misdirection of the nose. And more of an issue than the ground loop problem, we learned from the factory pilot that the FAA had refused to certificate it because of aerodynamic control problems. Besides the ground loop problem and the center of gravity and balance problems, there was yet another—serious problem: if in reducing the power (which you did by flattening the pitch of the propeller) you did it to a certain pitch angle, it lessened the airflow over the tail surfaces, and the nose pitched straight down! And this was the plane we were donating to the Cambodian Air Force? *One that LJ and I are going to instruct in?*

As an instructor, in spite of the likelihood of a ground loop on touchdown, if you want your student to progress in learning the landing technique, you have to let him go as far as possible towards actually touching down, before ordering him to add full power and abort a bad landing attempt. In the Air Force the abort is commanded by the instructor shouting *"Go Around"!* In the Navy the instructors shout *"Wave Off"!* In Spanish-speaking countries they shout *"Al Aire'!* Each of these is just a couple syllables and easy to get out quickly, so an instructor can wait till the last second before shouting them out. But listen to this: In French, the abort callout is *"Representez vous pour l'atterissage!"* If you waited till the last second to try to get this mouthful out, you'd be ground looping several times a week. I held a special ground school making sure all the Cambodian student pilots knew that *"Go Around"* was what they were going to hear instead of the longer French language phrase.

Thankfully, the training program went well (minus the negative feel to the controls and the 'pitch down' which both LJ and I noticed in the first few hours). Before we started "Rocket and Bomb" and "Aerial Gunnery" training, we had to just get our students able to take-off and land safely (which took twice as long as scheduled). One reason: the tallest pilot was 5' 3" and could barely see over the nose of the airplane. Being a tailwheel airplane, taxiing, taking-off, and upon landing, the tail is low (or on the ground), which results in the nose being canted upward—radically restricting a pilot's forward vision (especially if he is short). Becoming aware of this problem, after several days all the students were walking out to the airplane carrying a 6-inch-thick firm cushion. And when sitting on these cushions they *could* see over the nose, but it created another problem: Boosted up in the seat, their short legs were drawn even further from the rudder pedals. The one thing necessary to avoid a ground loop was instantly using your legs to get full throw of the rudders!

238

Part Three: The CIA Secret Airline and Eureka! She Exists!

An extremely high-level conference was scheduled to evaluate the flight training program and the future tactical use of the aircraft. Besides LJ and I, the US Ambassador, the Cambodian Minister of Defense, the head of the Cambodian Air Force, a couple other senior Cambodian officials, and the commander of the squadron being trained—Colonel Sompai, were there. It was held in the hundred-year-old historic Royal Cambodge Hotel; an edifice to view with wonder. It looked more like a German castle, being all made out of stone blocks with slate floors and fifteen foot ceilings; no glass or screens on the window, just huge wooden shutters. In the center of our large meeting room was a ten foot long glistening mahogany table. There was a chair for each attendee and in front of it a place setting of crystal goblets, pewter ashtrays, a quill pen, a tiny receptacle of ink, and a pad of linen paper. It was as urbane an event as I'd ever been a party to. The protocol was so thick you could have cut it with a pair of scissors. It took at least ten minutes to figure out how the seniority and status would affect the seating arrangement. I was nervous, since the meeting was going to be held using French, and having learned all my French from books, while I could speak and write it well enough, I had a hard time translating the spoken word. I would hear it, then in my mind's eye I'd write the phonetics of what I had heard on a blackboard, and then—finally, read it! I was thusly always a sentence or two behind.

Halfway through the meeting, the head of the Cambodian Air Force comes up with an idea that could mean WWIII; a *terrible* idea. I felt like saying, "Holy shit, that's ridiculous!" But knowing the sophisticated nature of the meeting, of course there was no way I could say anything that crude. I quickly searched for some kinder words—some way I could discourage this idea without causing an international incident. I happened to think of the stateside expression *Well, I have my doubts*. With no time, I chose it and responded to his idea by saying *"Puis, j'ai mes dutes."* I was shocked at the reaction by almost everyone, especially the general and the Minister of Defense. One was furious, the other seemed to start chuckling, and their aids began excusing themselves with bowed heads. The US Ambassador chimed his water glass with his knife and declared a ten minute coffee break.

As soon as the crowd disbursed I asked LJ what in the hell I had said. He answered that I had said "I have my doubts," and that as far as he knew I'd said it perfectly. Of course I told him there had to be more to it than that. He suggested I ask Colonel Sompai who was having a cigarette in the hallway. I found him and asked him. He responded, "Well Capin Yonk, I never be to Paris, but here in Cambodia, we only hear that expression one time. When young girl misses period and thinks she's pregnant, *she says 'j'ai mes dutes.' So you just told everyone that you were going to have a baby."* Fortunately, this event did not further derail the training program.

A Little Bit about the Training

We instructed the Cambodian pilots in rockets and gunnery. The plane had the whole port side of the cabin completely open, wherein was mounted a huge multi-barreled Gatling gun (that fired 900 rounds a minute)! When the gunner let go a burst the whole plane would shake and the instruments were unreadable. And a damn good thing the gunners were made to wear parachutes, *because one of them fell out!* I mentioned once before that anyone who thinks there's nothing worse than a fire at sea, has evidently never been in an airplane on fire! The rear bulkhead of the cabin was a huge electric panel that controlled the firing of the gun. On one flight I thought I smelled smoke and unfortunately I was right. That big rear panel had burst into flames. The gunner knew enough (proud of him) to grab the fire extinguisher and let go a burst. And I want to tell you here and now, two seconds after he did, *it was like an elephant stepped on my chest.* I could not inflate my lungs—could not even get a 'sip' of air; a hugely panicky feeling. Fortunately before I passed out (or died) the air gusting through the open side evacuated the extinguisher fumes. The breathing restriction was so instantaneous and critical, from that day forth, every aviation organization I worked for: no matter what the Maintenance Chief told me about our extinguishers having the right chemicals in them, I made him take one of our plane's fire extinguishers in the men's room, close the door, and discharge it—to prove it! The program was successfully completed and LJ and I were given accolades (and walnut plaques) by the US Air Force command that was responsible for the training and subsequent supervision of the new Cambodian squadron.

Back in Vientiane

Regarding my "other job"—trying to sell Playa Granada condos, while Ron did not seem as concerned as I was, we still had not received any commission checks' (This was 1973, and the $22,000 owed to me was a measureable sum.) And to complicate the issue, Ron got furloughed again! He had to leave and did—without his wife, who was still staying at their suite in the Lang Xang hotel. (Don't know what the plan was there, and I don't think she knew either.) I was pretty sure he was back in Spain, but wasn't communicating well with me (or his wife). I wanted to get paid and Ron was my only connection with the family that owed us the money.

Need to Get Some Answers

I scheduled an STO, flew to Spain—landing at the airport in Malaga on the Costa del Sol, rented a car and drove to Salobreña. I checked into that same family-run hotel—hoping Ron would be staying there. He wasn't. Since he was about the only American in the area, without them knowing his name, someone might have seen him. I asked the hotel bartender, and lo and behold (first guy I asked) he knew who I was talking about. Although Ron had recently stayed at the hotel he didn't know where he was living now. He said he thought Ron might be helping some real estate company in town. (I'm thinking, perhaps one started by the "family" to assist in the European sales of Playa Granada.) He said I could check with their office downtown. Since I was here to collect money from them, thought I'd better not do that until I'd talked to Ron. The bartender did give me what would turn out to be a good tip: he said Ron was often seen at a small café, fifty feet from the water's edge in the nearby small fishing village of Almuñécar.

The next morning I left the hotel at nine a.m. and made the twenty minute drive to Almuñécar. When the bartender had said a small town, he wasn't kidding. It was a tiny village of about a hundred fishermen! I parked the car a block behind the main street, which was a short street and the only street in town with commercial buildings on it. It paralleled and faced the water's edge just a hundred feet across from it. Obviously there were no buildings across from it since that side was the actual beach, strewn with upside-down, small wooden boats. No lie, this sole street in town was maybe only 50 yards long, containing only four or five small storefronts. In the distance I picked one which appeared to be a small café and perhaps the one supposedly frequented by Ron.

When still a hundred feet from it, *there he was!* He was sitting in front of the café, in a chair tilted back against the storefront, his legs crossed, feet up on a crate in front of him, and a drink in his hand—at ten in the morning. "Ron, Ron, it's Roger!" He turned towards me—well disguising what must have been a surprise to him. He was dressed casually in a silky, open-front shirt, a pair of cream-colored linen trousers, and light gray suede moccasins (with no socks). *Wow, living the good life.* I didn't waste much time before bringing up the objective of the trip: how was he doing getting our commission payments coming? While I knew it was Ron, I could hardly believe the words I heard come out of his mouth. Here was the most materialistic person I ever met, an award-winning maximum revenue salesman, accustomed to always having a one-hundred dollar bill in his money clip, who—between apparently relished swallows of his gin and tonic, commenced to tell me how *money wasn't that important; the good things in life were almost free.* I was stunned. Of course I stuck with it until I got him to promise he'd be more forceful with the "family." Finally he said he was pretty sure he'd have the money, and soon.

That solved, I was brazen enough to bring up the subject of his wife—still in the Lang Xang hotel in Vientiane. "Ron, what the hell is your plan for Wanda, are you going to send her tickets back to LA"? Surprisingly he didn't seem to have a plan for her. So I asked him what his plan for *himself* was. It was then the heavy duty stuff came out: The real estate agency had hired a tall thin, sultry and seductive German woman. According to Ron she was devastatingly attractive. He admitted they started dating, and then leaning forward, with almost a reverence he went on to describe what an incredibly passionate lover she was.

Well that explains it. Right about now my commission checks and Wanda were taking a way back seat, if any seat at all. I asked him if he was going to see the German woman today, and if I had any chance to meet her. He said "No, at the moment she's in the hospital." Of course I asked what the heck happened.

He answered: "She tried to commit suicide." What!? Geez, that on-the-edge mentality may explain the height of her activities in the bedroom. When we parted I re-established that (1) he was going to put on a full-court press for my $22,000, and (2) mail Wanda tickets back to the states (and maybe even tell her what's happening).

Back in Laos

The first night back in Vientiane I was invited to dinner at LJ's house. He, I, Ron, and two other guys had been a tight knit group since Saigon; so it was natural that LJ would care about Ron and want to know the latest. After dinner, sitting on a swing on his porch he asked me—caringly, *how was Ron doing?* At first—guarded, I replied with some innocuous, innocent details. Then—after a couple more direct questions from LJ, in a low voice and in confidence, I told him I was a little worried about the Ron and Wanda situation, inasmuch as Ron may be becoming interested in a German woman over there. To lessen the implications of the statement, you'll notice I said a "*little*" worried, and "*may*" be becoming interested in another woman. To further low-ball the situation, I made a point of saying that personally—*I never saw them together*. (I didn't tell him that was only because Kristina had put her head in an oven the day before!)

Two days later I was at the airport attending a necessary Air America ground school class on Taiwanese Air Regulations. There was a knock on the classroom door. The Chinese instructor went to the door and was handed a message. He returned to the front of the class, and holding it in front of him said, "Captain Yank, Yankee, Yonk, someone downstairs wants to see you right now." I had no idea who or what this might be. When I got downstairs, there—seemingly suspended a foot off the floor, trembling with anger and gesturing wildly with both hands, was *Ron's wife Wanda.*

Turns out, what I hadn't considered was that husbands frequently tell their wives everything they've heard that day. (Learned a lesson here.) Not only that, but worse: LJ's wife Brenda, *hated* Wanda. So the next night she invited Wanda to join them for dinner at the Chez Suzanne in town. Shortly after sitting down Brenda up and tells Wanda that *she was really sorry to hear that Ron was shacking up all over Spain.* Wanda contacted Ron and told him I was spreading the story of his infidelity all over town! *Ron never spoke to me again.*

Chapter Thirty-Four
A LANDING, BUT NO TAKEOFF

A Bridge Too Far

I can't remember the Lima Site number, but I do remember the name of the village, because I may have been the last guy that ever went there (if not the *first*). It was Muang Xon in northern Laos—almost on the same latitude as Hanoi and only about 40 miles west of the North Vietnamese border. *Not* a good place to be in early 73. You kept your ground time to the bare minimum never knowing when there'd be incoming artillery, or worse—an actual NVA ground attack on the village. The Customer told me it would be just this once, sounding to me like they were writing it off (which as far north as it was made this understandable). The war in Laos was now getting not-good publicity. Recent United Nations resolutions favored a transfer of power from the existing ruling royal (US-friendly) family to communist-supported elements waiting in the wings; a possible 'best solution' to end a twenty-year secret war. None of us knew what that might mean for Air America, but had suspicions it would spell the end of this long adventure.

At some strips the Customer had armed and minimally trained the old men and women to defend themselves if NVA troops tried to overrun it, when no Vang Pao Hmong soldiers were nearby. I sure hoped that was the case at Muang Xon. My cargo was medical supplies and *plasma!* I knew that was a bad sign. Bringing in blood means transfusions are necessary and there are seriously wounded soldiers at the strip or nearby; the result of recent, or worse—*currently* occurring fire fights! Took me an hour forty to get there and once there I couldn't risk circling the strip to check it out. That would draw too much attention (meaning ground fire). I made a 'straight-in' approach from the west, rolled out to the east end and spun her around for my hopefully soon-to-occur takeoff back to the west. The strip went through the middle of the village, most the huts to the right (south), some others and small rice paddies to the left (north). No American was standing there waiting for me. *Not a good sign.* (He may well have been just a a mile away leading a platoon of Hmong soldiers into battle.) As soon as the plane was stopped, a partially-uniformed villager yanked open the sliding side door and began unloading the supplies. Being able to keep an eye on him remaining at the rear of the aircraft—away from the prop, I did not shut down the engine; kept it running in anticipation of a quick departure.

Holy Shit!

I don't know how to describe what happened next: the deafening explosion, the flash, the concussion, or the breath being sucked out of me. An artillery round hit about fifty feet behind the plane, vaporizing the guy doing the unloading (a couple parts of him flying into the cockpit). The force of the blast against the tail spun the plane a quarter turn to the right. Once motionless and sitting there in shock I realized I was now pointing north, crosswise to the runway *and the whole windscreen had been popped out of the plane!* While trying to gain control over my shaking body and think rationally, another round hit somewhere further away; I think right in the middle of the thatch roofed huts. I could hear the pings as dirt, rocks, and pieces of metal hit the plane. I was parked about fifty feet from some rising ground to my right. Looking in that direction I saw villagers running towards it, and more specifically—towards a barely visible cave-like opening at the base of the hill. I took this to be the entrance of a shelter from incoming artillery, or as well disguised as it was—maybe even a hiding place that could go undiscovered if the NVA troops entered the village. Leaving the engine running I set the parking brake, leaped out and started running towards the opening. I am embarrassed to say this, but on my way there I was about twenty feet behind a running villager who went feet over head when a third round hit nearby. I guess I should've grabbed him on the way by, but I didn't. I ran right past him.

A Hiding Place

The entrance was so low and small, I had to drop to my knees to crawl in, sweeping aside the long grass that hung down across the opening—

perhaps purposely left growing there to hide the opening. These shelters had the same underground layout: the tunnel went in straight for about ten feet and then made a sharp 90 degree turn one way or the other (this one to the left). This was so people could get around that corner, and not be slaughtered when the enemy discovered the opening and began shooting straight into it. I made it around the corner and found myself next to a woman whose whole heel was missing and blood was pouring out of the gap. It was dark around the corner; had to strain to make things out. Above the desperate conversations and babies crying, I could hear lots of small arms fire outside, though couldn't tell where it was coming from; either the village or from atop the hill—*right over us*. In fact I could hear footsteps thudding on the ground above my head, causing me to wonder if any second a leg was going to come down through the dirt above me.

After who would know how long things quieted down and all I could hear outside were voices shouting commands, and by the inflection—questions. I had no idea if they were sounds from the villagers or the invading troops. I could hear the engine of my plane still running, but once again am embarrassed to admit I was too scared to venture out and make a run for it. I looked at the people with me in the shelter; men, woman, children—about twenty of us. Some of them were soldiers who had probably done this before and would know when we could exit. It was dead quiet now, no shots, no voices. I wished I could have gotten the nerve to make a run for the plane (of course if I did take off, with no windscreen I'd have a 100 mph wind right in my face)! I couldn't; stayed there. I think no one moved or spoke for at least twenty minutes. Finally I could tell by the grunts and gestures from someone further in—in apparent authority, we were being signaled to start out. Talk about a reluctant exit.

Coming Out

We emerged into a bright sunlit area; the aura of which was far removed from the actual situation. Nothing moving. I mean nowhere could I see a single villager. No idea where they could have gone or be hiding. While standing there mute and half paralyzed, looking at my windscreen-less shiny silver and blue aluminum escape capsule, I heard a loud outburst of shouts from behind me. I turned and my heart almost came out my throat. On top of the hill (right over our shelter) was about a dozen of what I guessed to be NVA soldiers, with their weapons pointed at us. They came stumbling down the hill screaming at us, and finding it hard not to be looking at me—with suspicion and motivations I could not interpret. I noticed that all the soldiers were not well-uniformed, in fact some were in ragged shorts and flip-flops, and no shirts; meaning they were Pathet Lao (the Viet Cong of Laos) assisting a North Vietnamese Army platoon.

Leaving Muang Xon

After a short—well not so short (but heated) discussion, it was obvious that several of them were assigned to do something with me. One of them approached me, on the way swinging off his haversack and opening it. He took out a coil of rope. Not good (but better than a knife or handgun). He made me stand with both arms hanging at my sides. He first tied my right wrist to my left ankle, and then my left wrist to my right ankle. I'd never seen that arrangement before (but he did it like he did it every day). After two hard shoves in the back and some hand gestures accompanied with foreign language instructions, I realized they wanted me to start up the hill that our shelter was under. I did, but tied the way I was, I was halfway up the hill before I'd figured out how to coordinate my leg movements with my arm swings. *God knows how I'm going to walk and function like this.* Over the hill and onto a path leading to the east and the North Vietnamese border (and possibly, eventually—*Hanoi)!* I was being escorted in a fearful direction. Fortunately I was so concerned with my immediate situation, I didn't have time to dwell on the fact that I actually could end up in the "Hanoi Hilton" with John McCain, and what that would mean; couldn't think that far ahead.

We continued walking for about thirty minutes until we came to a small clearing where surprisingly, *these soldiers had left their wives and several kids!* After gathering up them and their belongings, we were on our way, me bringing up the rear. We continued walking until darkness made it tough to pick the best path. In case I could escape and would need to backtrack, I tried to determine and stay aware of our heading, which I figured to be a little north of east, maybe 070 degrees. Wasn't sure if that was a base course or if these guys were just taking the easiest route to wherever we were going. As you might imagine, tied the way I was, walking was not easy, especially through the waist high brush. I didn't complain or say anything, trying to be as little trouble as possible— realizing that if I was too much of a burden they may give up on whatever the master plan was, and just shoot me here.

I GUESS I JUST WASN'T THINKING

The First Part of the Trek

By the end of the first day I had determined that the ranking guy was named Bao. He issued all the orders and wasn't challenged. During the day they had assigned separate individuals to walk with me. Most were noncommittal, except one bitter guy, who I was sure would shoot me if he had half a reason. That first night they started a fire, boiling some kind of broth, in a large section of bamboo that even in the flames never caught fire. They also heated something in a charred gourd—some kind of stew. Everyone ate except me. After dinner the soldier they assigned to watch me, was skinny and young—maybe fifteen or sixteen; not one of the married soldiers. He did not look at all mean. His expression seemed to convey that he was just doing what he had to, no other choice. It was his lot. I didn't have anything to lie on and the ground was damp, not to mention very likely crawling with vermin. I gathered some thin branches and fronds to keep me off the ground itself and cushion it somewhat. When I had lain down I had time to conjecture on the likely end of this trek; with that on my mind I was surprised that I dozed off at all. Not surprised when I awoke at midnight. Several of the soldiers and their wives were still sitting around the fire, apparently having a reasonable time, not at all concerned about their prisoner. Woke up several times more.

I didn't go to the bathroom the first day and half the second day, and having nothing to eat for about 30 hours; didn't think I'd have to, but about noon I did! No way to communicate my problem to my captors. Finally realized I had no choice but to just step off the pathway in full view of the soldiers (and their wives), squat and pull down my pants. Succeeded, but of course without toilet paper, wondering what kind of problems this would soon bring about. We walked basically the same heading until about four and then took a hard jog to the right—southeast, I'd say to about 120 degrees. I'll have to remember that. Well maybe not, because twenty minutes later we took a hard jog to the left—northeast, maybe 020 degrees. We walked about twenty minutes on that heading, and then turned back to the original heading of 070 degrees. Must have had to circumnavigate something; no other reason for the heading changes. With a limited view of the track of the sun, I was hoping my heading estimates were accurate, just in case I did get free and would have the chance to backtrack that heading. (I was now thankful that I was wearing well-made high-top flying jodhpurs and thick socks.)

That night I was included in supper. And I was hungry as hell. *But you should have seen supper.* A half-hour hunting venture netted several not-big birds. They did pull out most the feathers, but then on a flat piece of wood, using a cleaver-like knife, one of the women hacked these birds, scaly legs, claws, beaks, eyes, bones—everything, into small pieces, heated the mélange in that same gourd, and handed me a dirty metal plate containing a handful-sized portion. I knew that as distasteful as it would be, I needed the nourishment (and did not want to look ungrateful). Each swallow was a dreaded, pure mechanical act of necessity. I did not take one mouthful that I did not have to pick unknown things out of my mouth and sneakily flick them behind me in the dark.

After two days, having bragged about my jodhpurs earlier, I was getting blisters on the outsides of my small toes on both feet. Although I think it was sunny, the tree tops were so enjoined and thick that at high noon it was like dusk, plus most of the time there was no trail. They just seemed to pick and choose their way, but steadily to the east/northeast. If we were making eight miles a day—which I wasn't sure we were, *we could be inside North Vietnam tomorrow evening!* We stopped at what was about noon (not sure what time it was, because I had forgotten to wind my watch and didn't notice till a half day later). I thought they were going to have lunch, even though by now it should have registered that they only ate twice a day, late morning and dusk. It was a 'siesta' break—they were going to take a nap.

While they're lying there, a couple of the kids—maybe just out of curiosity, came over to me—looking as if they wanted to be friends with this different-looking being. I gestured for them to come closer, so I could demonstrate a trick my father did. I held my two hands together, fingers cupped together, and then quickly moved them apart, *apparently pulling off the last joint of one thumb.* You should have seen the look in those kids' eyes and heard the shrieks as they jumped back. After a few seconds—knowing they'd been sufficiently shocked, I unfolded my hand and displayed the missing thumb still attached. They were noticeably relieved to realize it was still on and just an illusion. One of them ran over to a nearby soldier—probably his father, and pulled him over to where I was. I knew he wanted me to do it for his dad and so I did. Had to do it several times for the at-first incredulous adult, who then brought the other soldiers over. I performed it again for them. *I believe I had just made a breakthrough here.* And I was right, the soldiers and their wives seemed to begin almost treating me like a traveling companion rather than a prisoner.

That was the highpoint of the day. The low point was I had to 'go' but was unbelievably constipated; think I hemorrhoided myself in having some sort of movement. Though I couldn't smell myself, my sweat soaked clothes and dirty behind must have made me ripe; small thing—in fact nothing, *considering the possible outcome of this journey.* Surprisingly I had less bites and scratches than I would have thought after this time. The ropes around my wrists had gotten wet, dried, muddied, dried, and shrunk, and the skin on my wrists under them was chafed and sore. I had to be thinking of this every time before I moved my arms.

The next morning we stumbled into a small hamlet. My captors exchanged greetings with those who came out to meet them. None of the villagers—after spying me, took their eyes off me. Some small, but tough-looking guy approached Bao and they commenced a long discussion. The mean guy in our group (the one who I said I had no doubt would shoot me if he could get away with it) whose name I picked up as Dinh, joined in the conversation, and seemed to be working at convincing Bao of something. The next thing I see is three villagers commencing some construction project with stalks of bamboo. Most of my captors showed no interest in the project—whatever it was. Both the women napped. I soon realized what the workers were doing. *They were building a cage!* (And I knew that when Ernie Brase was captured, that's how he spent most his time on the way to Hanoi.) Now, *talk about lucky*—at some point my captors must have realized that with me in the cage I couldn't walk, and I'd only be able to be kept in it at night, and they'd have to carry it in the day. This being the case, even though the project was half completed, Bao goes up to the village chief, and pisses him off by declining the offer, relaying that we were going to continue on as is. *Thank God for small favors.*

A Second Breakthrough and Guess What

That afternoon, one of the kids—I'd say about five or six, approached me and held up his hand. *My conclusion was, he wants to walk with me.* I was not about to take his hand, thinking that could end up bad. I glanced up and his mom was looking in our direction with what I would describe as a not-angry "wait and see" expression. She finally nodded, *so I took the kid's hand.* I suspected he would soon lose interest and it would be short-lived. But the kid held on for two hours! I had the feeling that this event even surpassed the thumb trick as humanizing me. And guess what, on the fourth day, by my very suspect calculations—shortly after crossing the

North Vietnam border, we stopped in a small clearing. There, the soldiers held several animated tête-a-têtes. When it broke up, Bao comes over to me and starts trying to explain something (evidently complicated) to me. Though he must have spoken for five minutes, it was all in Vietnamese and I didn't understand a word. Then he takes out his knife and—with a level of care I appreciated, cuts the ropes on my wrists (leaving the lengths still hanging from my ankles). He then points at me, and then over my shoulder in the direction we had just come from, and then he makes the same two motions again. *Don't tell me he's saying I can go?!* If so this was no time to dally. I was afraid to turn my back, so (carefully) began walking backwards out of the clearing. After my first two or three steps Bao was nodding approvingly. *My God. I can't believe it. They're letting me go!* Once I was sure they were in fact letting me go (and I can't believe this, I made a small wave-like gesture). I then turned and began walking quicker, on the reciprocal of the route we had just traversed; at least getting this first part directionally correct.

The Second Part of the Trek, Day One

I walked quickly for at least an hour—putting as much distance as I could between myself and my captors. (They may have a change of heart.) Although perhaps I should have been, I wasn't too worried about being recaptured by other Pathet Lao or NVA soldiers. One reason: excluding stumbling on the small hamlet we hadn't seen a single human being since we left Muang Xon. But being discovered was more than just a possibility, and the next people to capture me might not be so lenient. I also knew that since Muang Xon—much further to the south had been attacked, there had to be soldiers in this general area. I was much closer to North Vietnam (if not in it). Undoubtedly there were 'unfriendlies' between where I was and where I hoped to be going. I trudged doggedly ahead until dusk, not at all happy with my slow pace. (I'd untied one ankle attachment. The other one was too knotted.)

Under the strain of the last several days or the relief of being released, and finding myself completely on my own (still with a huge challenge), at the end of this first day free I just let myself sink to the ground, where the tears flowed. I stayed like that for a while, contemplating the perhaps 'undoable' task that lay ahead of me. I began weighing my options; trying to come up with a plan. I knew the walk back was going to be much tougher because I would have to stay off anything resembling a trail, or even any open areas where I could meet up with another traveler. I could stay within fifty feet of it, but be ready to duck down if I heard voices or saw a figure coming. I also considered whether to better avoid a recapture I should just walk at night. I quickly canned that idea. If I was going to stay on the back-tracking course of 250 degrees (the reciprocal of the 070 degrees they had walked me for several days) I needed daylight. Not because I'd be using the sun, but because the only way I could stay on that 250 degrees without a compass, would be to pick landmarks: (1) stand and face as close to 250 degrees as I could divine, (2) sight by a nearby tree to a distant tree that was right on that 250 degree line-of-sight, (3) use that distant tree as my first destination. Then do that over and over again, probably every fifteen minutes for who knows how many days. My chances of actually arriving back at Muang Xon were just about nil, *but I didn't want to*. If I did, it could well be occupied by North Vietnamese soldiers—who would be only too glad to see me again. If my southwest track was accurate, I should pass not too far either side of it.

Days Two and Three

I had no idea of any other strips in the area of Muang Xon, let alone ones that might have a Customer there. We never had any flights scheduled to this area so my chances of being spotted by another Air America plane were zero. And even though by now the company would have an "SAR" (Search and Rescue) operation going on, the tree canopy was two layers thick and no pilot could come close to spotting me. As I was navigating my way back, in the direction of safety and wondering about how I might be found, I reflected on having laughed at those SEALS and Special Forces guys who wore a small compass on the underside of their watchband, or the Air America pilots who always checked out survival vests for their flights. If I would have had one of those vests, I would have had a compass, at least had two flares and a signal mirror.

I would like to say that I found trails or paths that went roughly 250 degrees, but I didn't. In fact I hadn't found a single trail, 250 degrees or otherwise! (So I didn't need to worry about staying fifty feet off them.) All I could do was pick a projected route that appeared to go through the least foreboding brush. This caused me to not make as much progress per day as while being led by my captors. Plus these last two days, trying to stay on a course of 250 degrees was made much more difficult by bamboo thickets, high ground and swamps. I had to circle around, and then try to pick up 250 degrees again (having had no tree to aim at). I was proceeding generally southwest, which would be taking me towards central Laos, but that could involve a two-week walk, and I *could* end up walking into the center of the PDJ (where I would certainly be re-captured)! Now being so unsure of where I was, made me think that in addition to having maps in the cockpit, it would have been a good idea to carry another map of Laos on our person. Sure could have used one about now. The biggest thing I'd had to eat for three days were berries. (You hear about mangos, papaya and kiwi in Southeast Asia, but I can tell you, there were none of those trees up here.) I know I was lucky to find anything growing wild, and though I wasn't sure if they were toxic. I spent an hour yesterday, sitting alongside some berry bushes and eating about a hundred of them.

Day Four

I was very unsure of my position and not making good time; couldn't believe there was this much geography without any people. As much of a pickle I was in, and as discouraging as it was, I couldn't help but shiver with relief, when I speculated on *where I might have been right now*. And boy was I dirty. I'd walked through deep mud a dozen times. Woke up last night when something bit me on my calf; jumped up and in the dark shook whatever it was out of my pants leg (or at least hoped I did). I was almost afraid to slide my hand up through the cuff and feel the area of the bite. In the morning I examined my calf which was mostly a big red lump, real hot to the touch, and hurt. Not very glamorous to relate, but I spent most of this day with the "runs." The berries may not have been toxic, but diarrhea hit me full force and repeatedly. I knew that would dehydrate me; would now have to find water for sure. Still hadn't seen or heard another human being, which I guess was good.

Day Five

The next day I started early, but still—between the trees the scrub brush was so dense that I couldn't make good progress. Even on the days when I did, I'd be surprised if I made ten miles. At this rate it would take me at least another week to reach an area far enough south that it might be "ours." If so, and I came upon an open area—some grassland without any trees, I could lay out a distress signal and wait there. Rest! And just hope some Air America search plane would see me. But even laying out a signal would not be easy. I had no contrasting man-made materials. In an "SAR" over supposedly uninhabited areas (like this) the search pilots are most likely to notice a signal if it is comprised of geometrically shaped or arranged—man-made materials. (A 4x8 piece of white drywall cut into four big triangles would be just fine.) The only thing I had and likely to be sufficiently contrasting, but way too small—was my white undershirt. Not that I had needed it thus far, but in the whole trek south, I hadn't come across a single piece of paper or cloth, of any size. I spent the day just trudging along, shoes ruined, trouser legs torn, aching, hungry, and tired by noon, so not much to relate—during the day that is; the night was another thing!

Never Thought About This

That evening I found a sheltered and possibly *comfortable* spot. A hollowed out big log filled with leaves (that I first scavenged through in search of rats or snakes or frogs). I nestled in for a hopefully—all-the-way-through-the-night sleep. I did fall asleep quickly, which I think was because of my rundown state and hobbled mind. But I was awoken sometime around 2 a.m. by the most fearfully loud explosions, rumbling, and violent shaking of the earth beneath me. The retorts coming every few seconds were not only deafeningly loud, but a second or two later were accompanied by concussive waves that sucked the air out of my lungs and as I was to notice later, had undone a couple buttons on my shirt. It lasted at least five minutes. It was another of the almost nightly B-52 bombing raids (of this neutral country). As terrifying as it was, I'll bet the drop zone was at least five if not ten miles from my position. I was well aware of these strikes. We often could hear them when we RON'ed at Long Chien; three B-52's in tandem, each with over one-hundred, 750-pound bombs. I'm sure that from Langley or the Pentagon they had intelligence declaring the targets as enemy positions, but to me the program could easily be called reckless—almost random "carpet bombing" of mostly uninhabited wilderness! Many times, flying out of Long Chien the morning after one of these extended "Rolling Thunder" raids had occurred, we would be the first to see it from the air, and the destruction was so dense that the ground was *75 % tan (new dirt craters) and only 25% green (remaining jungle)*. One time the B-52's accidentally dropped some cluster bombs on the outskirts of Long Chien, resulting in a case officer named Shep Johnson having most his left buttock taken off. After that, the big joke was saying Shep was doing a "half-assed" job.

Day Six

I knew (everybody knows) you have to keep up your liquid intake, especially in this hot climate. Like I had (only once before), I came upon a small drainage creek (three feet across at the widest) and found an area in it where the water ran over rocks and looked clear. I had no canteen (or any other receptacle) so couldn't take any with me. Just cupped my hand and drank about a hundred handfuls. The good news was, I wasn't eating chopped up birds. The bad news was I wasn't eating much at all, but thank God, that was about to change. I suddenly realized I was hearing voices and quickly dropped down in the brush. I didn't think there was a path nearby, and I didn't see anyone coming. Scanning ahead, through the trees I saw structures and realized *I was about to walk right smack into a tiny village.* Can't do that! This far north it was probably visited daily by NVA soldiers, and the villagers would turn me in—*at the least!* (The B52 bombings had annihilated many a small village like this one. They were *not* keen on Americans!) I crawled up to the edge of the clearing and looking about a hundred feet across an open area I was able to get a better look at the village. There were quite a few open-sided (*no* walls on *any* side) gazebo-like structures that served as homes. They all had raised floors—at least three feet above the ground. And there was some type of cultivated area behind each one, and stretching to the edge of the wooded area where I was now crouched.

And the best news was, behind each house (on the side towards me) there was a long table upon which were rows of specially-shaped ceramic jugs. Having seen this exact type jug in many villages, I was willing to bet what was in them—something called "sticky rice'! *"Khao Niew."* It's the staple of half of Southeast Asia and all of Laos. Hmong soldiers would go into battle with a three-inch ball of it in each trouser pocket. It's a glutinous rice with a high sugar content, so when it's steamed it sticks together; you can make 'snow balls' out of it. My plan was to slip in after all the villagers had retired for the night—probably after midnight. (Would have to make sure not to fall asleep myself.) I'd grab a jug and sneak back here, and if lucky, eat my fill. I was hoping I would find some kind of small container to steal, since I wouldn't be able to carry the large jug with me. On some of the tables there were smaller sacks, stuffed with something— maybe turnips, potatoes, or some kind of rounded vegetable. Here, and good, I was perhaps going to get some nourishment, at least help a little with that problem,

A half hour after the last lamp in the village was extinguished, and only one small fire was burning itself out, I ventured to the tables. This only took about one minute and was not too bad, except I was cutting through what might have been rice paddies. Halfway there I was able to make out a raised dirt path between the wet quadrangles. I'd use it for my trip back. At the tables I was thrilled to find the ceramic jugs were filled, and I was almost sure—with that sticky rice. (They could have been sitting there empty, ready to be filled.) Grabbed one and snuck back to the wood line, sat down, pulled out the clay top of the jug. It *was* sticky rice and I dug in! Even with no sauce, I almost had tears in my eyes, swallow after swallow. Pure joy to chew something. When I'd had my fill I made another trip back to check out those sacks of whatever. Did so and brought one back to the woods. Didn't know if it was turnips or potatoes or what (and wouldn't be sure until first light in the morning). This fortunate delay accomplished, at some hour before dawn I left, putting as much distance between me and the village as I could. When there was enough light I examined the contents of the sack, and it was a fruit I was familiar with, called rambutan (I think). It is not appealing to look at. Its outer layer being comprised of hundreds of stringy, dark red appendages, but once pealed there is a soft white and sweet interior. I was quite sure this would be very good for energy, and was glad I had brought the sack with me. About noon I began to get some appetite and started in on the rambutan; eating at least ten of them. (They're only a couple inches across, about the size of a lemon.) If I just didn't get recaptured, I was beginning to think I might make it far enough south to get to a safe, and possibly discoverable location (such as that hoped-for, grassy open area I spoke of earlier).

Day Seven

Halfway through the following day I heard a noise that was unrecognizable at first; almost like a distant engine. It must be ahead of me, since as I continued the sound became more pronounced. *Holy shit—that's the sound of a river.* I was excited because everyone knows it's on rivers that towns and cities spring up. Still keeping myself hidden in the wooded area I snuck to within fifty feet of the bank. It could be my bad luck to stumble onto some 'unfriendlies' getting water. Only thing was, I knew from flying to Muang Xon, there was no river near it. The closest one (as I recollect from my maps) was at least thirty or forty miles west. And if this was it, it would mean while I had intended to go mostly south, I had actually gone more to the west. Damn, I wish I knew where I was—how far south I was. The river was flowing to the south. It would have been nice to have a raft, and just be able to float south. Of course no way I could risk that exposure (or be able to make a raft). Or, I could have made much better progress walking south on the hard sand bank, but that would also make me easily seen. Too dangerous now, gotta wait until I'm at least one more day south. I trudged south alongside it—about fifty feet in the woods, and noticed the stretch of water was becoming much wider; in fact, turning into a major river. There'd have to be a village on it soon (or at least eventually).

Day Eight

About ten in the morning I did come upon a village—on the opposite side of the river. *And miracle of miracles, I saw a jeep and heard a generator!* That would mean this place had been visited by USAID with whom Air America also had numerous contacts (and the Customer used for cover for many of their operatives). Pretty sure it was friendly, but I hid in the wooded area for another hour, observing the people on the other side of the bank. And then I saw an American! *And I knew him!* He was a longtime USAID volunteer: Pop Buell, an Indiana farmer who had been travelling all over Laos for the last 15 years—often to villages this far north, where he instructed the inhabitants how to better cultivate their land and plant and grow pest-free, nutritious crops. He was known and respected country-wide (even by the 'unfriendlies'). Unfortunately—stunned by my good fortune, before I could shout to him Pop disappeared back in the village. I ran down the bank to the river's edge, but was afraid to try to get across. I didn't know how deep it was, and the current was fast. I hollered and waved, gaining the ears of some villagers. They in turn started shouting back towards where Pop had disappeared. In a few minutes he was in view again, *waving at me!* He launched two guys in a small boat powered by one of those "pop, pop" two stroke engines, to come across and get me. Good thing I didn't try to swim, coming across to keep the boat from being rapidly swept south, the guys in the boat kept the bow pointing 45 degrees to the north—upstream, against the current, arriving at a spot fifty feet upstream, and getting to my location by riding a rapid drift downstream.

Pop Buell recognized me from the many times I had flown him to remote locations like this, but he was not aware of my being captured or the Search and Rescue mission. He radioed back that I was there, okay. A joyous night was had by all. The next day I found out this was the Nam Ou river—a major river in Laos, and that if I had continued to follow it south, in three more days, I would have arrived at the bustling city of Luang Prabang, the cultural and religious capital of Laos, frequented daily by Air America planes. I was bought back to Vientiane the next morning, greeted well, and badgered to tell my story so many times I didn't get home till late afternoon, where I sat in deep thought for a long time. It was sort of a wake-up call for me. *What would Sara and the kids do if I was no more?* At this moment, I missed them all, very much.

Chapter Thirty-Five
KICKED OUT, BLACK OPS, AND GOOD-BYE

The Move Across the River

After over ten years of operating "in-country" on a daily but publicly unacknowledged basis, Air America's tenure in Laos was coming to an end. The communist elements in the government took over and we were immediately declared "persona non grata." So what did this mean? *It meant Air America had one week to get all its personnel and equipment out of Laos!* The plan for operations (which would not cease that rapidly) was to relocate the whole Vientiane setup across the river in Thailand— to the joint Thai/US Udorn Thani Air Force base (where our helicopters had been based since the early sixties). With no warning this move had a negative impact on almost every employee; no way to arrange for the transport of even half our belongings; many of us had paid a year's rent in advance (that we would not get refunded), and for me specifically—I didn't have time to find a buyer and had to abandon that baby blue Fiat sports car!

Danielle was still living with me, and this sudden expulsion was going to be a problem, since she had no Thai visa. In spite of its singular 'saving grace' our coexistence had been so rocky I toyed with using this event as being a justifiable reason (excuse) for us to make the big break. But I failed to capitalize on it! I went along with her getting a visa and she did accompany me. Missed a big chance that would only delay a harrowing experience. In Udorn—not too far from the base, I found a small, two-story, well-windowed house. It was unique in that it and one other home next to it, were brand new, oddly built in the center of a flat ten-acre expanse of marshland. In the other home lived the head of "Det One" (the moniker

259

for the CIA office running highly-classified operations out of Udorn). His name was Buddy Rogers and he was a prince of a guy, admired by all who knew him.

Becoming a "Project Pilot"

Det One was conducting a significant number of "Black Ops" operations; not just in northern Laos, but into North Vietnam (and quite a while after the January 1973 supposed "Peace Accords"). This included 3 a.m. landings in a black "Twin-Otter" aircraft *on dikes just 13 miles outside downtown Hanoi!* Secret negotiations were still going on, and U.S. representatives wanted inside information on what the North Vietnam government was really up to. Thusly what we were doing up there *was tapping the phone lines!* Actually not we pilots; we had Thai mercenaries that shinnied up the telephone poles and did the actual handiwork. We just flew them in and out. There were only about ten pilots involved in this and other similarly secret and hazardous aviation operations; they were called "Special Project" pilots. Shortly after my arrival in Udorn there was a vacancy for one more Project pilot, I was humbled to hear I had been nominated by the pilots already in the program, and approved by Buddy himself (who was willing to take a gamble on a guy he knew nothing about; for which I will always be indebted to him).

Air America pilots in general enjoyed a lofty regard, but as a Project pilot one had an even more elevated status (as well as the associated danger of being part of "Black Ops"). Now, instead of the couple dozen daily trips from Long Chien to village strips, that I'd been doing in the past, my days (or I should say *nights*) were occupied training for a landing on a dike just outside Hanoi city. We carried out this training near Pakse, Laos, deep in the woods, in the middle of the night, on an unlit five hundred foot long, 15-foot-wide dirt path (and without using the aircraft landing lights)! To define the landing area (now and during the coming real thing) we had one guy standing at the far end of the strip, shining his flashlight at us coming in, and another guy standing on the touchdown end of the "runway" also shining his flashlight at us. On landing we'd only clear this first guy's head by five or ten feet! (We had to be this low in order to touch down soon enough that we wouldn't go off the far end.) Just two lights—*small* lights, defining the ends, and no lights defining the edges.

I can tell you, during training—making those approaches, skimming the tree tops, hitting and careening down the narrow rutted landing area, scared me to death. I can't believe my wobbly control of the aircraft, last-second corrections, and to me—barely acceptable landings, weren't seen as such by the senior project pilots. As far as I was concerned, I wasn't up to the task. Usually riding in the right seat and evaluating my performance was the senior Project pilot, Pete Packer (who had been Wernher Von Braun's private pilot, and at 19 years of age piloted one of the B-26's in the famous and failed Bay of Pigs Cuban invasion). Not on even one landing did I feel as if I had proper control of the aircraft!

My First Black Ops Mission

About three weeks later we got the 'go-ahead' for a mission, and though I cannot think of any reason they would have chosen me; I was scheduled for it. The good news was I was going with Pete Packer, and he was—like Jim Ryan: the "best of the best." I would be the copilot—in the right seat, primarily doing the navigation to get there. Oh, and let me tell you about that. First of all, there were no accurate maps for our intended route inside North Vietnam, and even if there were, it would be at night, so we could not navigate by observing the terrain features below us. *So how did we get there?* Installed in the aircraft was something called "Terrain Avoidance Radar," which by its name you know was not there to avoid thunderstorms; it was there for us to read the 'ground return' to keep us in the valleys that led to Hanoi (while only 50 feet above the tree tops)! Interpreting the returns on the scope and selecting a series of headings was almost an art—a real scary art, because without immediate recognition and proper interpretation of what you were seeing on the radar, you could easily end your life by flying into suddenly rising terrain (which more than one Air America Project Pilot had done).

About one in the morning Pete and I got a last-minute briefing and were driven to the ramp where we met our two Thai mercenaries at the aircraft. These two guys had been selected after a dozen of them with gaff-hooks on their ankles, competed to see who could dig them in and get up the un-barked tree (simulated telephone pole) the quickest. At the aircraft I got a real surprise: *Pete was going to ride in the right seat, and let me fly the mission! Whoa!* Half the reason I hadn't been really sweating this thing was because I knew that Pete would be flying. Although, now that I think about it—since the biggest danger was flying into the side of a hill, he may have concluded that the safest thing he could do was *not* be occupied controlling the aircraft, but sit in the right seat *interpreting the ground radar returns*, and keep us out of rising ground.

We were airborne at one-thirty and headed north. The first hour and a half was no problem. As we approached the North Vietnamese border we started paying particular attention to the "Holy Shit" gauge. *Oh, I hadn't mentioned that yet.* The anti-aircraft weapon we feared the most was the SAM-7 missile, fired by a single person using a four-foot long shoulder-supported firing tube. The damned missile—about the same length, had a sophisticated infra-red homing device in its nose, and not only traveled in excess of the speed of sound, but supposedly could make sharper turns than the aircraft! While it was in "Search Mode" and hadn't locked onto you, the gauge was blank. As soon as the missile system locked onto you, the gauge started flashing and a beeping tone began. When the missile was actually fired, the beeping tone went to a shrill, steady tone, increasing in volume, the scope went bright orange, and your fate was just about sealed. That's why it was called the "Holy Shit" gauge.

Navigating the last five miles to the east/west oriented dike was accomplished using what we called the "Skippy" system. Earlier in the day of our arrival a special sound-modified aircraft made a quick 'in and out' pass over the dike and dropped an empty peanut butter jar as close to it as he could. The jar shattered upon hitting the ground, allowing a small radio beacon to tumble out. On it was a lever (like on a grenade) that now out of the jar was free to spring open, starting the transmission of the signal. It was low-powered beacon with a battery life of only 24 hours (so the North Vietnamese would have less chance of picking it up). When I over-headed the beacon I knew I was somewhere near the landing site. (The jar had only hit *near* the dike.) I didn't want to, but had to pop up to a hundred feet of altitude to visually spot the dike. Great! Spotted it and one of the flashlights. I flew a half mile west, made a quick 180 degree turn, and started in for the landing, heading due east—the dike orientation. (Like in practice—with the aircraft landing lights out.) Saw both flashlights now. Had to slide over to the right a bit to line up perfectly. Reduced the power, began my descent. I may have—for some reason, been *less* scared than I was when making those practice landings during training. We hit (hard) but on the dike, and mercifully—centered and not too far down it. Couldn't see anything left or right, just kept the nose pointed directly at the light at the far end, which was suddenly only twenty feet in front of me! Stopped. Out of prop reverse.

Oops, a problem that should have been anticipated: Surveying the narrow patch of raised ground I was on, it was going to be a real tight maneuver to turn the aircraft around for take-off; in fact, *maybe not possible!* One main gear might go over the side, and then we'd be stuck here and captured for sure! Pete knew what I was thinking, grabbed a flashlight and jumped out. There was a road paralleling the dike—I could see cars going by at what seemed to be only a hundred yards away. Pete appeared in my line of vision, shining his flashlight at the edge of the raised dike and motioning me to continue my turn, with full left brake. The left main gear could not advance (in fact, had to back up)! This required the use of reverse power on the left engine. Pete was walking with the nose of the aircraft, holding a 'thumbs-up' as I jockeyed the turn. My right main gear stayed clear of the edge. Great! Pointed back down the dike ready for take-off. Even before I got positioned the Thai guys had jumped out with their gear and the gaff-hooks already strapped to their ankles. Of course, in spite of the noise, I left the engine running, since we might have to make a hurried departure! I stayed in the cockpit. In a couple minutes Pete joined me.

I didn't know for sure how long it would take our guys to accomplish what they had to do, although I did know what it was they had to do: first—get up the pole; second—unscrew the several ceramic insulators on the cross-bar that supported the wires; third—when the cross bar was clean, overlay it with a vinyl solar strip (to power what we were about to install); fourth—screw back in the ceramic insulators, *including one bogus insulator that was actually a tap, that would retransmit all the telephone conversations carried on this line.* These transmitters were not omnidirectional. They only sent out a narrow signal. The Thai guys would position it so the transmitted signal went southwesterly (so someone to the northeast in Hanoi would not pick it up).

And this was not even half the job; the power of these insulator/transmitters was so weak, the signal only went out about thirty miles, so we were going to have to place another receiver/transmitter in the top of a tree, every 30 miles for 150 miles—to get it to a listening post. And as hard as this is to believe, the CIA at Langley, not only gave us the coordinates where each of these five re-transmitters (huge, artificial tree-top canopies made out of thousands of green-painted aluminum leaves) would go, but actually sent us a U2 photo of each of the precise trees that we were supposed to put them on top of! At the final listening post we had captured NVA soldiers in headsets, listening 24/7. If they heard a high level, pertinent conversation, they would key a recorder and later translate it. The English translation was coded and sent to the Joint US Military Advisory Group in Bangkok, who got it to the people who needed it (Henry Kissinger—in France). We were a key part of the "Paris Peace Talks."

I sat there a bundle of nerves, imagining persons in nearby neighborhoods hearing the engine, and coming to investigate. (I was just outside a suburb thirteen miles from city center!) *Please God, give us another five minutes.* It was less than that when I heard the Thai guys jumping back into the airplane. They hollered that it was done and we could leave. I jammed the power levers forward and we were accelerating down the dike. Shortly after takeoff one of the Thai guys comes up to the cockpit, apparently well satisfied with his work. We asked him how it went. He said, no problem, except his gaff-hooks weren't much help, *the telephone pole was concrete!*

Udorn Just Before Dawn

The trip back was gratefully uneventful, that is to say until I parked the aircraft. As Pete was exiting the right side cockpit door (about eight feet above the ramp), his foot slipped off the exterior step and he began falling backward. Instinctively he reached upward to grab something to arrest his fall, and he caught the sill of the door opening. This abrupt stop in his rearward plummet snapped his head back, the effects of which were worsened by him wearing a heavy WWII 'shrapnel-proof' helmet. When I got around to that side of the airplane Pete was getting up and saying he wasn't hurt, but at the same time turning his head from side to side, indicating to me he wasn't really sure about his neck. We attended a short debriefing and then went to the Air America cafeteria, feeling euphoric at having successfully completed our mission and being back—safe! The cafeteria had been told to be open just for us. Pete's wife "Smiles" and Jim Ryan joined us.

While we were eating I could see something was bothering Pete; he was only taking an occasional bite. He soon stopped eating altogether and just leaned back in his chair, silent. After a minute or two he said "God, I feel terrible." With that he pushed back his chair, stood up (but not steadily) and then just lay down on the floor. It was obvious for him to do that, this could be serious. We called the Udorn Air America clinic (open 24/7). A nurse was there in three minutes. She did wellness checks but did not look like she had determined anything. I told her about the incident on the ramp. She immediately used her hand-held radio to call the US Air Force clinic, and five minutes later an ambulance arrived. Smiles was understandably—extremely worried. (You never could tell what Jim was thinking.) Two days later Pete was flown to the Stanford University Medical Center. Not sure they would have done that for any of us. While most of us were just "contract" employees with the Agency (big bucks but no benefits or retirement) the word was that Pete was on the official Agency roster. He was gone three months getting treatment for varying stages of lower body paralysis. When he returned he had no paralysis, but had no feeling in his right leg. He wouldn't know it if you held a lit cigarette against his leg. He was obviously off the flight schedule.

Perhaps the Most Beautiful Words a Husband Ever Said

Being as close to Pete as I was, after he was back in Udorn recuperating, I would often stop over to his house to check on him. One afternoon, approaching his house on the incoming stone walk, that would take me past an open window (which I knew was right over the couch where Pete most often rested), I heard Pete talking to one of his sons. He had four boys—no girls. He had no idea anyone was coming, I was positioned there by pure coincidence. Evidently one of the boys was pulling that famous ploy of playing something the father said, against something the mother said. I heard Pete say: *"Danny, I was in love with your mother long before you came along, and I'm going to be in love with her long after you're gone, so don't ever try to come between me and my wife again."* (How many wives would be thrilled to hear their husband make a statement like that!)

A reality check: Along with what you've just read—for us to be nostalgic for a moment, Pete died of esophagus cancer not too many years later, and his beautiful smiling wife is in an assisted living home with dementia. I still see Danny from time to time.

Finally, Making the Big Decision

May of 74. I don't know about the rest of the world, but all of us here knew we'd lost the war in Vietnam, and even operating out of Udorn, conducting operations in Laos was all but over. The NVA forces were driving the lesser trained and armed Hmong soldiers backward ten miles a day. I feared it could only be a matter of months before Air America shut down. Should I struggle along to the bitter end or just quit now? I'd spent nine and a half years in Southeast Asia. I was going to have to go back to the states (or somewhere) sometime. Of course I had no idea what I'd do (especially with a one-eyed pilot's license). Still, somehow, the luster was sufficiently off the operation. I made the decision to quit and did so, but cannot adequately relay here the array of confused thoughts and strange emotions that plagued me while making and right after this parting decision.

Major White

The tough thing to do would be to find individual buyers for each of my possessions (a dozen pieces of furniture, a bunch of kitchen stuff, a Hi-Fi setup, and a neat Mazda truck), and also take my Doberman watchdog. The *ideal* thing would be to find someone to take the whole lot! Someone being transferred here who would like a 'turnkey' move-in. (They would have to acquire all this stuff anyway.) With only a little more than a week to go, no buyer had yet materialized. Of course with things winding down there were few new-hires arriving. I was beginning to panic. And then a miracle: my advertisements were answered by an Air Force major. This surprised me, because all the active duty military personnel I knew were living in quarters on the base. Why would he be looking for a house in town? After a bunch of negotiating we did settle on a complete deal—the house, all my stuff, my truck, *and the dog!* And with a week left to go!

Bad news! A couple days later, he contacts me and says for some reason he can't do it! *What do you mean you can't do it?* Turns out it was a money issue; he had switched banks and his military direct deposits got screwed up. He said he just didn't have it available now. "Okay, tell you what Charles, how about this: I'll give you the address of my bank, leave without the money, but as soon as you have your funds squared away, send the bank a check for the $2,400 dollars." He was thrilled and we shook hands on the deal, and set a date for him to move in. The next day he stops by, *with his wife?* That should have made me suspicious. I already knew that for military personnel this was an "unaccompanied" tour—no family members allowed. Two days before I'm schedule to go to Bangkok to fly out, Major White contacts me and tells me the deal is still good, but he can't take the dog. (His wife got bitten once.) I spent the next 24 hours begging Air America friends to take the dog. Thank God, one does. *Much more on Major White later.*

Danielle

As I said before, two people could hardly have been less likeminded than Danielle and I. The sole benefaction—sufficient to forestall me from abandoning the relationship early on was the merciful relief I found in being able to at least consummate the act—something so long absent and desperately craved. Although knowing I was falling way short, my passable performance with Danielle at least allayed a decades-long devastating fear of total impotency (that I could just not imagine reliving)! While Danielle definitely had a measure of that aura I sought, I clung to the hope that there was a woman *who would have her aura, plus!* But being in this relationship I would not have the opportunity to find that woman (wherever the hell she was). I tried to make the break when Air America was kicked out of Laos. Didn't do it then, but now here's another chance! Sadly and embarrassedly I'll admit to you, I still wasn't able to do it, or at least do it "cold turkey." But I did have a plan to cowardly bring it about as a result of me quitting. Before leaving for the states I gave her tickets to Paris and told her I'd meet her there in three weeks. Since she knew I'd be in Europe to meet Al at Playa Granada the last weekend in July. (Remember? He had bought one of the condos there, from me.) So it was credible that on my way to Spain I'd come through Paris and pick her up. (I had her brother's phone number.) *Although, while discussing these plans aloud, in my heart I knew there was every chance this Paris pickup would not come about.*

Chapter Thirty-Six
A SUMMER TO REMEMBER

First Things First

Arriving in the states my first order of business was to visit Sara and the kids. To facilitate this—with no residence of my own and my employment location not nailed down (to say the least) I chose to move in with my folks. They were retired of course, but actively managing a cute little beachfront hotel just north of Fort Myers on the west coast of Florida. It was a three hour drive from there to the kids' house in Hobe Sound. I bought a green 1966 Mustang, which was pretty cool. Checked it out for a day or two and then drove over to the east coast. Certainly couldn't stay in the house with Sara, so got a motel in Jupiter (the next town south of Hobe Sound). I do have to thank Sara—she made every effort to give me unlimited and undisturbed contact with the kids. For a solid ten days the kids and I did just about everything a guilt-ridden father could offer; starting off by going to Disney World, Universal Studios and Busch Gardens. As far as Sara's security and leisure, I was pleased to see the Air Force major was a fixture around the house. Interspersed with our trips to Florida's main tourist attractions, were fun-filled days at the beach. I bought a whole volleyball setup, boogie boards, and a shade tent to sit under. Of course the boys (and Donna) were into surfing (like every other kid in Hobe Sound), but only had one second-hand board. I corrected that, buying them two new twin-fin short boards. The waves were better about fifty miles north so we took a two-day trip up to Canaveral pier, and we all gave it a go (even dad). It turned out to be a great ten days. I felt as if I'd repaired at least some damage. I would learn as the years rolled by, when a father abandons his kids—like I did, for whatever reasons, that damage is never repaired (so you young fathers reading this, take heed).

Returning to the Promised Land

After almost a month of priceless time with the kids (but no worthy job offers), it was time to temporarily disappear; boomerang back to Europe and sample—perhaps for the last time, the environs and lifestyle about which I was hopelessly nostalgic. Although I knew there was virtually no chance of finding employment anywhere on the Continent, I was surely going to keep my eyes open. I'd heard that since half the runway at the Basel, Switzerland airport stuck into France, the Swiss government let the aviation companies based there, *hire up to 50% of their employees from other countries.* I had an assortment of tickets, among them the ticket for my first flight: Miami to Paris. When I bought the ticket back in Vientiane, Danielle was with me so I had to use Paris (rather than Amsterdam or London) for my arrival airport, to convince her I was really going to meet up with her again. After this much time separated, my awareness of the stateside culture, and particularly, my unemployed status *I now was confident the best thing was to pass through Paris unannounced.* I was too cowardly to envision a face-to-face breakup; not showing up would do it. My plan was to maybe spend a day in Paris (jetlag), then spend about ten days visiting spots I had been to and had fond memories of (such as Cannes and maybe the Clinica Barraquer in Barcelona); more or less just wasting time before my July 27th meeting with Al in Salobreña. (Remember? Months ago in Vientiane he and I had scheduled this July meeting so I could show him his condo at Playa Granada.) Since he bought it just on my word, I felt I owed it to him to walk with him on the dark hardwood floors and out on the balcony of his new Mediterranean holiday residence.

A Meeting Meant to Miss

Arriving in Paris I got a room in my favorite hotel, the New Hotel—which on its business card says: *en face du gare du nord* (meaning across the street from the north Paris train station) which is where the train from the brand new Charles de Gaulle airport arrives. Unfortunately, almost all flights from the USA east coast to Europe leave about 8 at night and take 7 hours. But instead of arriving at 3 in the morning (providing a chance to get *some* sleep), with the time zone change it's about 9 in the morning. Everybody is up and starting their day while you are just looking for a place to crash! I thus wasted the first day.

Back in Europe I would have loved to pay a visit to my wonderful June, but had no idea where the Stafford Ballet was performing and thus no way to make phone contact. June as usual was and would always be out there somewhere—never out of my thoughts. Sadly—regardless of my love for her, her great character, personal worth and her love for me, she had proven not to be the female who could unlock my manhood. Therefore—having already confirmed I could not perform my husbandly duties with her, I predicted a marriage would likely end sadly. For this (noble?) reason, and this reason alone, I excluded her as a marital partner.

Now just in case you thought I had a brain in my head, after spending a half day debating it, *I called Danielle's brother!* Can you believe that? I was unable to carry out my spineless plan of just being a "no-show," which would have been a sure solution. Jacques was excited to get my call, a meeting with Danielle was arranged, and some travel plans were formulated. (It was surprising my lack of enthusiasm wasn't immediately apparent to her.)

The Greek Isles

I had a sheaf of MCO's and exchanged some for a set of tickets to Athens. We spent two days in the city and then took a steamer to the island of Mykonos. There we were met at the dock by hundreds of locals aggressively hawking their 'B&B's, of which the one we settled on was fresh and clean with spectacular views of gleaming white and turquoise. Each day we took an old bus over the top of the island and down to the beaches. There were three beaches, which progressed according to how much bathing attire was required. (The third—Elia, required *none*.) Although things went generally fine, it was evident Danielle and I were not a union made in heaven, and had already lasted longer than anyone could have thought. After Mykonos we went to a place neither of us had been—Crete. As you may know, it's the largest Greek island, about 150 miles long (just a little bigger than Puerto Rico). We flew into Heraklion, rented a Volkswagen beetle and spent the whole day driving an elevated road that scribed the perimeter of the island. It was carved out of steep cliffs, perhaps five-hundred feet above the water. It was spectacular and scary! (Similar to the drive I took with the kids around Corsica.) We looked down into emerald green cove after emerald green cove. The beauty was hypnotizing. I knew I wasn't going to find work here, but what a place to live!

That night Danielle and I had a great Greek dinner; a creamy split pea puree, baked eggplant, and our share of that honey-soaked baklava desert. At the conclusion of the meal (including several retsinas) the mood couldn't have been better. We decided we'd finish the evening by visiting a local taberna. I asked the waiter and he recommended we make the short drive to Hersonissos and go to some place that started with a "K" or hard "C." Even without getting the name in full, it was easy to find in the tiny village. The place was rocking, with musicians in—I guess, 19th century attire, playing apparently old and lively traditional Greek dance music. We spent almost two hours having drinks and watching the locals (and some tourists) go up on the stage and get with it, robustly dancing to the Hellenic music.

A Vacation Abruptly Ended

I cannot remember what provoked it, but seemingly out of the blue—perhaps because of something I did (or didn't do) the next thing I knew Danielle was strongly voicing a sudden and serious disapproval of me. She was more vocal and direct than she had ever been with me, in fact putting her hand on my chest and pushing. Although I had witnessed similar displays in the past, I had never seen her rise to this level of expressed distaste for me. After finishing one especially degrading sentence (of which I failed to grasp the meaning) she jumped up, turned on a heel and marched assertively towards the stage crowded with dancing tourists. There she mounted the steps and wedged herself in between two Greek guys, looping her arms over each of their shoulders. Starting the next second she appeared to be having the time of her life, and not at all upset about perhaps having just 'washed her hands' of me.

I wasn't at all sure what the rest of the evening would hold, and for the next few minutes just sat there befuddled, pondering what would be an appropriate course of action on my part. What I did amazes me to this day; nothing was further from my disposition and I can't believe I had the guts to do it! Although I failed to make the break in Paris (and at least three times in Vientiane) I was going to do it here and now—in a manner that would leave no doubt; an action that would definitely mark the end of us. I left money on the table to pay our bill, got up, walked out, found the Beetle and drove the few miles to our hotel. I was there just long enough to gather my belongings and stuff them in the car. That done I drove to the Heraklion airport, which I must've thought was open 24 hours a day.

But no, it was pitch black and completely deserted; not a single security guard or maintenance personnel in sight. Abandoned! It was about 3 a.m. I had no choice but to just wait there until it opened at six or seven or whenever. The Volkswagen was the sole vehicle in a ten acre parking lot. I can tell you getting comfortable enough to sleep in a Beetle is no easy task; think I was still awake when the sky began to turn pink in the east. Turned in the car and was on a flight back to Athens at 8:15. I spent several days in Athens, including a two-day visit to the island of Santorini, which was built on the slopes of a volcano, and as beautiful as Mykonos, with white beaches and crystal clear water. I was back in Athens on Wednesday, July 24th—three days before I was supposed to meet Al in Salobreña. Used another MCO to get a ticket for my flight to Spain the following day.

Salobreña Again, But No Al

Like I'd done twice before, landed at Malaga, rented a car, made the one hour drive to Salobrena, and checked into the same small hotel. The hotel was perched atop the rising ground to town and provided a beautiful view of the few sugar cane fields remaining, the Playa Granada condos under construction, and the beach. I was a day early but there was always the chance Al would have also shown up early. No such luck, but tomorrow is when he was supposed to arrive. But he didn't arrive the next day—the date we'd specified. This was a long time before cell phones and there was no way to contact him, or him— me. I passed most the day relaxing in a chaise lounge on the patio (that I'd twisted around so as to see the entrance in case Al arrived). That arrival did not happen. I hadn't heard from him, but knowing his punctuality, if he hadn't arrived on the specified day, it was a good bet he wasn't coming. Accepting that fact, there was no reason to stay in Spain, or anywhere in Europe. My month was over and I had to start thinking about my return (*unemployed)* to the good old USA.

That day (as I had done each day to save time and money and not risk missing Al), I took the evening meal in the hotel. The dining hall was on the south side of the hotel, facing the Mediterranean beach below. To facilitate tourist sight-seeing, the back wall was all glass (of little value now—in the dark and being completely steamed over as a result of previous requests to lower the air conditioner). Being later than I normally ate, all but one other table had been vacated; just me and my asparagus soup in this large, cold and abandoned dining hall. I was sitting where I'd sat for three nights— with my back to the glass, facing the entrance in case Al did come walking in. When seeing something incredulous we often say, "My jaw dropped." Well if ever that expression was applicable, it was now—to me. While my eyes were on the entranceway, my blood ran cold; *who do I see march through it, but Danielle!*

I realized she had known of the date of the scheduled meeting with Al, and just somehow (and I fear to imagine how) was able to get the money and tickets to get here. She spied me and without a falter in her step proceeded straight towards me, pulled out the chair and sat down across from me. There were no words exchanged for a sufficiently awkward time. She spoke first. "Well, you finally did it. I'm almost proud of you." This 'proud of me' comment on top of her wholly unexpected arrival, further took me aback, but could not generate a comment on my part. I was just smart enough not to say anything to indicate I was contemplating us getting back together, *but by the same token did not immediately reaffirm we were through.* I told her I'd be flying from Malaga to Paris, for my return to the states. I'm not sure if I said this to indicate I'd escort her back there, or some other possibly more futuristic reason. I walked her to her room and she invited me in. Sitting alongside her on the edge of the bed I could feel the same heat and arousal that had started this whole thing back in Vientiane. However, she gave no indications that she was intending to have me spend the night, and in retrospect it would not have been a good idea. We did agree I would get her a ticket and she could come on the same flight as me, back to Paris.

Never, Ever, Had I Been So Unsure

Although in Paris we were together during the daylight hours, at night I retreated to my favorite New Hotel and Danielle went to her brother's. The one thing both of us were frightenly aware of—thinking of nothing else, but speaking all around it without saying it, was: *was I going to take Danielle with me back to the states?* I was able to put this crucial decision off until the last minute. This was way before online e-ticket purchases. You could buy your tickets at the airport before walking to the gate; so I didn't have to stop by a travel agency and resolve this issue while we were sitting there (and suffer the response in the office). I had never been struck so indecisive and irresolute, or fearful of the pending consequences (whatever they would be) as during the cab ride to the airport. Yes— Danielle went with me. As usual she was wearing her knapsack, which appeared to be more full than usual (perhaps with a couple changes of clothing in the event of me making a positive decision). We didn't speak, but as they say: "the silence was deafening." She was just there like an appendage to my side. And she was there like that in the line at the Air France counter. Not holding hands; not speaking, just every couple minutes the two of us moving a yard further forward as a passenger in front of us completed their purchase and moved on. (The person in front of us, meaning to be sociable asked a question for which neither of us had an answer, other than looks of panic.) I was soon going to be out of time. Only one person left in front of us, *and I still had not come to a decision.*

I have no idea what muddled thoughts spawned the choice or how I suddenly mustered the fortitude, but when it came to the moment, *I asked for just one ticket.* Danielle's eyes widened, her lips tightened, she said nothing; just turned and walked away. Myself, I was a numb statue of a person. Ticket in hand I proceeded to the 2nd floor gate which had a glass back wall looking down into the lobby. Danielle hadn't left. I could see her. Having figured out where I was she was looking up—right at me. The next twenty minutes, waiting for them to call the flight seemed endless, and they were; then thirty, then forty-five minutes. When I snuck a peek, Danielle was still there. Five minutes later, an announcement: "*Air France flight six has been cancelled, all passengers please return to the lobby for assistance.*" I was dumbstruck, thinking of bolting for the ramp, go in the opposite direction—hide somewhere. With no way to avoid it, I went back down to the lobby. Tried to walk as normally as possible, past Danielle towards the line at the counter, with just a casual (can you believe) aside about my flight being cancelled. She waited motionless but not expressionless while I got rebooked—on a flight that (thank God) was about to be called!

Once again, had to pass reasonably close to her on my way back to the gate, and was somehow able (don't know how) to pull it off. We exchanged glances and I think I nodded my head. Only had to wait thirty minutes at the gate before they called the flight. No jetway. Had to take a bus out to the aircraft. Everyone boarded. Doors locked. Taxiing to the runway. Airborne! *I've done it! I've escaped.* I heard the wheels coming up, looked out the window and saw the flaps retracting. I was on my way. It was then I realized I my hands were vice grips on both armrests. Took my first deep breath in two days. Stretched my legs. Laid my head back and closed my eyes, for who knows what next. This was next: *Ladies and gentlemen we have a small problem and will be returning to De Gaulle for minor maintenance.* To myself I shouted "Oh No"! And then by the looks I was getting from nearby passengers, realized I had shouted it out loud. *What is this God? Are you trying to tell me something?* Am I supposed to give this Danielle thing more thought? This last thing was almost too much. We were told to wait in the same gate area, from which I could again see the lobby. *Danielle was gone.* The flight was soon boarded, and was promptly airborne. I laid my head back and closed my eyes, for another in a long line of "who knows what next."

Chapter Thirty-Seven
BACK IN THE U.S. AND ELSEWHERE

I'm Going to Need a Job

Of course the first thing to do was see the kids. I did and we had as good or better time than our first reunion. But I was plagued by the always with me: *what the hell was I going to do to make a living.* (I won't even tell you how little I saved after nine years with Air America; too embarrassing to mention.) Of course I knew the most likely work would be flying something, somewhere (hopefully in Florida). I took out ads in *Trade-A-Plane*—the most widely read weekly aviation newspaper, as well as in *Flying* magazine (not mentioning I had a waiver on my license for deficient vision in one eye). This *did* garner a handful of offers, but they were scarcely credible; ones flying old and poorly maintained aircraft, out of rusted hangers on rundown airports, in areas of congested airborne traffic or brutal winter weather—*for almost no pay at all.* (Made it clear to me why aircraft from these type organizations are always crashing: only the youngest and least experienced pilots would take these flight positions.)

Hard to Believe but True

Remember Major White? The guy who just a few days before I left for the states, rented my house in Thailand, bought my truck and all my furniture. He had told me he was switching banks and it would be a couple weeks before he'd have access to his money. He promised me that as soon as he did, he'd mail a check to my stateside bank. Well it's two months later and still no check. While visiting the kids in Hobe Sound and staying in a motel in Jupiter, I got thinking about that and got more and more irritated. I decided I was going to call him over there and tell him to get that money to me now! From there in the motel—after getting an international operator, I was connected to the Air Force Base in Udorn, Thailand. Once in contact with the base operator, I was able to get connected to his unit— the 432ⁿᵈ Tactical Air Force Wing. *But lo and behold, they tell me he's been transferred. Gone!* I got switched over to the Base Locator, who I knew should know what unit at what base he had been transferred to. Surprise number two: Turns out he wasn't just transferred, he was discharged! *He wasn't even in the Air Force anymore!* I tried to get the Base Locator to give me the "Home of Record" address he had left with them. Wasn't easy, they kept insisting that was information they were not authorized to give out. I finally succeeded, and *what they told me was a one in a million break*: He was now living in West Palm Beach, Florida. Six miles south of my motel! I was able to easily take care of the situation.

An Old Friend Comes to the Rescue

Back to finding a job; fortunately (or initially thought to be fortunate) Earl Richman who had been the Vice President of Operations with Air America contacted me. He was presently managing a large aviation operation at the old Stewart Air Force Base in Newburg, NY, which the federal government had recently sold to the county to run as a commercial airport. He was familiar with my reputation and the job I had done as Chief Pilot, and asked me if I would like to be his Director of Operations. Earl said, being only sixty miles north of the Big Apple, the rumor was that it would soon be designated the "alternate" (overflow airport) for aircraft that couldn't get into JFK or LaGuardia. By all rights, this would guarantee a bright future for his operation. The pay was okay and it was a position I could be reasonably proud of, but man oh man, did I not want to go up north! A thousand miles from my kids and I'd be knee-deep in snow half the year. Plus it involved another stressful thing: I would be supervising and flying small (Piper and Beechcraft) "puddle-jumper" aircraft—that I had no experience in, having started in military aircraft and then gone straight to Air America.

I will never forget the foreboding reservations I felt standing in front of my folk's house—the loaded trailer behind my Mustang, ready to go but stalling. I left, but it was with no conviction whatsoever that this was the right move. It was a two-day drive. Earl appeared thrilled to see me and could not have been more accommodating. Earl came from a blue-blooded family; in his hallway was a photo of him sitting in a chair with his father and grandfather standing behind him—each in their Yale sweater. His company was called Banner Flight and it had four sources of revenue: Aircraft storage and fuel sales, aircraft maintenance, a flight school, and a charter business. However it was late 1974, the country (and particularly this area) was in a deep recession, and to me Earl's company appeared to be struggling. As an example of how the recession had affected the area, in Newburg the Ford dealer had closed down his business. When I strolled the streets, and especially when I walked into the local Kmart, tears almost came to my eyes when I saw the rusted, banged up cars in the parking lot, and the unkempt, slovenly dressed shoppers inside (and compared that scene to what I had seen on the Haufbahnstrasse in Zurich).

I struggled in the job, never for an hour feeling as if I understood what I could do to jack up our revenue (what little of it was coming in). Even the other pilots seemed to display a pessimism about the future of Banner. Fortunately, the existing chief pilot when I arrived was a solid, 100% guy—Stu Carlton. He was young, but had started flying young and had a wealth of experience in "general aviation" (what this kind of operation was called). Stu and I would go on to be lifelong friends. With my lack of experience and floundering efforts at Banner, it was Stu who kept me out of trouble, and I had one memorable encounter with him: I had noticed that when someone asked Stu a question, he would consistently put his fist to his mouth and clear his throat before answering. Anyone seeing this would easily recognize that he was just stalling to assemble his thoughts. One day I said to him, "Stu, as long as we have become such good friends, let me mention one habit you have, that you may want to consider doing away with." I went on to describe the above. Stu seemed to take it okay but responded that since we were such good friends, he 'd share something with me: He wondered if I had ever noticed, that almost every time—just before I began to talk, I would put a hand in my pocket, find the elastic in my jockey shorts, pull it away from my leg, and jiggle my hips to let my balls hang free.

Earl scheduled weekly departmental meetings during which the marketing guys got their chance to make their pitches about huge imminent contracts—not just in New York, but across the country (including contracts in California with helicopters utilizing earth-penetrating sonar, to discover potential underground oil reserves). I would listen but was unable to make sense of their claims (leaving each meeting feeling I wasn't even qualified to be attending it). I had no business background and couldn't put it together. It didn't seem real. Nothing seemed to be adding up. I knew just enough to ask Earl for two financial records kept by every company, which he gladly gave me (not suspecting I had never looked at these type records before and was ill-equipped to understand them or come up with any positive suggestions). As unfamiliar as I was with these documents, after studying them I felt even more at a loss; for example: the numbers for the flight school indicated every time we took a student up we lost money! Another month: two more meetings of glad handing and high-fiving. I concluded I just wasn't cut out to understand the business world. The following month Earl announced we were declaring bankruptcy and shutting down the operation.

Sometimes You Have to Consider Every Offer

I was contacted by the owner of a small aviation company in Wichita, Kansas. His company had contracts with Beechcraft (the largest manufacturer of small civilian aircraft, and whose factories were there in Wichita). The owner sent me tickets to fly out for an interview. I did. Turns out he was a tennis doubles partner with the Vice President of Sales for Beechcraft. (The best way to get contracts, next to being a golf partner.) Beechcraft made a fast, small, single-engine plane (often purchased by doctors and lawyers) called the Bonanza. It was the 'queen of the fleet' of general aviation aircraft. Well the Iranian Air Force ordered 12 of these Bonanzas—specially designed and built to fire rockets and drop bombs. The owner (Dave) had sweet-talked himself into getting the contract to deliver them to Iran. (This purchase was when the Shah was in charge, and just doing whatever American corporations wanted.)

I realized if I did hire on with Dave I might have to move to and live in Wichita. To enhance its appeal, Dave had planned an elaborate barbeque at his house that night, so we stopped by the local grocery store to buy a steak. While walking through the store, Dave—in attempting to point out the good things about Wichita, *was actually stumped*, and could not verbalize a single point. By chance and fortunately for him, in the next isle we bumped into his business partner. Dave is relieved and asks *him* to tell me what's good about Wichita. The partner gets pensive, finger tips to his lips, glances skyward for a moment or two, and finally responds, "Well there's not much bad about Wichita."

A Little Bit about My New Job

If you needed any further indication as to how little I think ahead, and how little I consider the details and consequences of what I am about to do, I agreed to hire on, *to fly single-engine, slow, propeller-driven aircraft, alone—solo, sitting on an aluminum gas tank instead of a seat, for ten hours, across the icy Atlantic.* (Of course it didn't matter if it was icy or not. It's a big ocean, and even if the water was 70 degrees you'd die of exposure before you were found.) Prior to taking my first trip I had to go to Moncton, Ontario, where the Canadian Civil Aviation Authority (now the TCCA) made me watch videos of Canadian Air Force pilots bailing out into the Saint Lawrence Seaway, and going motionless—dead, in the frigid waters, *in the first one minute!* The CCAA wouldn't allow any pilot to fly a single-engine aircraft from anywhere in their country, across the ocean, until he has attended this seminar and passed a written test. (I later discovered that I was one out of only nine approved!)

On the first trip I was nervous as hell; picked up my plane at the factory (all painted in a camouflage design) and flew it to Gander, Newfoundland. After a restless night's sleep I got up at three a.m. and by five, was airborne and heading east—bound for Shannon, Ireland, across the soon to be sun-streaked glassy Atlantic. Now what makes this trip even more difficult is our aircraft *did not have any long distance navigational aids!* Airborne out of Gander I would just 'aim' at Shannon and hope that for the next 1,702 miles the winds would be as predicted, that I wouldn't drift too far, and would be able to visually orient myself when the west coast of Ireland came into view—a lot of if's. (Some guys missed Ireland altogether, and arrived at the Scottish coast to the north or the southwest tip of England to the south.) My first trip and approaching the Irish coast I was only forty miles north of Shannon (which I found out was a record for the company).

After arriving in Europe, the rest of the trip to Iran took me over a southerly route, which had me passing over the northern edge of Syria (violating their airspace). As small as we were ground radar rarely picked us up, but somehow Damascus Control must have seen me and asks me for my "Overflight Permit" number; furthermore he says if I don't have one, *they're going to launch fighters and shoot me down!* Of course I didn't have one, so I would just spout out a series of bogus letters and numbers for them to look for, repeatedly insisting they had to be able to find it, because that was the one their consulate issued me. (My hope was, and I did—exit their airspace before they realized I was "BS-ing" them). This kind of quick thinking impressed Dave and his partners, and after my first trip I was promoted to Flight Leader. From now on I would lead two other guys over each time.

A Humorous but Embarrassing Anecdote

My next trip therefore was a flight of three. After the ten-hour crossing of the Atlantic and landing at Shannon, our route would be: first to Le Bourget, France, then to Malta, then to Ankara, and then finally, to our destination—Teheran; each about six hours. Although the last four legs were much shorter than the Atlantic crossing, they still exceeded our bladder capability, so a 'must' on each trip was an empty milk jug. There wasn't room to stand up and pee normally, and getting my small dick through two layers of clothes and sufficiently into the neck of the jug, *while seated*, and not have two or three 'almosts' was not easy! Well, on the leg from Le Bourget to Malta I couldn't find a milk jug and (stupid me) made the bad decision to believe I'd have no problem 'holding it' for just five hours. Sure as hell an hour and a half after take-off, crossing the south coast of France and venturing out over the pitch black (not a single light) Mediterranean sea, my teeth started tickling. It wasn't long before I was in dire straits, extreme discomfort—threatening permanent anatomical distortion. I bore it for as long as humanly possible, but knew I was going to have to relieve myself. *But into what?* I thought of a possible solution—my flashlight! It was a long multi-battery steel tube. I screwed off the big end (the lens end), dumped the batteries out and was ready. But being seated I realized I wouldn't be able to tip the flashlight down low enough to keep the pee from running right back out. No way to stand up, the top of the cockpit was only about ten inches above my head, but I would somehow have to raise my hip area enough to allow me to angle the flashlight down.

I raised ten inches until my head hit the overhead, then bent over 90 degrees at the waist, allowing me to raise my hips even further, straighten my legs almost as if I standing. However, to have room to do this required that I wedge my head and shoulders forward across the top of the instrument panel; in fact, all the way to the windshield (which space narrowed, causing me to have to turn my head sideways to jam it the last few inches). Of course with my head there *I couldn't see the instruments or manipulate the controls!* A few seconds later (before I had a chance to start peeing), on the radio I hear one of the other pilots urgently shouting my name (having seen my aircraft peel off on a wing and start down towards the black water)! Tried again, and the same thing happened. I righted the aircraft again, and was pretty sure I had it trimmed up to maintain straight and level flight while I took care of business. *I was ready to start.*

The one thing I had to avoid was over-filling the flashlight. I'd have to stop before the pee rose to the level of the opening. Since I couldn't see the flashlight, I slid my index finger a half inch down inside the opening. The plan was: as soon as I felt the warm liquid hit my finger I would stop peeing (which I knew might not be easy). I peed, and peed, and peed some more. There were tears in my eyes and warm shivers went through me. I continued, couldn't believe my bladder was so full. *And the good news was the tip of my index finger was staying dry!* In fact I was able to complete the whole urination successfully—or so I thought. That was before I realized the screw in the other end of the flashlight was missing, and a quart of pee had run right through the flashlight, out the screw hole and soaked where I would have to sit the rest of the trip!

A UFO Encounter over the Caspian Sea

The last leg—from Ankara to Teheran, was usually flown from sometime after midnight to just about dawn. On this leg we had to climb to 13,500 feet to clear the high mountains in eastern Turkey. This was something prohibited by FAA Regulations. Pilots are not supposed to fly above 10,000 feet without oxygen. We didn't have oxygen in these airplanes and had to be on guard that we weren't succumbing to hypoxia, which at the least makes you light-headed and slows your thought-process (if not cause you to pass out completely and spiral down to impact)! The check was to see if your finger nails were turning blue (not easy to determine in a cockpit with nothing but red lighting). It was about 2 a.m. We were north of Syria and south of the old Soviet state of Georgia. The Caspian Sea would be coming up off our left wing in just a few minutes. When it did we would be able the make our right turn southeastward, cross the Iranian border and towards Teheran.

Our flight of three was the epitome of isolation. We were not being monitored by any flight following facility. We were absolutely alone, just droning eastward in the pitch black night. Even monitoring the airline "gossip" frequency (123.45) for the last couple hours we had not heard even one wise crack. We had endured several straight hours of black pit silence. Our only friends were the stars. And then it happened, over southern Armenia and just coming up on the Caspian sea, I glanced to the north—over my left wing, and *about a yard outside of my wingtip, I saw what appeared to be a bright lime green luminescent golf ball!* This was sufficiently incredulous that I was afraid the lack of oxygen was getting to me. Then I thought it might be some reflection of the cockpit lighting, so I turned all the aircraft lights out. No luck, it was still there. Try as I may and I really worked on this, I couldn't tell if it was something the size of a golf ball a couple yards off my wingtip, or something the size of a basketball twenty yards off my wing, or something the size of a beach ball fifty yards off my wing. I strained and did every trick to determine the distance. It could even have been something a mile across and fifty miles away. I couldn't tell. Just then—and making me feel a lot better, Eddie Fitzpatrick (a furloughed TWA pilot) flying the second airplane, keyed the mike and said, "Is anybody seeing what I'm seeing?" At least I wasn't going crazy.

In ten minutes my golf ball had turned into a beach ball. In fifteen minutes it occupied half the northern sky, and in twenty minutes it had increased so much in size, that it occupied the entire scope of our vision northward. I actually had to rock the airplane left wing down to see the bottom of the ball, and then up, to be able to see the top of the ball. I considered that it might be some kind of nuclear explosion up in Russia, but that would be gaseous, and being gaseous the changing atmospheric pressure would squeeze it or elongate it, and this ball was 100%, perfectly round—like a dinner plate. We were never sure if it was something at a fixed distance growing in size, or worse—something of a fixed size rushing at us, making it appear to grow larger! *Maybe it was another planet on a collision course with us. The end of our earth!* The sight merited the much overused expression of awesome, if not terrifying. And sufficiently so, that Sheldon—flying the third plane in the formation, turned right—to the south, added full power and broke away from the formation, attempting to outrun it. When Eddie and I called him back he didn't even answer. As the ball had increased so dramatically in size, it lost some of its brightness (whatever that would indicate). A few minutes later it suddenly disappeared. It didn't shrink or sink or fade, it just did away with itself. Zap!

We landed at Teheran about dawn, scavenged the aircraft for the company items Dave had installed, plus the life rafts and life vests, and thus laden down trudged to the gate for a cab to town. It was a good thing it was morning, because there was not a hotel in town with a vacant room. We stored all our stuff in one and tried to find an English language paper that might have an article on what we had seen. As big and bright as it was—if it wasn't something airborne, it would have been seen by hundreds of thousands of people on the ground. However, even staying there a second day, awaiting our commercial flight back, we could find no reports of what we had seen. Oh, that second night, there still was no vacant room in Teheran. I found a meeting room off the lobby in one hotel, with a whole bunch of tables and chairs, but no people. I snuck in there and slept under one of the far tables. The commercial flight back was uneventful.

I continued in this job until all twelve aircraft had been delivered. It looked like Dave had another good contract for aircraft delivery—over *terra firma,* to South America! That sounded better and involved a few-week delay, which would allow me a good visit with the kids. However, while down in Florida doing so, I got the word that Dave's company would be no more. His partner and a group of investors had brought a suit against him for lack of fiduciary responsibility, claiming Dave was rifling through the profits to enhance his lifestyle. (And from what I had observed—the Porsche and private club memberships, could well be true.) Well so much for this adventure, I was back in search of a sufficiently revenue-producing, and hopefully more orthodox aviation position; one that might have a future, or a retirement!

Chapter Thirty-Eight
HALFWAY AROUND THE WORLD TWICE.
TRIP NUMBER ONE

Evergreen International

R emember Ernie Brase? The Air America pilot who had landed at a
strip in Laos—not knowing the North Vietnamese had overrun it the
night before. He was captured and marched to Hanoi (over 100 miles)
where he was held with John McCain in the notorious prison, nicknamed
the "Hanoi Hilton." He was part of the well-publicized POW release in
1973 (and I believe the second longest held captive). *Well guess what, I get
a call from him!* He's now the Operations Officer for a young and growing
lumber company in Oregon, called Evergreen International. Their never-
tried-before method was—in lieu of hacking roads into the dense forest
and using trucks to get the wood out, they used giant helicopters to pick
up and haul the long and multi-ton pieces of freshly cut timber directly to
the mill.

They just secured a new contract, but not involving timber. It was
with the World Health Organization and for it they had just bought two of
Air America's Pilatus Porter aircraft (still in Saigon). The Porter's unique
capabilities were precisely what were needed for this contract. They
set about finding the most capable Porter pilot available, perhaps with
international aircraft delivery experience, and speak French. Guess whose
name came up? Ernie offers me the one-time job of flying commercially to
Saigon to pick up two Porters and deliver them to the city of Ouagadougou
in the French colony of Haute Volta (new name, Burkina Faso) in West
Africa. In view of the challenges this would entail, including a low-level
crossing of the whole of North Africa, I asked what compensation they

were envisioning. It was good—in fact more than I was expecting. I asked him to give me two days to think it over. He said no problem. We made some small talk about our time in Southeast Asia, and I hung up feeling good, although mostly about the nostalgia of old times, not about what would lay in store for me if I took this job.

President Trump referred to some African countries as "shithole" countries, and rightly received a lot of flak for it. But I must admit, my experiences had led me to believe the most dangerous and corrupt countries of any continent were in Africa, and your safety is not guaranteed more than a hundred yards from a five-star hotel! Knowing the limited range of the Porter with no extra gas tanks (like I had in the Bonanzas) even with a zero payload, I would not be able to fly legs longer than 800 miles, which would mean I'd have to make many refueling stops. A look at my maps showed the route would overfly Cambodia, Thailand, Burma (now Myanmar), East Pakistan (now Bangladesh), India, West Pakistan (now just Pakistan), Iran, Saudi Arabia, the Red Sea, Sudan, Chad, and Niger, before arriving in Haute Volta. Wow, that's a lot of countries for something to go wrong in (with absolutely no one or nowhere to go for help). When Ernie called two days later I still had nothing else on the horizon and told him I'd do it, warning him how much cash I would need to be in possession of to start each journey. (Bribes and credit card refusals being the "fait du jour" in the third world countries I would be transiting.) I ordered all the maps and aviation info I'd need for the projected trip (a third of the way around the globe)!

Arriving in Saigon, the new Air America guy in charge of Porters was acting like he wasn't sure I was qualified, and worse—like the aircraft was still his. It started as a delicate relationship, but I was finally acknowledged as the new owner and ready to commence my journey. Most pilots nowadays don't file their own flight plans or get their own overflight permits, the owner of the aircraft does it for them, or if not, the pilot contracts with a company like Universal Services that specializes in this. *No pilot now flying can imagine what this procedure entailed in the 70's.* The individual pilot had to do it on his own, and for international flights it required the use of a now forsaken correspondence system known as teletype. These were typewriter-like machines connected through international telephone lines, that went click, click, click, and when successful (about a third of the time) jerkingly spit out a half-inch-wide, long ribbon of paper containing the individual letters that spelled out the answer to your request. In the third world countries I needed approvals from, their offices were only manned during daylight hours, the occupants often didn't come to work, or when they did, had extended cigarette breaks, coffee breaks, or prayer times, and often—to save electricity would turn off their teletype machines. The flaws in this procedure usually caused me to skip it, choosing to make the flight in the middle of the night when all the senior airport officials at my landing site were asleep and only the most junior ramp workers would meet me. When I did go in the day without clearance and landed unannounced, I usually found the airport personnel who met me were none-the-wiser as to whether or not I had any pre-approval. (If they were, extended conversations and several meetings ensued.)

First Leg - To Burma

7 a.m. I topped off the fuel and launched for Rangoon (now Yangon), Burma (now Myanmar), with no flight plan, no overflight permits, and Burma not apprised of my arrival. The flight took me over Cambodia and Thailand, before crossing into Burma. When I had the Rangoon international airport in sight I called for landing clearance, but—believe it or not, could not raise anyone on the published frequencies. I landed anyway. In no way did this aerodrome appear as an international airport. There was only one runway and it was uneven, with rows of foot-high grass sprouting up through the cracks between the concrete slabs. Herds of cattle and wild animals were milling about in the high weeds within fifty feet of it. The terminal was a small one-story building in major disrepair and apparently deserted. I taxied to the parking ramp in front of it and shut down. Surprisingly the single ramp attendant did come to the aircraft. I pulled off the gas cap for him, pointed inside the opening and showed him my Shell credit card. He showed me a big smile and a mouth filled with almost no teeth. I spied the proper jet-fuel truck about a hundred feet away—walked over to it, pointed to the letters JP4 painted on the side, and made sure he knew this was the truck to use. The Porter having a *jet* engine, but also a *propeller*, caused many refuelers to think it took the type of gas used by most propeller aircraft. (If that blend was put in, you were in for a lot of work.)

Next, I had to fill out the arrival forms and hand in the passenger manifests (never mind I have no passengers), pay for the fuel, and file my flight plan to East Pakistan. The office to do this was in the top of the control tower, which did not have an elevator. One had to take a none-too sturdy exterior staircase, which I did—noting with some concern the well-rusted bolts holding it to the side of the building. Of the four large windows in the control tower, all but one had the glass completely broken out. Inside, the operator on duty was asleep in a cloth hammock strung between two opposing posts (that used to hold glass). Scratchy music was coming from a radio on a desk in the center of the office. Its plastic case had long since departed, as had its antenna—which was now a bent hanger-wire. I waved two of the required blank forms in front of him. He sleepily pointed at them, gave me a weak "thumbs-up," made a writing gesture with his hand, and appeared to doze off. I went about the job, filling in all the blanks with at least some information, whether or not it applied or was accurate.

Done, I again awoke him and handed them to him. He took them but held up one finger, which I assumed meant he needed another. I went through the process again, trying to repeat the same lies as on the first two; halfway through I saw him signaling me with two fingers. I commenced a fourth copy. When finished I gave him the second two and a flight plan which normally requires a copy of the landing approval at the other end. I didn't have it of course, *and he didn't ask for it.* The next step: him calling in my flight plan to the proper authorities (which required a tip of 20 U.S. dollars) I knew would not be done and was just as happy. Back in the aircraft (fuel level visually checked) I started the engine and knowing the tower controller was awake—played by the rules and called for taxi clearance. Can you believe it, and I can see him through an open window raising one finger; on the radio he tells me before he can release me, he needs one more copy of a passenger manifest. Fuck him. Let him try to stop me.

The Second Leg: To Calcutta, India

I had a choice: carry out my original plan, stay over land and fly up to East Pakistan (now Bangladesh), or fly directly across the Bay of Bengal to Calcutta (now Kolkata), India. It would be about 80 miles further, but still within the aircraft's fuel range. Since I was already going to have to stop in India twice, doing this would save me the hassle of immigration and customs in East Pakistan. (If I lose an engine I'll just drown quietly.) I crossed the bay without a problem and landed in Calcutta about 5 in the afternoon. At the airport, as primitive as it was—and it was, the people were more than accommodating and spoke perfect English. Of course this made sense, it having been a British colony for over a hundred years. By the time I had everything taken care of it was almost six. Let me tell you about the cab ride to town, although no words can adequately describe the scene: we drove past mile after mile of cardboard tents—thousands of them, trash, garbage, waste ditches and impoverished destitution! Emaciated figures as far as the eye could see. I could not imagine how any governing bodies could enact what would rectify this situation in the next fifty years.

I had no idea of the name of any hotel and told the driver to take me to a good one. Before we arrived there—not more than two streets from the main street in Calcutta, we were on a completely unpaved street, in deep, wet, rust-colored mud, following a wooden cart being pulled by two large-horned whitish oxen. The driver dropped me off at a reasonable hotel. I got a fourth floor room and felt somewhat normal once inside it. I ate in the hotel as you might imagine, had a couple glasses of terrible-tasting wine, and crashed in the rack. When I awoke in the morning, I went to the window to peruse the early morning activity. What I will tell you now is the gospel truth. Just two streets from the hotel—in the middle of that same rust-colored mud street was a similar large oxcart to what I had seen the night before, but this morning with a macabre mission. The sidewalks on each side of this apparently thriving commercial street, were wooden—a series of warped, sun-bleached boards. On them were rows of side-by-side, still-sleeping figures, wrapped in their native dress of white swathing which encased them like a sleeping bag. Workers *were picking up the ones that had died during the night and throwing them into the oxcart*. It was—I guess, a morning hygienic ritual; just two blocks from a four-star hotel! Checking out, I asked the concierge about what I had seen. He said, "Think that's something? Too bad you're in a hurry. I could take you to where those who perish with some family to do so are taken." He went on to describe a 100-foot-across, humped 'hibachi pot' metal grillwork mounted on top of a circular cement base. On it, members of the family would throw the bodies of their deceased relatives. Carnivorous birds would then set about eating their fill—de-fleshing them, until all that remained were bones, that then fell through the holes in the grillwork to a pit below.

Legs Three and Four: To Somewhere Near Agra, India, and then Karachi, Pakistan

There was no way I was going to be able to get completely across India in one leg. I would have to find a midway refueling stop. Having already landed in India, I didn't need to go to an airport for international arrivals (a hassle and time-consuming), so chose a rural airport near Agra, which my world aerodrome book described as "reasonably well-used." Upon arrival in the area I saw no airport at all; not even a city or town that might have one. After twenty minutes of circling over barren dirt acreage and scrub brush wasteland, I was able to make out what appeared to be a barely discernable outline of a dirt strip. There was a small group of people near it and a road leading up to it. I still had a hard time believing this was my destination, but fuel becoming an issue, I had no other choice but to hope and land. Out of the airplane, standing more or less at a loss and scanning the area, I realized there was not a single building on the airport; no terminal, not even a shack on or near this landing site. Luckily I did see one parked fuel truck. A gathering of shabbily dressed onlookers, some of whom approached me, were apparently excited to see me—as if some anticipated cargo might be aboard my aircraft. They spoke in a dialect not close to being decipherable. Fortunately—a few moments later, a better dressed individual speaking perfect English (thank God) arrived on the scene offering assistance. I told him I was just stopping for fuel and would be out of his hair as soon as that was accomplished. I knew I was in luck because at the edge of the airport was the only man-made structure in sight: a giant Shell Oil billboard! After the refueling was complete (most of which I did myself), there was one more task that had to be taken care of: I had to pay a landing fee and sign some forms relating to my travel in their country.

To accomplish this, the new arrival gestured me to join him in about the oldest Land Rover I'd ever seen. We bounced about a mile (across flat fields without a single tree as far as the eye could see) to a lone building, which appeared to be an old and unoccupied two-story residence; the only structure in sight across the entire horizon. On the second floor was his office. In it was a safe containing the monies paid by other pilots passing through, as well as the forms I would have to sign. The safe was locked and my new friend *could not get it unlocked!* He tried the combination a dozen times, becoming more apologetic and more frustrated with each try. His grimaced face was now glistening with perspiration and his white shirt was soaked. I could see—to him, this inability to get the safe open constituted a major problem. *But did I really have to sign those forms? And couldn't I just leave the money with him. He could put it in the safe later?* A frantic, desperate shaking of his head indicated to me that my suggestions were unthinkable. He made several phone calls. A slight relaxation of his face after the second one gave me a glimmer of hope. I just sat there, time-a-wasting. After almost thirty minutes of us both sitting there, I decided to try to bribe him, which in third world countries I had yet to see go unrewarded. But here in the middle of nowhere I must've met the most honest guy born. He not only would not take payment on the side, he held up his hand as if to stop the words coming out of my mouth! It was more than another hour before the guy arrived with the proper combination, and it was four in the afternoon before I was able to take-off.

The next leg would be about 700 miles—six hours, to Karachi, The trip went smoothly and I arrived there about 10 p.m. In so doing, I learned something I didn't know before: Pakistan and India have had an adversarial (and that's putting it mildly) relationship for centuries. Me arriving there *from India* was like going to a NY Yankee baseball game wearing a Boston Red Sox sweatshirt. I was about to be 'put through the wringer' and my aircraft thoroughly inspected for contraband. It is understood that when you first fly into a country you have to declare your cargo: what you are carrying in the cabin and the hold. Because I had the audacity to come here from India, they wanted to see everything in the two places mentioned above, and anywhere else. They declared that the oil inside the engine was being carried into their country and had to be inspected. *I actually had to drain all the oil out of the engine!* In case any of you readers are aviation mechanics you know that once this is done, that oil should not be put back in the engine. But I was going to have to do so. I found a reasonably clean pail and something that would work as a funnel, scrubbed them good and used them. The chief of customs was obviously bent on causing me the most uncomfortable time possible. (After all, I had just been in *India!*) When it appeared this drill could extend into the early morning hours, I located the guy in charge of the whole process, complimented him on his work ethic and offered him a generous tip for his extra fine work. And that did it. He waved his guys away from the plane, and they all (gladly) left—except one, who continued to pilfer through my gear. I approached him and started a conversation. Once established, I showed him my ball point, which when you pressed a knob on top of the pen a small window on the side of the pen lit up with the day and date. This *did* impress him, his eyes lit up like the little window, and he looked at me with anticipation. I gave him the pen, he left, and I got a cab to town.

Leg Five: To Dhahran, Saudi Arabia

Due to more forms and regulations, my departure was delayed till almost noon. This leg was over 800 miles and was going to be a stretch. Meteorology swore to me that I could expect a light tailwind the whole way, which would make it "doable." The most memorable part of this leg was flying over the Gulf of Oman, just off the south coast of Iran. The

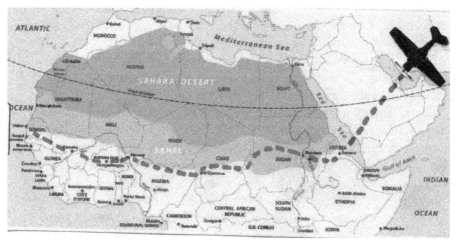

Iranian topography inland from its southern coast displays the results of a perhaps catastrophic prehistoric event. I had never read of it, but now viewed it aghast: at least a hundred-mile wide area of what looked like dried and hardened, dark gray molten lava, with weathered bubbles and caverns. (If we ever did want to fake a moon landing, this would be the place to do it.) I don't know what tectonic or volcanic events could have ever produced such a barren wasteland. It was completely absent of any type of life or structures; not even a single road!

I landed in Dhahran, which fortunately was more westernized than most places in Saudi Arabia. Perhaps a thousand American petroleum engineers employed by Aramco were living there. Since Bahrain was my initial entry point into Saudi Arabia and they didn't know I was coming, I was ready for a fair amount of mistreatment, which did ensue. Having been told to expect this in Saudi Arabia, I had been advised to bring something with me—something not available there, that would work miracles. That miracle worker was a case of the stateside cookie product, Fig Newtons. With this offering, I was able to smooth things over, get dinner (without a beer or glass of wine), and lodging for the night.

Leg Six: To Jeddah, Saudi Arabia

Was airborne early on the 750 mile leg to Jeddah—the large cosmopolitan city on the Saudi west coast, right on the Red Sea. Landing there was not a problem since they were accustomed to all sorts of arrivals, and I had already been 'stamped' into the country. The only problem was: they were going to play by the rules, and would not let me take off until I had gotten a teletype approval for landing at my destination—Khartoum, Sudan. (The teletype operator let me know that $100 would markedly reduce the wait.) Still, I knew it would be at least a couple hours, and decided to put the time to good use: find my old Vientiane Air America boss—Jim Ryan. (Remember? The forged check story.) I knew he was here on some project for the CIA, but as a cover he was flying pipeline inspections for an American oil company.

A True Story, but Hard to Believe

I asked every American I spied, describing Jim: over six foot tall, dark hair, a crew cut, *and a wooden leg!* The third guy I asked knew him and drew me a crude map to get to his apartment. I hailed a cab and sped to the address. His apartment was supposed to be on the second floor, the end unit on the right. I raced up the steps and to the door and knocked. It opened, but it wasn't Jim. Fortunately, this guy *did* know where Jim lived, and also drew me a map. *Why all these maps?* Well in Saudi Arabia the streets don't have names. They are referred to by the leading attraction on that street; thus there's Chicken Street, and Coca Cola Street and Chop-Chop Street (where the beheadings occur). Back in the cab and to the new address. Knocked on the door, and *Bingo!* I heard the clump, clump of someone with a prosthetic leg approaching the door. I was excited knowing how thrilled he would be that I took the trouble to look him up. The door swung open, and there was a six foot guy with a crew cut and an artificial leg, and it wasn't Jim! *There were two Americans with prosthetic legs flying in Jeddah!* This guy did know Jim, and directed me back to the first apartment I had stopped at. (Jim lived in the far *left* unit.) I went there and Jim and I had a short but good reunion.

Leg Seven: to Khartoum, Sudan

My clearance to land in Khartoum finally arrived, and even as late in the day as it was, I decided to get in a short leg—across the Red Sea and into Sudan. Landed in Khartoum at about 10 p.m. Went through all the rigmarole I've described earlier, and then got a cab to town. The driver asked me what hotel. I told him I had no reservations. "Just take me to a good one." If we went to one, we went to ten; from four-star to one-star, to what had to be no-stars; from main roads to less travelled roads; to roads where the brush on each side scraped the car. *Nothing.* Then an idea evidently hit him and we proceeded further out of town into a remote, wooded area, with no buildings—commercial or residential. I was beginning to worry for my own safety. On this dirt road, previously bordered by woods on both sides, we finally emerged into a clearing on one side. In it was a wide, three-story, old wooden-sided building, with nothing to indicate what type of building it might be. He stopped the car, jumped out and urged me to follow him up the steps. Since he led me to what appeared to be a registration counter, I guessed we'd finally found my lodgings for the night. Once I was met at the desk, he smiled, accepted his fare (in US dollars) and left. I filled out the necessary paper work and the attendant motioned for me to follow him. He led me up the steps to the second floor, and then—strangely, slowly, walked the entire length of it to the stairs at the far end. And what was more strange (by a *lot*), all the rooms were brightly lit and had glass-paned (see-through) double-doors. You could look right in! And each time I did, I was not only looking directly at the bed, *but most the time there were two men sitting on it—I think, holding hands!* We mounted the stairs at the far end and started down the third floor. (I can only guess the object of my tour of the second floor.) Halfway down this third floor he gestured into an empty room, the glass doors wide open. I went in, closed them, locked them, and went to sleep (a restless, worried sleep).

Legs Eight and Nine: To El Geneina, West Dafur, and then Fort Lamy, Chad

Would have like to have made it from Khartoum to Fort Lamy in one leg—non-stop, but too far, couldn't make it. I was going to have to make a refueling stop, and let me tell you, in in sub-Sahara Africa there aren't that many refueling locations! I chose El Geneina. One of the few villages on the western border of Sudan that my aviation publications stated had jet gas. Since my Porter had no useable navigational aids, I had to navigate by reference to terrain features. *Well for this flight, I may as well have thrown my maps away and clipped a brown paper bag to my leg.* The whole way and as far as I could see—ahead, left or right, there was nothing but sand beneath me. No towns, no railroads, no rivers, not a single terrain feature that would merit being marked on a map. I was on a 500 mile leg with no navigational landmarks and unknown winds. You'd think I would have just aimed directly at El Geneina and hoped. However if you do that, when the flight time is up and you should have arrived, if you don't see your destination, you won't know whether to search to your right or to your left. You're not sure which way it may be, and you waste critical fuel searching both left and right. So what you do is purposely aim to miss it just a bit—say to the right: then if it you can't see it when you should be to it, you only have to search to your left.

Well it didn't show up when my flight time was up. And this was serious, because I was low on fuel and could easily run out looking for it. I did a decades-old search pattern called a "Square Search", flying an expanding box-like pattern. But no dice, and my fuel was getting critically low. In fact, so low that I entertained the idea of—before I ran out of fuel and crashed, *just making a controlled, power-on landing.* (At least I'd climb out of the aircraft alive.) With no more than five minutes of fuel remaining I did find it and landed. Besides a herd of goats to meet me, there was a group of tall natives with eight-foot spears, dressed in skins (and standing on one leg). Thank God, once again there was that damned Shell Oil billboard! Except this time no truck; the fuel was in 55 gallon drums. Getting them open wasn't easy, and then I had to use a hand pump, and rigged hose arrangement to refuel the aircraft. Since no one of any importance arrived at the strip, I was airborne again having filled out no forms or paying any fees!

I was excited about this second leg into Chad, and to my landing site— the city of Fort Lamy. It was the original headquarters of the first French Foreign Legion! In an effort to Africanize the name, Fort Lamy became N'Djamena in 1973 (but still kept most its French population and all its flavor). At Fort Lamy I filled out the required paperwork, refueled the aircraft and hopped a cab to a hotel on the outskirts of town; a spreading two-story white wood building that I think was the only hotel utilized by European travelers. Even so, most the front lawn was covered by natives' blankets, displaying a wide assortment of handicrafts for sale (including a fake watch, artfully carved out of a block of silver, that I could not resist buying).

Legs Ten and Eleven: To Niamey, Niger, and finally, Ouagadougou, Haute Volta

Arrived at Ouagadougou about 5 p.m; having had to make a midday refueling stop in Niger. Nothing better or worse occurred during either flight than I have already described in the preceding pages, (except in Niger, where they claimed they couldn't accept my Shell card, so I had to pay cash—at an exorbitant price per gallon)! Chapters back I spoke of the ambiance and the simple but charming cosmopolitan nature of Vientiane in Southeast Asia—a truly French-provincial town (and where you felt safe). Ouagadougou—while still a city in a previous French colony was not of this ilk. Even more than the remote locations I had just transited, it oozed being isolated. It was a small enclave, surrounded by an ever-stretching dark wilderness. I sensed the small French community likely considered itself lucky to have thus far gotten by without a horrendous occurrence. There was an aura even inside the white-linen dining room of the best hotel, that you were little more than prey to something lurking behind the nearest tree-line. And what's worse, for the pilots Evergreen would hire to fly these aircraft, they weren't even going to be based here in the capital; they'd be based at a smaller and even more primitive city: Bobo-Dioulasso. Once the aircraft were signed for and the paperwork done, I would take a vintage and thread-bare African airliner to Dakar, Senegal, and wait for the once-a-week Pan Am flight back to New York.

The Next Chapter

Dear reader, having waded through three parts, your kind patience will be finally rewarded as the next chapter unfolds....

Chapter Thirty-Nine
DAKAR, SENEGAL AND EUREKA, SHE EXISTS!

A Brief Turn-Around in the States

The timing of their contract was such that Evergreen didn't mind if I took off a week between the two ferry flights; such being the case, after arriving in New York I booked a flight to West Palm Beach, and was able to spend some time with the kids, albeit school had just started and their time was limited. I tried to show my interest in their academics, by— at least a couple nights, getting involved in their homework assignments, which though I don't know how much help I was, I think was appreciated. Hobe Sound had turned out to be a great idea. Everyone loved the town and the kids and Sara had a ton of friends. We had a screened in back porch with a persistent but undiscovered leak in the roof—that I was luckily able to fix (and at least do one thing that was worthwhile). Satisfied here and grateful for how things were going for the family, I booked my flight back to Saigon to pick up the second Porter.

Delivering the Second Plane

No problem in Saigon. They'd seen me before and knew the plan. And this time I'd arrived early enough in the day to fuel, file and depart for Rangoon at 2 p.m. Decided to take the route I'd considered (but not done) for the first delivery. I would stay over terra firma, flying northwest to Dacca, East Pakistan. (Instead of cutting across the Bay of Bengal directly to India.) Jumping off from Dacca allowed me to avoid Calcutta and get further into India, landing at Lucknow—a dirt strip in central India. Because of weather systems—mostly headwinds (and one previous refueling stop now being a disputed facility in a civil war) this last delivery required a different (more northerly) route than on the first trip, unfortunately resulting in a memorable overnight in Egypt.

I arrived at Cairo airport just before midnight. Ground Control had me taxi to a remote, unlit, crumbling tarmac, parking among about a dozen half dismantled aircraft—at least a mile from the terminal. Although I called for it no transportation was provided. I had to walk (loaded down with stuff) to the terminal, which was poorly lit and smelt. With a $20 bill here and there I was able to migrate my way through inefficient, logic-bending customs, immigration, and other associated delays. When finally cleared and after a thirty minute wait I was able to get a taxi to town (which turned out to be an exercise in futility). First: after a long and desolate drive, upon finally entering the city the traffic we encountered was crazy—horns and screeching tires. Late hour chaos. We just barely avoided an accident every other block. Second: an hour of checking hotels did not result in us finding one with a vacancy, which was just as well since I did not feel comfortable or safe in any of the ones we visited. I told the driver to just take me back to the airport. I went back into the terminal, through it, made the mile walk back to my Porter, and slept in it (though you might imagine, not well).

The rest of the trip to my destination—Ouagadougou, would take three more days; one leg each day. Being north of my first delivery route, the first two legs would be over the Sahara Desert. Unable to get permits from the countries I would overfly, to improve my chances of staying out of jail I chose to depart about 10 p.m. on each of these first two. (This way—landing at 3 or 4 in the morning I would only encounter low paid, low ranking peons.) This resulted in two six-hour flights without hearing a single call on the radio or without passing over a single light on the ground. It did provide a moving experience. The Porter's clear acrylic windscreen stretches back over the pilot's head, so during each flight I had a spectacular view of the heavens above. I found it hard not to keep gazing upward, at the million stars, the constellations, and the majesty of the expanded cosmos above me. I also was able to note—for the first time, the extent of the little known circular movement of the stars during the night. The panoramas on these all-night trips will always remain with me.

The Two Plane Delivery Completed

There were just a few things to settle upon officially turning this second aircraft over to the contract representatives here. I was able to complete them fairly quickly, so only had to stay in Ougadougou that first night, and took a flight to Dakar, Senegal the next day. At this time the only way to return to the states from West Africa, was out of Dakar on the once-a-week Pan Am flight to New York. I was going to have to wait in Dakar three days for that flight, but better there than here in Ougadougou.

Arriving in Dakar I checked into one of three surprisingly plush oceanfront hotels—perhaps recently built for the burgeoning French tourist business. My room was of a most interesting design. It was split level. The left side of the room was at entry level and contained a living, eating area, and bathroom. The left side wall faced the ocean and had narrow windows reaching to the ceiling. The whole right half of the room was elevated

Postcard from Dakar

an eight-foot high loft with the bed and nightstands—arrived at by a ladder (as opposed to stairs). I cleaned up and then rested in the room an hour or so before deciding to do some exploring and people-watching.

That First Day, Late Afternoon

Since it wasn't far and would probably hold some things worth seeing, I went down to the hotel lobby. Upon viewing it a second time I had to admit, it was first class—everything clean and proper. Most eye-catching were the various groups of French tourists checking brochures and discussing the next day's activities (with sufficient drama). After about a half hour of "people watching" I remembered that in picking this hotel, right next to it was an even more impressive (and likely more expensive) lodging I decided to pass up. Maybe I'll wander over there and check it out. *Wow!* I thought mine was first class, but this one was really 'top of the line'! Elegant furniture, polished marble floors, tall figurine statues, immaculately uniformed desk attendants and fawning bellmen—all more than eager to render assistance. There was a display of artwork on a balcony above the foyer and I chose to check it out more closely. Mostly modern art, maybe done by local artists; lots of oranges and red and burnt umber (to me, making most the paintings look like abstracts of forest fires).

299

Something Special, Very Special

While alone in this advantageous lookout, I spied a most impressive entourage entering the hotel. They strode erect and quickly across the lobby; almost as if they were royalty. They were led by a tall honey-haired blonde in high heels and a floor length fur coat. I wasn't sure if she was a super-model or just a super-rich tourist, but either way, it was obvious she was not accustomed to encountering the type of obstacles we mortals dealt with on a daily basis. Her hair was pulled straight back, tied in a pony tail that hung down to the small of her back, and bounced with each strutting step. I realized it wasn't just me, no one could take their eyes off her. She wasn't cute or pretty like Debby Reynolds or Doris Day, *she was sultry mean like Greta Garbo or Lauren Bacall.* Her eyes were steely-gray and fortunately she stayed looking straight ahead, because you knew it would not be comfortable if you were caught in her razor gaze. She was closely followed by a well-dressed couple and one lone woman. Wow. Enough of subjecting myself to this belittlement, I'm going to return to my safe hotel and check out the dining hall.

The Early Part of the Evening

After a fine meal I decided to take a stroll behind the hotel—towards the beach. The temperature was perfect, just about 70 degrees, and a light breeze. You could easily feel good about yourself and the world at a time like this; or maybe I was feeling good knowing I had successfully accomplished a not-easy mission, and was on the way home. Although I was planning on an early evening, just in case this would be the night that mysterious woman would appear, I was wearing a pre-washed ("de-lave" in French) shirt and trousers I had bought in Athens (accented by a puka shell necklace I had bought when I was in Hawaii with Sean Flynn). Having heard what sounded like high energy music coming from the beach, I continued, and after rounding a large clump of tall kenkiliba bushes I spied the hotel's main draw for nighttime activity: a large thatch-roof-covered cement slab, right on the beach. In it were about a hundred people dancing their booties off. Those not dancing were reclining on over-stuffed furniture located around the perimeter of the dance floor. About fifty feet from the hut was a small outdoor bar. Not feeling bold enough—by a long shot (irrespective of my "cool" outfit) to just walk right into the middle of all those laughing and sophisticated French tourists, I made my way to a stool at the nearby bar.

After one drink I wagered I would not be any more ready to take a look at what was going on inside the hut (sadly the translation to that being: what single woman might be available that I could get up my nerve to approach). Just inside the entry way, at the edge of the dance floor, sprawled on a large floral-print love seat *was the imposing and privileged looking group I had seen cross the lobby in the hotel next to mine!* This included three women and two guys. They were speaking French (in the same elevated, careless and superior manner so common among *la crème francais de la crème*). Being a bourgeois American and with only a rudimentary French capability, it appeared a bevy I should not even consider approaching. Then while in the midst of these prohibitive thoughts, one of the women—a thin brunette, pops up, comes over to me, grasps my hand and pulls me out onto the dance floor! I think I was able to get out a couple appropriate words in French before she put the length of her body firmly against me and we started dancing. (It was a slow dance.) I was startled as I could immediately feel her firmly press her mound against my thigh, and one hand was above my collar—her finger tips moving on the back of my neck. I was dumbstruck! (And soon feeling the beginnings of that long-absent and desperately longed-for possible capability.) I couldn't believe how she was so purposefully against me.

After the dance I escorted her back to her lounging group, who did not take exceptional notice of us, being involved in conversation among themselves. Starting to leave I was surprised when she gestured for me to take a seat. At a loss for what else to do, I did. But *boy,* was I out of my element or what!? Sitting there in silence, feigning to understand what was being said, a man to my left (who hadn't been with the group this afternoon), leaned over and whispered into my ear: *Son mari devient jaloux.* After a minute of labored translation I worked it out: Holy Shit! The woman I was dancing with was the wife of the guy sitting to my right; understandably becoming jealous. Then he said, *Mais la blonde est disponible.* The blonde was available.

Up to this time, mostly because I was afraid to make eye contact, I had not studied the blonde—who from this afternoon's procession was apparently the ranking member of the group; the one to whom homage was due. In commencing to observe her more closely I came to the same conclusions I came to this afternoon. A man—any man, desirous of approaching her would definitely think twice before doing so. She was no kitten waiting to be picked up and petted—not by a long shot!

While her features: forehead, nose, mouth, jaw (and 30-inch-long pony tail) were perfection and hard to look away from, *her eyes were cold and filled with distrust.* It appeared the group as a whole had no objection to my lingering presence. (I obviously did not dance with the brunette again; in fact I didn't dance again.) My real problem was that while my evening study sessions with a textbook had gotten me to where I could (given the time) write French passably and even verbally form sentences, when listening—the spoken word flew past my grasp. I was able to add just enough responses to lead them to (erroneously) believe I was understanding whatever it was they were talking about. While from time to time the others threw out an English expression, I gathered the blonde spoke no English at all, never having uttered a single word in English (or for that matter—hardly any in French).

Later in the Evening

After an hour or so in the hut (me listening to the music and all of them smoking), it was apparent the evening was over and they were leaving, and to my great surprise *motioning me along with them!* Strolling as a group—when we got to the narrow walk I found myself walking gingerly (and at a safe distance) alongside the blonde, whose name I now knew was Mireille. We made our way back to their hotel and up to one of their rooms (whose room was more than I could ferret out). There, after another hour of light-hearted conversation (of which at best I may have understood a quarter of) and a couple snifters of brandy, I hazarded to believe the suspicion radiating from Mireille's eyes had softened, perhaps even to a mild trust—at least of those in this room. Throughout the evening and even here, she had barely added a word; her silence amplifying her mystique. And I was taken aback because when she did voice her thoughts they were in striking contrast to her stern appearance! *The words came out as if from an unsure and innocent preteen school girl!* That frightened tone, so differing from her self-assured, even intimidating aura, had the effect of causing me to feel a new concern for her—want to be protective of her and reassure her she need not be afraid. (What? Me?! I must be crazy.)

During the whole time in the hotel room she just sat on the end of a bed, and I think or imagined, *from time to time looking up at me;* almost as if something (God knows what—perhaps being an American, or my humble ineptitude) had struck a vein of curiosity within her. I don't think I can adequately describe my trembling sensations of cautious excitement at this moment. Dare I, dare I be so presumptuous as to even imagine this could end, *with me finding the courage to ask Mireille to spend the night with me?* (Though it's true, the guy had said she was available, whatever that might mean.) I could think of nothing further from reality than that scenario, which should it wondrously occur could be described as the most benevolent miracle ever! But on the other hand, if my almost unanimous historic coital failures are any indication, *this particular attempt could also bring me the worst embarrassment and disappointment I would have ever suffered!* I cannot recall the thoughts or events that could have given me the courage, but I did ask the question, and it was all I could do to keep my balance when she responded with a warm smile and a nod.

The short walk to my hotel was without conversation; even if we spoke the same language I am doubtful my state of mind would have allowed me to think of anything to say that would have been meaningful. (I was barely able to put one foot in front of the other.) Still silent, into my hotel and into the elevator, although encouragingly, in the elevator—she did look at me with a warm and trusting smile, a very warm and very trusting smile (that caused me to pray to the gods of love-making, that just this once, even if never again, they would grant me what would be necessary). Walking down the hallway I was terrified, thinking of the excuses I would have to come up with. If I would not have had my jaws clamped shut, my teeth would have been chattering. I doubt I had ever been more overcome by apprehension and fear; here in a position any man would have killed for. Into the room—still without speaking. The windows were open and the lace curtains were blowing in, almost up to the ceiling. (Shades of Belkis and that abandoned hotel on the Bosphorus.) She excused herself and went into the bathroom. I climbed the eight steps to the bedroom loft. In bed I listened to her activity below and waited, trembling and feeling cold.

When her head appeared at the top of the steps she still had that almost silly, not understandable, but warm and trusting smile. I noticed now for the first time, that while anyone seeing her during the day would have considered her slender, she was thin enough to be called skinny. I raised the sheet offering her a place next to me. As soon as our bodies touched, it happened—like never before! A rock hard arousal that would unquestionably be up to the task; one that would have to be satisfied, and have no mind of quitting! In my adult life—in all my life, I had never been so surprised, so gratified—this euphoric. In possession of this hardened tool, natural quests took over. We made passionate love, and I truly felt a love for her. She kissed me, repeatedly and hard, and wrapped her arms around me. Between her heartfelt murmurs of approval I could hear her breath coming in quicker and deeper gasps. I finally knew a pleasure I had never known before; *not my own*, but just *seeing and feeling* this special woman take her pleasure with me inside her. I now knew—after twenty years of deprivation, *what every other man regularly experiences and never questions.* After several moments, when her movements slowed and then subsided, she forced me over onto my back—but carefully, so as not to dislodge me and just lay atop me, arms around me, speaking to me (of course in French) with what I interpreted as being the most loving utterances, while her tears ran down my neck. *At last. At last my entire view of the world around me had changed; changed into one that allowed me to be a part of it, to at last talk and joke with other men as one of them!*

The Next Three Days

It wasn't over. It had just been the beginning! There was not a moment the following two days that she was not at my side, holding my hand with one (or both) of hers. I never looked at her face that she was not looking into my eyes with the most loving and trusting expression (which just upon observing provoked that same newly experienced heat and hardness). I was in a state of mystification and a never-before experienced delight. Two more intimacies were the same or better. No doubt about my premise now, there *is* that chemistry thing that I'd hung my hat on for twenty years. When it's right—this happens. The day before my scheduled Pan Am flight, I got another gait-altering surprise: "*Je veux que tu viennes avec moi en France.*" Mireille was asking me to cancel my reservations to New York, and return with her to France! Having never known such exhilaration, such gratification—such pride and power. Now, at last with a *meaning* to my life, in spite of no idea about what the future would hold, I knew I would follow her to the ends of the earth—sacrifice anything, *and I agreed!*

Epilogue
I GUESS I JUST WASN'T THINKING CONTINUES

Part Four: At the End of the Rainbow. Now, as a result of the no less than miraculous occurrence at the end of this part—his long-awaited, wholly unanticipated mastery of the unapproachable and eminent femme fatale in Dakar, he is a changed being, emboldened and empowered, having at long last found that one woman! However, he is now faced with a daunting challenge—one for which there could be no solution: he has to come up with some way to construct a life with Mireille—in France, the states, or somewhere. During this quest we observe Roger in drudgery-immersed positions, and a real "first" for him: reeling in the disgrace of being "outplaced for management convenience." (Fired.) We cannot expect Roger to "change his spots" and we again find ourselves screaming instructions at him as he retreats to more familiar territory, engaging in a string of dangerous, disjointed and sometimes illicit activities (one of which ends up having him rescuing a friend from a dirt-floored cell in Colombia). The unfolding of events in this part see Roger having the highest hopes and then enduring the gravest disappointments, and finally the surprising, startling consequences of past events. Having slogged alongside Roger for the first three parts, you will not want to miss the shocking finality of his story.

CPSIA information can be obtained
at www.ICGtesting.com
Printed in the USA
LVHW081345021121
702247LV00014B/523